D0398633

INDUSTRIAL
ERGONOMICS
A PRACTITIONER'S GUIDE

INDUSTRIAL ERGONOMICS

A PRACTITIONER'S GUIDE

David C. Alexander
Babur Mustafa Pulat

Published by
Industrial Engineering & Management Press
Institute of Industrial Engineers

The views and concepts presented are those of the author. Publication by the Institute of Industrial Engineers does not in any way constitute endorsement or approval of the book's contents.

ISBN 0-89806-073-7

Additional copies may be obtained by contacting:
Publication Sales
Industrial Engineering and Management Press
Institute of Industrial Engineers
25 Technology Park/Atlanta
Norcross, GA 30092
404/449-0460

Quantity discounts available.

Contents

ERGONOMICS APPLICATIONS IN INDUSTRY

Preface

The field of industrial ergonomics deals with the person on the job — one of the foundations of the industrial engineering profession. Yet too few industrial engineers have ergonomics as one of their more commonly used tools.

This text explains through example and illustration the use of ergonomics in the industrial setting. Virtually all aspects of industrial ergonomics are covered. Of particular importance is the wide range of contributing authors. Leading researchers and respected practitioners have shared their work and experience in this text. All of the articles are original works or derivatives written especially for the particular needs of this book.

The work assumes that the reader has no (or minimal) background in ergonomics. Therefore, the initial section deals with the fundamentals of industrial ergonomics, from traditional plant-site concerns to product design. The second section covers a number of ergonomics groups and how they work. The third section deals with applications of the technologies, covering problems encountered in industry. And the fourth section provides resources needed by the practitioner.

Academicians may find this work useful in supplementing short courses, workshops, or seminars to industrial audiences. It may also serve as a handy reference book.

Our contributing authors were great to work with — they made the job seem fun and exciting. We appreciate their enthusiasm and hard work. Thanks also to the Ergonomics Division leadership during this effort — Mahmoud Ayoub, Steve Johnson and Bob Dryden.

And, we want to thank our families for their patience and encouragement — Janie and Lucas Alexander, and Simin, Önder and Özgür Pulat.

Dave Alexander
Kingsport, Tennessee

Mustafa Pulat
Greensboro, North Carolina

May 1985

FUNDAMENTALS OF ERGONOMICS

1

Introduction

B. Mustafa Pulat, Ph.D.

Ergonomics Defined

The term *ergonomics* is not one of those words that we encounter during our day-to-day operations on the shop floor, at home, or in any other environment. In fact, many professionals have not even heard the term. Yet, we all experience the inconveniences of poorly designed products, work stations and work methods. A garden shear which imposes stress concentration over the soft tissues of the hand, causing blisters and other ailments, is a good example. A spray device which requires a bent posture (due to a short nozzle-handle mechanism) while spraying roots of dandelions and other weeds in the lawn is another example of the inconveniences experienced during use. A work surface that is two inches too high results in a 20 percent or more drop in the production efficiency of an assembly worker. In such a case, the worker will have to raise the shoulders and/or abduct the arms in order to have proper access to work components. This posture is in conflict with the normal biomechanics of the upper body, and will soon result in muscular fatigue which will have to be compensated for by short periods of idle time.

Ergonomics have been defined by many over the past several decades. One can describe ergonomics in practical terms as *the study of the interface (or interaction) between humans and the objects they use and the environments they function in*. This definition seems to catch the most important components: humans, objects, environments, and the complex interactions between them.

The origin of the term can be traced to 1949 when K. F. H. Murrell (a British ergonomist) combined two Greek words, *ergos* meaning work and *nomos* meaning laws, to create the term ergonomics. In the USA, the equivalent expression is *human factors*. Thus the two terms will be used interchangeably in this chapter. *Human engineered* is the expression frequently used by ergonomists to describe a design which conforms with human expectations, or which humans can use effectively without undue stress.

Another slightly different definition of ergonomics is *design for human use*. Again, the stress is on human effectiveness in working with different designs of products, equipment, machines and other systems.

McCormick and Sanders (1982) provide a more comprehensive definition of the discipline. In summary, the authors attempt a three-pronged approach; namely the central focus, the objectives, and the central approach of human factors. The *central focus* is the consideration of human beings in the design of man-made environments, objects, work procedures, etc. The *objectives* are to increase the effectiveness of resulting man-machine systems, while maintaining human well-being. The *central approach of human factors* is systematic application of available data on human characteristics (capabilities, limitations) to the design of such systems or procedures. Thus one can identify three major objectives of ergonomics as shown in figure 1.

The central theme of ergonomics is *fitting the task to the man*. To a certain extent, the converse is employed when one is selecting workers for jobs. If jobs and work stations are human engineered, however, the need for selection is minimized. We can neither train humans to be seven feet tall to reach overhead controls and have proper line of sight with displays, nor

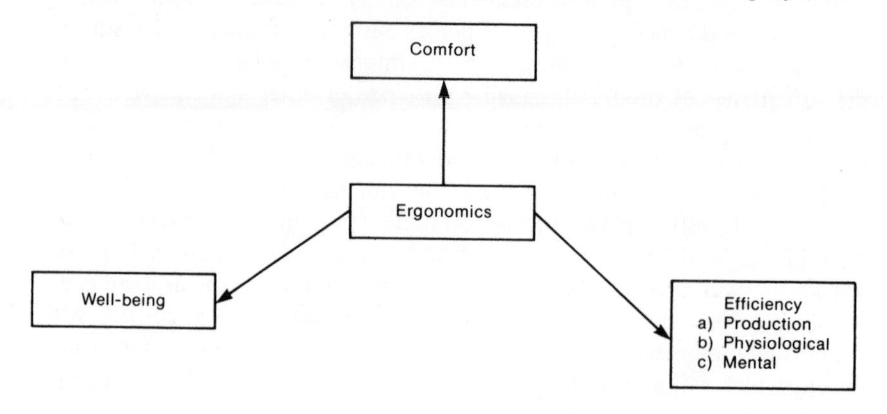

Fig. 1 The three major objectives of ergonomics

can we motivate people to hear sounds having frequencies outside the audible spectrum or see wavelengths outside the visible spectrum. We simply have to design such interfaces so that job demands will be within the human capability ranges, or use job performance aids such as displays, controls, materials handling equipment, and magnification devices, which make previously incompatible conditions compatible.

Another point for ergonomics is taken from general systems theory. For any system to function efficiently, the two major prerequisites are: a) the components must have been designed properly, and b) the components must function together cohesively toward the common goal. Take an example: If one wanted to build a superior car engine, and chose the best-built engine components (carburetor, engine block, crank shaft, etc.) on the market and put them together, that engine would never work. No matter how well the individual parts are designed and constructed, they will not fit and function together. Similarly, the user or operator is an integral part of a man-machine system. If he/she cannot effectively function, the performance of the total system will be affected and sometimes major mishaps will occur.

Frequently, we hear that human error was the cause of a major accident. However, detailed investigations show that the real reasons are primarily related to design or procedural errors that lead to a human error. The mishap at Three Mile Island in the late 1970s is a good example. One of the major reasons for the late discovery of the low reactor coolant level was that the status of a valve draining coolant was erroneously indicated as closed on the instrument panel, when in fact, the valve was open. Naturally, under a wrong assumption, control room operators looked for the problem elsewhere. After several hours, the problem was spotted, but before then a considerable amount of coolant had been lost.

Illustrations

One experiences many situations in everyday life which can be pinpointed as posing ergonomic problems. Assume that you have just about completed picking out your groceries in a grocery store. At that instant, an announcement is made that counter seven is open with nobody waiting. You immediately look toward the distant counters to see where counter seven is, but cannot spot any numbers. By the time you find the correct counter, there are already several customers in line. It is only when you bend to get your first item in the cart to place on the belt conveyor that you are able to see a black number seven against a dark brown background located at waist level on the panel.

We all have seen "No Turn on Red" signs, located next to traffic lights. Perhaps the idea here is to provide some illumination to the sign at night for visibility. At night, however, traffic lights are sources of disability glare that block the visibility of objects within their close vicinity. Thus, the whole purpose of locating the "No Turn on Red" sign is defeated. It took a whole year once for this author to spot a speed limit sign in a speed transition zone (high to low) along a very busy road. The sign was located on the left-hand side of the road. Luckily, no speeding tickets were issued.

In literature, there are many examples of ergonomics problems in industry. Both throughout and at the end of this book, there is a good selection of such works. At this time, however, it would be appropriate to provide two short industrial examples which personally involved the author.

The first case was concerned with the programming of an Automatically Guided Vehicle (AGV) used for materials handling purposes at a textile plant. The vehicle followed a magnetic tape on the floor. On this path, there were thirty possible stop points. The stop-go action of the AGV was controlled through thirty small toggle switches positioned next to each other on a control panel. The AGV stopped at a particular point on its path if the corresponding switch was set at the "up" position. The down position implied "go." The plant was experiencing many inefficiencies in this handling operation. The problem was traced to programming errors with the switches (a seemingly human error). The two underlying causes, however, were a) the short lever arm of the toggle switch, and b) poor color and brightness contrast between the switches and the metal plate they were mounted on. Both the switches and the plate were silver in color. For the two reasons stated above, the programmer could not visually identify switch positions with high accuracy. He was not motivated to utilize touch senses on each switch either, under the current incentive wage payment program. Thus at any given run of the AGV, several switch positions did not necessarily correspond to the intended stop and go actions. The plant experienced at least a 30 percent productivity increase in this particular operation after small, dark adhesive tapes were placed on the tips of the switch lever arms for better contrast with background and improved visual discrimination of switch positions.

The second illustration involved a riveting operation at a flashlight and lantern plant. An expensive machine was designed and built to automate the label riveting operation on flashlight tubes. The task involved the placing of oval-shaped plastic labels (1 inch major axis length, ¼ inch minor axis length) on a rotating table (1 foot diameter) with very close fit requirements. Labels were picked up from the table by suction and positioned on a tube delivered to the riveting station by a conveyor mechanism. Instantaneously, with two simultaneous strokes, the label was riveted to the tube at both ends. The plant was experiencing many rejects on this operation. Again the problem was traced to the task of the operator. Most of the rejects had the label missing. Thus it was immediately evident that either the suction mechanism did not work properly, or the worker could not keep up with the speed of the rotating table. Visual observations led to the conclusion that the second alternative was true. It was simply impossible for the operator to keep up this pace with the rotating table, especially under the current fit requirements (the two small holes at both ends of the label had to fit through two pin-like recesses at each label station on the rotating platform).

Three adjustments helped turn what was an extremely costly operation into a profitable one. First, the angular speed of the rotating table was reduced. Second, a female operator who displayed good finger dexterity was assigned to the job. Third, the vendor was contracted to deliver the labels with proper alignment, eliminating many finger movements at the work station. After the changes were made, the operation achieved close to a 50 percent productivity increase, with a tremendous reduction in the reject rate.

Most of the above illustrations may seem to be common sense. However, our experience shows that most engineers fail to exercise basic ergonomic principles in designing work stations and work methods.

Assumptions

The basic assumption of ergonomics is that equipment, object, and environment characteristics influence human and thus total man-machine system performance. Thus, if products, equipment, work stations and work methods are designed keeping human capabilities and limitations in consideration, then the performance of the resulting system will be optimum. Conversely, if ergonomics is ignored during design, one should be prepared to accept the costs detailed in the next section.

Costs of Ignoring Ergonomics

Our experiences tell us that the following may be expected if ergonomics is not exercised:

1. Less production output
2. Increased lost time
3. Higher medical and material costs
4. Increased absenteeism
5. Low-quality work
6. Injuries, strains
7. Increased probability of accidents, errors
8. Increased labor turnover
9. Less spare capacity to deal with emergencies

Naturally, converse statements can be made for the potential gains of ergonomics.

Procedures

Data concerning human capabilities and limitations are generated through basic research with human subjects. This information is published in technical and professional journals such as *Ergonomics* and *Human Factors*. Better sources for human characteristics information and ergonomics design suggestions are handbooks such as *Human Engineering Guide to Equipment Design* (1972), *AFSC Design Handbook* (1977), *Human Factors Design Handbook* (1981), and other sources such as this book, Kvålseth (1983), the Eastman Kodak Co. study (1983), and the work of Diffrient et al. (1983).

Applied research aims at applications and testing of various design principles and suggestions generated as a result of basic research. Ergonomic case studies appear in various sources, especially in the *Applied Ergonomics* journal.

Ergonomics Position Survey

Ergonomists are employed by industry, government, consulting firms, and educational institutions. A recent position survey (Pulat 1984) of the members of the Ergonomics Division of IIE resulted in twenty responses. Although this number is quite small compared with total membership in the division, the following will provide the reader with a flavor of position duties, background of respondents, and other pertinent information:

a. A majority of the respondents had been members of the division for three to five years.
b. The FTE (full-time equivalent) of ergonomics positions and size of the workforce displayed great variety. However, approximately one person in 6,000 is employed in manufacturing industry with 20 percent ergonomics duties. In service industry, one person in 1,500 is employed with 60 percent ergonomics-related duties. In consulting, educational and government research institutions, employment density and percentage responsibilities are much higher.
c. The degree of autonomy in initiating and/or executing ergonomics projects on a scale from zero (no independence) to ten (full independence) showed that ergonomists employed in industry enjoyed less freedom (five to six) than their counterparts elsewhere (seven to eight).
d. Industry people report that management displays mild support of their activities. The labor force is equally divided between full and mild support and indifference. Consultants, academicians and government ergonomists enjoy more support from management, but not necessarily from the labor force.

e. Most ergonomists (industrial 60 percent, others 70 percent) hold an advanced degree. Others stated their background in the field as on-the-job experience, seminar attendance, or completion of at least one course.
f. Published information in literature contributes to 50 percent of the daily routines of advanced-degree holders in manufacturing industry, educators, consultants, and government specialists. Their counterparts in service industry display a lower percentage in this respect (25 percent). The percentage decreases as educational sophistication drops.
g. Subjects that attract most project work, thus attention, by all respondents are: VDT (Video Display Terminal) ergonomics, office furniture and layout, general work place design and improvement, manual materials handling and biomechanics, and handtool design. Other subjects of interest are: human-computer interface, seating, training, cumulative trauma disorders, physiological and psychological stress, environmental effects (ventilation, heat stress, noise, lighting), systems safety, job/task design, job evaluation, selling ergonomics to management, equipment design, hospital ergonomics, and work physiology.

References

AFSC design handbook, DH1-3. 1977. Personnel subsystem. January.

Diffrient, N., A.R. Tilley, and D. Harman. 1983. *Humanscale 1/2/3, 4/5/6, 7/8/9*. Cambridge: The MIT Press.

Eastman Kodak Company. 1983. *Ergonomic design for people at work*. Belmont, Calif.: Lifetime Learning Publications.

Kvålseth, T.O. 1983. *Ergonomics of workstation design*. Kent, England: Butterworths & Co.

McCormick, E.J., and M.S. Sanders. 1982. *Human factors in engineering and design*. New York: McGraw-Hill Book Co.

Pulat, B.M. 1984. Ergonomics position survey. Unpublished report. North Carolina Agricultural and Technical State University. Greensboro, N.C.

Van Cott, H.P., and R.G. Kinkade, eds. 1972. *Human engineering guide to equipment design*. U.S. Government Printing Office. Washington, D.C.

Woodson, W.E. 1981. *Human factors design handbook*. New York: McGraw-Hill Book Co.

2

Physical Work

Mahmoud A. Ayoub, Ph.D.

Work in its many varieties taxes the human body in predictable and measurable fashion. In a purely physical sense, work represents the performance of a task of given attributes. Regardless of the title given to the task or job, there are parameters that define the workload which will be imposed on the body. These are *force, distance, time*. The three parameters define the physical work to be performed (force × distance), as well as the energy level that would be generated (force × distance/time). Work is usually measured in terms of Newton-meter, while energy is given in terms of Newton-meter/sec. The units are those of the metric system. Other units (pound-force, inch, etc.) can be used interchangeably. Any system of units can be used as long as consistency is maintained throughout the analysis or application.

Example: Consider a situation in which a worker is required to stack boxes in a warehouse. Each box weighs 50 pounds (22.2 kg). Boxes are taken off a conveyor that is 30 inches (0.75 m) above the floor and placed on a shelf located 12 inches (0.3 m) above the conveyor surface. The worker is expected to stack the boxes at rate of ten per minute. What is the job workload?

Workload is a function of the following:

a) force (weight in this case) = 22.2 × 9.8 = 217.6 *N*
   (9.8 = gravitational force)
b) distance = 0.3 m
c) time per lift = 0.10 min.

Combining a, b and c yields a workload of 652.7 N-m/min. The computed workload represents what the human body has to contend with.

The response of the human body to this workload will involve both the musculoskeletal and cardiovascular systems. This comes about as follows: (a) Muscular forces are required to enable the person to hold and move the weight between different levels; (b) the cardiovascular system provides the fuel that is necessary to maintain muscular work at a level appropriate for the job at hand. We consider these two aspects in some detail below.

Muscular Forces

Muscular forces developed in response to an imposed workload depend on (a) the muscle or muscles used; (b) the posture assumed throughout task performance; and (c) the amount of force required to meet task demand. Consider the following example:

Example: A person is holding a box with both hands. The box weighs 22 kg and is carried equally with both arms. The box is maintained in front of the body, with elbows bent at right angles (90°). Compute the muscular force required. Figure 1 shows the posture and load described.

To proceed with the computation, some assumptions have to be made:

a) Hand and forearm form one link.
b) The weight of the hand/forearm segment is 1.6 kg and is located 0.17 m from the elbow. This information is obtained

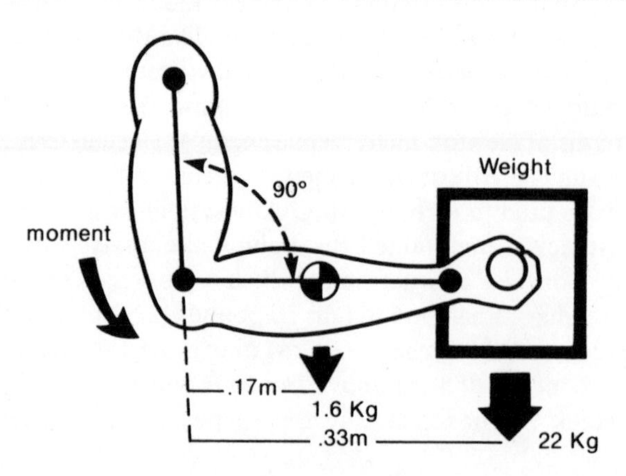

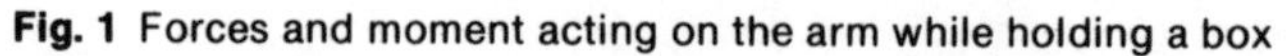
Fig. 1 Forces and moment acting on the arm while holding a box

from anthropometric tables using body weight and height (see Roebuck, Kroemer, and Thomson 1985).

c) Muscular forces necessary to balance the load will manifest themselves as moment (torque) about the elbow.

By definition, Moment = Force × Distance

Based on the above assumption and the data in figure 1, elbow moment $= 22 \times 0.33 + 1.6 \times 0.17 = 7.53$ N-m

This moment has to be resisted (balanced) by a moment developed by the elbow flexors. If for one reason or another the elbow flexors cannot develop the required moment, then we conclude that the demand exceeds the strength capability of the articulation joint. Accordingly, it would not be possible for the person to perform the task, that is, holding the box.

Strength limits of various body segments are readily available from many sources. For some specific data, see Laubach 1978.

Muscle Force

We can refine our analysis slightly by considering the work of individual muscles. In this case, we will assume that the biceps will provide the resisting moment (see figure 2).

To compute the muscular force, we invoke the three conditions for equilibrium.

a) Sum of all horizontal forces = 0
b) Sum of all vertical forces = 0
c) Sum of all moments about a given point = 0

From condition c, we write

$$- F \times 0.06 + 1.6 \times 0.17 + 22 \times 0.33 = 0$$

from which we compute $F = 125\ N$

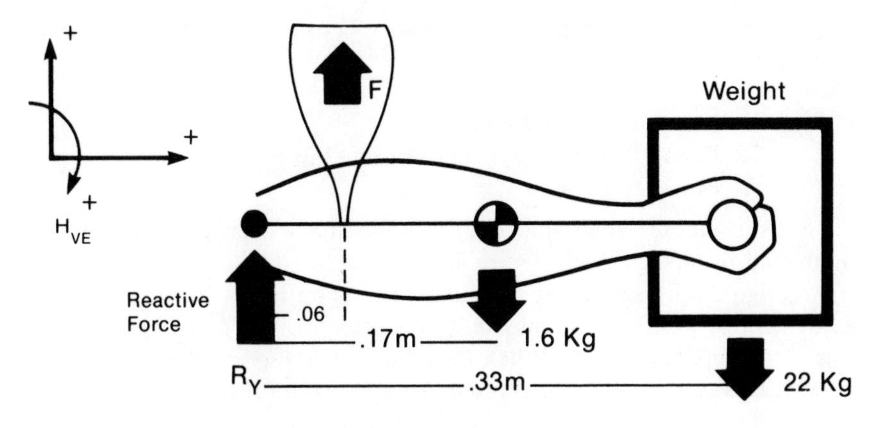

Fig. 3 Biceps force

We continue and compute the reactive forces at the elbow joint by applying conditions a and b; thus

$$R_x = 0 \quad N$$
$$R_y = 104.4 \ N$$

In all the above expressions, we used the sign convention shown in figure 2.

Force vs. Posture

To see the effect of posture on the required muscular force, we perform the same analysis from the previous example while allowing the hand/forearm to assume different positions (figure 3).

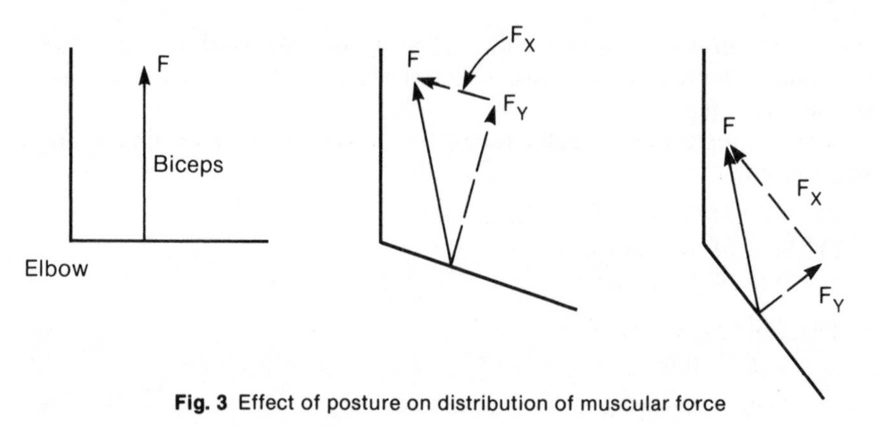

Fig. 3 Effect of posture on distribution of muscular force

The computation is essentially the same as before. At any position, elbow moment is $= m\,x \sin\theta$.

where

m = Mass of body segment

x = Distance of center of mass from elbow

θ = Forearm angle

Substituting different values for θ in the above expression, we obtain the overall results shown in figure 4.

As figure 4 indicates, the muscular force is optimal when the elbow is at 90°. In this position, the muscle is very effective and most of its power is used to support the load. When the elbow angle increases to point close to 180°, however, most of the muscle force is taken up as a thrust applied to the elbow joint. In this case, the effective lifting power is reduced con-

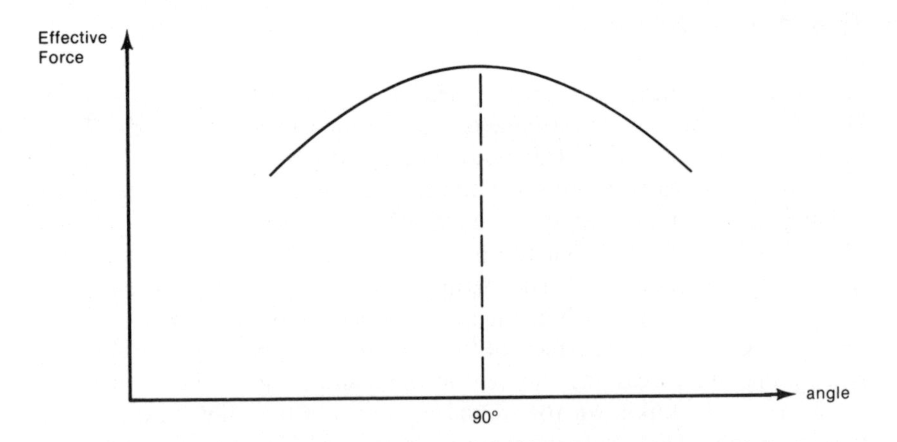

Fig. 4 Optimum elbow angle for maximum force

siderably. It is this last observation that demonstrates the importance of posture. That is, for every muscle or muscle group there exists an optimum posture which will yield the maximum force. It is important to notice that maximum muscle force (the force a muscle can generate) depends very much on the initial length of the muscle. If the muscle is shortened or stretched beyond its normal resting length, then its power (maximum force) will be reduced. Figure 5 shows this relationship. This can easily be demonstrated by using a hand grip dynamometer and having the handle size vary from minimum to maximum.

To summarize, available muscular force will depend on posture for both definition of initial muscle length and the amount of force that will be used to handle the external force weight.

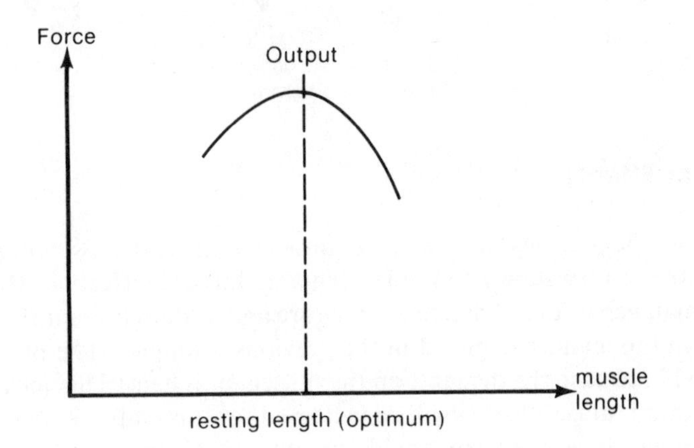

Fig. 5 Muscle force vs muscle length

The Whole Body

So far, we have dealt with one segment and in a very simplified fashion. However, we can expand this analysis to encompass the entire body. To do so, we use the concept of free body diagram (figure 6).

Notice that reactive forces and moments at the articular joints are applied to both corresponding ends of the segments. Each body segment is in a state of equilibrium by itself. Therefore, the three conditions for equilibrium (previously stated) do apply. To determine forces and moment at the articulation joint, we consider each of the body segments separately. For each segment, we account for the effects of the other body segment by appropriately placing reactive forces and moment at the common joint. Following this, we solve for the unknown forces and moments at the joint. Starting with the most removed link from the support, we proceed until the point of support is reached and all links are covered.

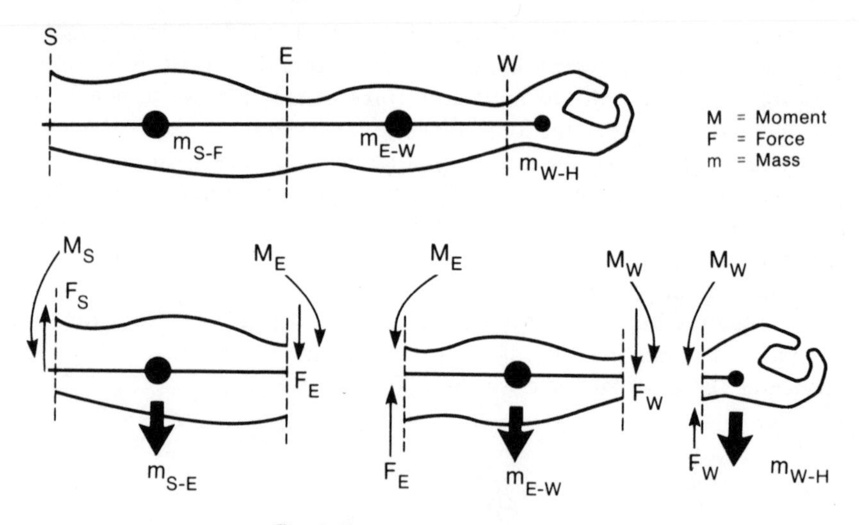

Fig. 6 Free-body diagram

Dynamic Effects

Throughout the previous examples, we considered the body as simply motionless or moving very slowly to render dynamic forces ineffective. However, most human activities are dynamic in nature and seldom present themselves as static in the manner depicted in the previous examples. The presence of motion will increase the demand on the muscular system. This means that, due to motion, muscle forces will be increased substantially. Increases of up to 500 percent have been computed for some motions.

The amount of increase depends on the speed with which the motion is executed. Dynamic analysis can be used to compute actual forces and moments at different articulation joints generated as a result of performing a given task. The computations are typically laborious as well as tedious. For this reason, use of computers is very advantageous (Plagenhoef 1971).

Electromyography (EMG)

Dynamic analysis yields information on the forces and moments to which the body and musculoskeletal system respond. As is known, motion recording and the corresponding analysis are cumbersome and may be of little interest to the practicing IE. The IE is typically interested in finding out the degree of muscular loading for a given task—that is, the determination of how hard the muscles work under specific task conditions.

Electromyography (EMG) offers a reasonable alternative to dynamic analysis. EMG is a technique for measuring the tension (force) developed as the muscle is shortened or put to work. Action potential that accompanies muscle tension is measured in terms of microvolts. Monitoring a specific muscle consists of placing a pair of electrodes on the muscle "belly." The signal from the electrodes is picked and then conditioned before it is displayed on a meter or chart. For some applications, the raw EMG signals are integrated or averaged over a specific period of time. (See Basmajian [1979] for details of EMG recording and analysis.) Muscle action potential (EMG data) varies as a function of several task, person, and workplace variables. The list of variables include: (a) posture, (b) speed, (c) force (weight handled), (d) range of motion, (e) muscle mass used, (f) work/rest schedule, (g) initial muscle length, (h) individual degree of fitness, (i) clothing, and (j) static loading.

EMG can be used to express objectively job muscular loading as a percentage of the monitored muscle maximum. If the computed percentage is less than 30 percent (or even 40 percent), then we may conclude that task loading is acceptable. For higher percentages, the task must be examined closely for possible redesign or adjustments.

Posture Targeting and Analyses

Posture analysis may be used as a substitute for both dynamic analysis and EMG measurements. Describing the posture of various body segments versus time does provide much information concerning (a) static loading, (b) concentration of job motion, and (c) extreme motions and positions at various body joints. This information is very important when a job/work place is evaluated or redesigned. For example, knowing that the job is characterized by much static loading would help the IE to define and then modify/change the work place component or method element that may be the source of the problem.

The advantage of posture analysis over other methods is the ease with which the assessment/evaluation can be carried out. The procedure involves the following steps. First, the person is filmed (videotaped) while performing the job. The person is filmed from two angles in order to record body segment motions in all planes. Filming should continue until several job cycles are covered. For repetitive jobs, this is usually accomplished in a few minutes. For most jobs, five minutes of recording would be long enough to cover hundreds (or more) of cycles. Recordings should be made for a representative sample of the persons assigned to the job being evaluated.

Following recording, the film or videotape is viewed in a systematic manner to sample for the occurrences of certain segment positions. A special form should be used for this purpose (see Corlett, Madeley, Manenica 1979). The form should be designed to document the various positions the segment assumes throughout the task cycle. The standard posture descriptors (flexion, extension, etc.) are used. The films or tapes are sampled for these positions for each body segment. The analyst goes through a frame-by-frame sampling until sufficient data are obtained to profile the various body segments on an eight-hour basis. Again, such information can be very useful when the redesign of jobs/work places is contemplated.

Physiological Responses

Muscular forces are the result of muscle shortening that involves consumption of fuel. Fueling the muscles taxes the cardiovascular and respiratory systems. The response is directly related to level of activity (workload). Physiological responses are assessed in terms of changes of some specific and measurable parameters such as heart rate, blood pressure, skin temperature, rectal temperature, oxygen consumption, ventilation rate, respiration rate, and concentration of metabolites in blood and urine.

These physical parameters can be measured using a number of well-established techniques and methods. For example, in the case of oxygen consumption, the Douglas bag method involves collecting the expired air in a bag. Collecting the air over a specified period of time and emptying the bag through a meter will yield the volume per unit time. This volume should be corrected for standard temperature and pressure to give the ventilation rate (V_E), expressed in liters/minute (l/min). If a sample of the expired air is analyzed for oxygen content, the oxygen consumption can be estimated as follows:

$$\dot{V}_{O_2} = \dot{V}_E\ (.209 - X)$$

where

$\dot{V}_{O_2}$ = Oxygen consumption, l/min

$\dot{V}_E$ = Ventilation rate, l/min

X = Oxygen concentration of expired air (sample), varies between .15 and .20

.209 = Oxygen concentration in ambient environment

If we assume that each liter of oxygen would yield 4.8 to 5.0 Kcal, energy expenditure (E) can be estimated directly from oxygen consumption; that is, $E = .29\ \dot{V}_E$. The respiration rate can be estimated by monitoring chest movement using a special transducer and corresponding equipment.

Each of the physiological responses (for example, heart rate and oxygen consumption) follows a pattern as shown in figure 7, which shows a profile of a typical heart rate vs. time.

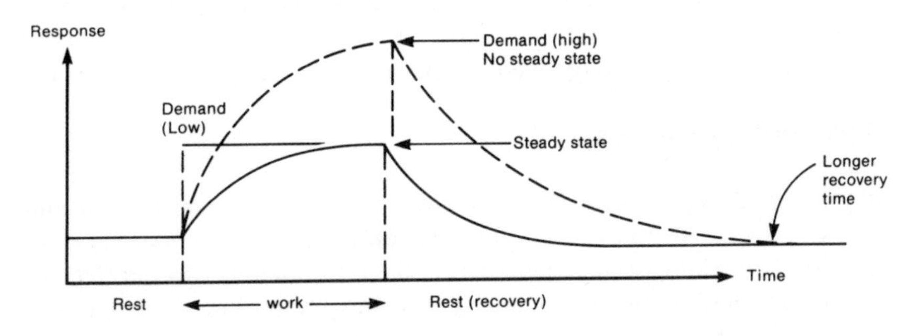

Fig. 7 Response pattern

At rest, the heart rate is at a minimum. When work commences, a brief time will pass before the heart rate is elevated to the level compatible with the workload. If the heart rate maintained by the body is sufficient to meet the demand imposed by the workload on the muscle, a steady state is achieved. This is indicated by the plateau in figure 7.

On the other hand, if the demand is such that it requires a maximum heart rate, then a steady state will not be realized. Instead, a steady climbing of heart rate will be observed until the work is stopped. Upon termination of activity, the heart rate will start to drop gradually until it reaches the resting level. The rest-work-rest pattern shown in figure 7 gives a cyclic pattern that may be repeated hundreds of times in the course of an eight-hour day. From figure 7, it can be seen that work/rest periods depend, to a large extent, on the workload level. For light to moderate levels, the length of the work cycle could last for two or so hours without any scheduled rest periods. However, for heavy and highly demanding work, the work cycle will, by necessity, have to be short and should be followed with rest periods of proper duration.

Another alternative to this would be to enlarge the job to encompass tasks with varying levels of demand. Job rotation (assigning two or more tasks, different in demands but related otherwise) will tend to bring the overall demand to managing levels.

Maximum Response

There are limits for the physiological responses that the human body can make. The following are examples of these limits:

Oxygen Uptake

Males

$$\dot{V}_{O_2} \max = 60 - 0.55 \times \text{Age (years)} \quad \text{ml/kg/min} \quad (SD = 7.5)$$

Females

$$\dot{V}_{O_2} \max = 48 - 0.73 \times \text{Age (years)} \quad \text{ml/kg/min} \quad (SD = 7.0)$$

Heart Rate

The maximum heart rate that can be attained in the absence of heart disease is given by

$$HR_{max} = 210 - 0.65 \text{ age (years)} \qquad (r = .96)$$

Contributing Factors

Physiological responses are influenced by a number of factors. These include age, sex, degree of fitness, nutrition, task duration, and the intensity of the workload. Physiologists maintain that for the same intensity of work, females' responses would be higher than males, assuming everything else being equal (Brouha 1960).

With age, maximum capacity declines. For example, with every decade, maximum heart rate decreases by ten beats. A fit person would become apparent in his or her response to a workload. The physiological responses of fit persons are markedly lower than those of individuals who might be classified as average or unfit. In other words, a fit person will be able to perform the same work but with less strain on the body.

Fitness can be gained through proper training (designed to enhance aerobic power, as well as to increase muscle strength). Fitness and adaptation can play a decisive role in the body's response to a hot environment. A fit and acclimatized person will be able to handle and tolerate a hot environment in a manner far superior to a person who otherwise is less fit. A person handling a highly intense task for extended periods of time will undoubtedly exhibit some signs of fatigue. This fatigue will take the form of higher levels of physiological responses. This means that as time goes on the heart rate, oxygen consumption, etc., will increase, even though the work load has remained the same. Introduction of proper rest periods (duration and timing) will tend to control or moderate the onset of fatigue.

Muscle mass used in task performance affects levels of physiological responses. Tasks with predominant arm movements tend to tax the heart more than those performed using the powerful muscles of the lower extremities. This is attributed to the size differences between blood vessels of the arms and lower extremities. Small blood vessels in the arms cause an increase in blood pressure, thus higher heart rate.

Wearing tight cloth may cause an increase of stress on the cardiovascular system. For example, tight pants impede blood flow to and from the lower extremities. This causes an increase in heart rate.

Standing jobs which do not allow the person to move around or utilize the feet much of the time impede return of the venous blood to the heart. In other words, the phenomenon known as "muscle pump" will be drastically reduced, if not lost. Slowing venous blood return results in blood pooling in the lower extremities, accompanied by an increase in heart rate. Heart rate is increased to compensate for the lower stroke volume caused by blood pooling.

Smoking and drugs do influence physiological responses. Smoking increases breathing resistance, which may become a limiting factor during exercise. Two cigarettes may raise the heart rate by twenty to thirty beats above normal level (Astrand 1977). Smoking lowers the oxygen-carrying capacity of the blood due to the combining of carbon monoxide and red blood cells. This means that, for the same level of effort, more blood must be pumped to the working muscles in order to compensate for loss of oxygen supply.

Alcohol affects the body in a number of well-defined ways: impaired judgment, loss of coordination, speech disturbances, memory loss, and loss of manual dexterity. In addition, alcohol causes changes in blood circulation, which in turn increases the workload on the heart.

Good posture promotes better circulation through proper positioning of internal organs. All of this reduces the strain on the cardiovascular system.

Relationships

The body's responses to an imposed workload can be assessed by measuring several parameters. However, for all practical purposes, only one or two parameters need to be measured. This is because the relationship between any two parameters (for example, heart rate and oxygen consumption) is basically linear. Furthermore, the relationship between workload and any of the physiological responses is also linear. It follows that, to assess a given job, not all the possible parameters need to be monitored.

Indeed, for most physically demanding jobs, monitoring the heart rate would be more than adequate to assess the physiological responses. This is particularly true in the case of hot jobs, for heart rate will reflect the degree of body strain due to the physical aspect of the job and thermal load imposed by the hot environment.

The following are some empirical formulas depicting these relationships. They represent data averaged over many jobs which involved several individuals with varying degrees of fitness.

Heart Rate $= 72.34 + 0.145 \times$ Workload (beats/min)
(Workload, kg-m/min)

Oxygen Consumption $= -1.3 + 0.02 \times$ Heart Rate (l/min)

Ventilation Rate $= 3.22 + 18 \times$ Oxygen Consumption (l/min)

Energy Expenditure = 5 × Oxygen Consumption (Kcal/min)

The above expressions serve as a means for estimating the limiting responses for individuals. And as such, individual differences may not be reflected in the limits computed. To avoid this pitfall, many individuals are assessed on submaximal or maximal tests. Based on the measured responses (such as oxygen consumption and heart rate), the limiting responses are computed (see Astrand 1977 for more details on how this can be done).

Example: Suppose that we have a group of men handling boxed materials in a warehouse. The boxes are lifted from the floor and placed on shelves 0.75-m high. Each box weighs 44 kg. Boxes are moved at the rate of twenty per min. What would be the expected physiological responses?

$$\begin{aligned} \text{Workload} &= \text{Force} \times \text{Distance} \times \text{Frequency} \\ &= 44 \times 0.75 \times 20 \\ &= 660 \text{ kg-m/min} \end{aligned}$$

Using the above expressions and for the given workload, we obtain the following estimates:

Heart Rate = 168 beats/min
Oxygen Consumption = 2.06 l/min
Ventilation Rate = 40.3 l/min
Energy Expenditure = 10.3 Kcal/min

Two additional methods can be used to estimate (predict) the physiological response on the job. These are to utilize regression functions and table-look ups. An example of these methods is given by Aberg, Elgshand, Margnus, and Lindholm 1968.

Job Classification

There are many schemes for classifying jobs based on physiological responses (table 1). The differences among classifications stems from (a) the number of classes assigned, and (b) the response range assigned to each class. For example, a light classification may be assigned a job that elicits a heart rate in the range of 70-100 beats/min. Another scheme may expand this class into two classes, light and very light, with two ranges for heart rate: 75-85, and

TABLE 1
Job Classification (Grandjean 1982)

	Very Light	Light	Heavy	Very Heavy
Oxygen Consumption	0.5–1.0	1.0–1.5	1.5–2.0	2.0–2.5
Heart Rate	60–100	100–125	125–150	150–175

85-100, respectively. Regardless of the classification scheme employed, a job that targets a heart rate of 100-110 beats/min can be considered moderate and acceptable for many manufacturing operations. Jobs that require levels in excess of 160 beats/min are unduly heavy, if not hazardous, and should be redesigned.

Applications

Being able to define physical workloads, as well as measuring or estimating the body responses to these loads, would allow the industrial engineer to perform one or more of the following:

1) *Job Evaluation*
   For a given job (carried out under a specific production schedule and personnel assignment), demand can be estimated. Following demand determination, the job (or group of jobs) may be classified on a scale from light to very heavy. With this classification in hand, a decision can be reached concerning what can be done (if anything) to change the job demands to bring them within reasonable levels.
2) *Job Redesign*
   Several job parameters contribute to the intensity of the workload. These include posture, tools, task time, force exerted (or weight handled) and the layout of the workplace. If a task is determined to be too excessive or demanding, then one first looks at the job parameters to see what can be changed/modified to reduce the job demands. Knowing job constraints (that is, what must remain or not be changed), it should not be difficult to change some of the parameters to bring the overall job demands within acceptable limits. See Ayoub (1982) for some specific examples.
3) *Pre-employment Screening*
   The premise behind any screening program is that of matching job requirements (demands) with potential employee capabilities. Given job demands and a means of assessing candidates' abilities, the desired matching can be obtained.
4) *Manual Handling Tasks*
   Materials handling jobs span a wide cross section of many industries, from light to heavy manufacturers, from service and light-assembly plants to warehousing and distribution centers. In all these cases, lifting, pushing, and pulling tasks (in all forms and varieties) do impose the greatest hazard to the musculoskeletal system, primarily that of the back.

   There are many measures that can be taken to lessen the load sustained by the back. These include (a) reducing the weight handled; (b) reducing the distance through which weight is moved; (c) increasing the time allocated to each lift; (d) training the worker in means and methods of handling a given load without subjecting themselves to excessive stress; (e) improving workplace layout to promote proper posture and handling methods. There are some specific guidelines for the evaluation of lifting jobs. As a minimum, *NIOSH Work Practice Guide* on lifting should be consulted when a job is being designed or evaluated.

5) *Static Loading*

There are many jobs in industry in which the physical demands and associated physiological responses would be considered light to moderate. Consequently, they tend to be considered as satisfactory, based on their demands. The majority of these jobs can be found in assembly jobs, in the electronic industry, in apparel and textiles, in data processing, etc.

Females are the predominant workers in these job categories. These jobs share some common characteristics:

a) Repetitive motions.
b) Most of the task motions are highly concentrated on few segments of the body, primarily the hands and forearm.
c) The uninvolved segments remain basically motionless over many job cycles—that is, most of the body is statically loaded.
d) Production rate (standard) is based and developed on the use of the principles of motion and time study. The job is viewed as performing a sequence of motion over well-defined points.
e) Work/rest schedules are not well-defined, or followed when defined. Indeed, more often than not, workers do work through their breaks. Therefore, some workers may simply put in eight solid hours with no breaks, and no more than a few visits to the bathroom.
f) Most workers are on incentive pay (piece rate). Under such systems, employees are expected, and indeed encouraged, to perform at a pace higher than that compatible with the standard rate (the so-called 100 percent rate). In developing these standards, IEs incorporated fatigue allowances in their estimates of the time. These allowances are based on data compiled some years ago and may not be reflective of today's work environment. The majority of workers may be physically unfit.

Considering all the above factors, one can see why those jobs are known for their high prevalence rates of cumulative trauma disorders. Tendinitis, carpal tunnel syndrome, and bursitis are some of the well-known disorders that affect many of the involved joints. Although there are many causative factors involved in producing the disorders, the presence of static loading is taken to play a major role, either as a causative or aggravating factor. Many studies and researchers have cited static loading as the leading cause of tendinitis or the more general class of cumulative trauma disorders. Static loading coupled with extreme posture may lead to pain, the severity of which will depend on task duration. We can illustrate this relationship by considering the following example.

Example: A person is asked to maintain the arm fully stretched in the front of the shoulder (in the sagittal plane). Assume that the weight of this arm is W and is located at a distance X from the shoulder. Further, let the arm be placed at an angle from the vertical (figure 8). What is the total effort extended by the person after a holding time of t minutes?

Moment M acting on the shoulder due to having the arm placed as shown in figure 8 is given by

$$M = W \cdot X \cdot \sin\theta$$

This moment M will be maintained for t minutes. By combining M and t, the effort E associated with the imposed posture is

$$E = M \cdot t$$

or

$$E = W \cdot X \cdot \sin\theta \cdot t$$

By rearrangement, we write

$$E/W \cdot X = \sin\theta \cdot t$$

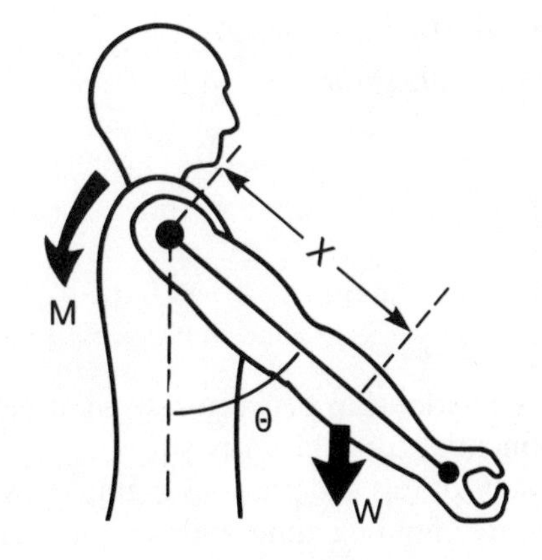

Fig. 8 Arm posture

For a fixed level of effort, the above relationship becomes figure 9.

$$\text{Sin } \theta \cdot t = K$$

Where K = constant with a value = $E/W \cdot X$.

It follows that, for a constant effort, the relationship between holding time and posture is basically exponential. That is, as the arm angle increases, the holding time decreases.

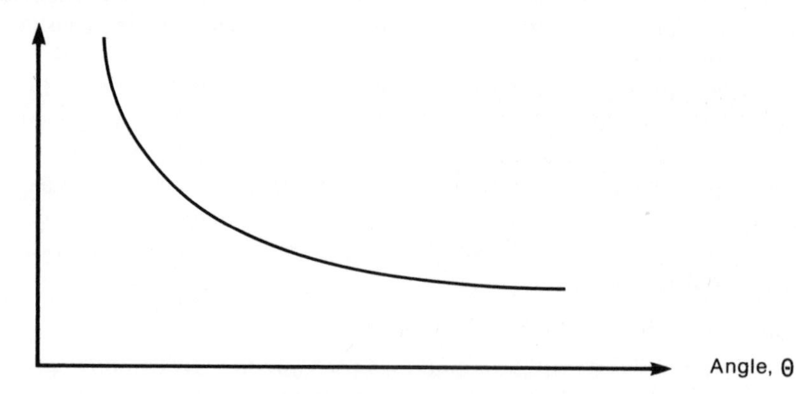

Fig. 9 Holding time vs arm position

Example: In the previous example, we limited the analysis to posture and holding time. Here, we like to look at the effect of having a weight carried in the hand. To simplify the calculation, assume that the load in the hand is at a distance $2L$ from the shoulder. Let F be the weight held in the hand. Find the total effort E for ± minutes of holding, while the arm is maintained at θ degrees from the vertical, where L = X.

Moment about the shoulder M is given by

$$L \cdot W \cdot \sin \theta + F \cdot 2L \sin \theta$$

The effort E =

$$(W \cdot L \cdot \sin \theta + 2F\,L \cdot \sin \theta)\,t$$

Rearrangement yields

$$K = (W + 2F) \cdot t \cdot \sin \theta$$

where K = Constant = E/L.

It follows that the relationship between F (weight held in hand) and t (holding time) is exponential for a given posture.

Combining the results of this and previous examples, we express the relationship between posture, holding time and weight carried as shown in figure 10.

Figure 10 shows that, as the weight and the angle increase, the holding time decreases—again assuming that the level of total effort is fixed for all

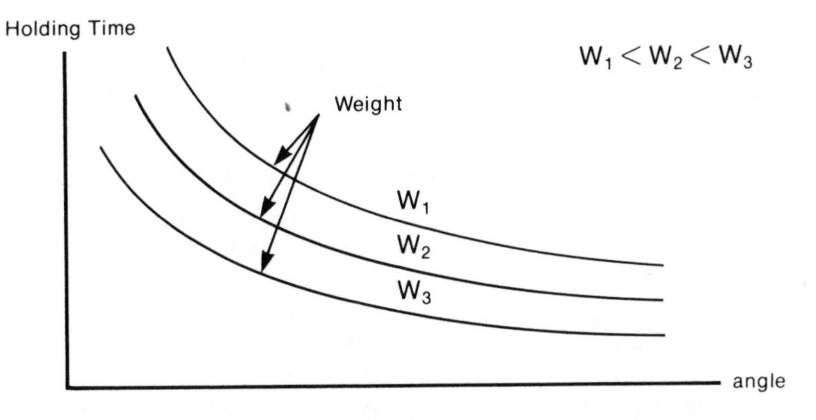

Fig.10 Effect of handing different weights on holding time

possible combinations. Chaffin and Anderson (1984) have provided a similar relationship between posture, weight and time to severe pain. It should be obvious that the time to severe pain is equivalent to the holding time in our examples. Caldwell and Smith (1966) have also given similar results.

The interpretation of the above relationships is evident when one reflects on the physiology of muscular work. A muscle contracts with a force that is sufficient to handle the imposed load. As a byproduct of muscle work, lactic acid is produced. When the muscle is forced to maintain a constant state of contraction (as in the case of static loading), much lactic acid is accumulated. In other words, the muscle becomes acidic and pain results.

In addition to accumulating lactic acid, a muscle in a continuous state of contraction will not receive direct fuel from the body (aerobic power). Instead, the muscle has to rely on the stored fuel within its cells. It follows that if the load imposed increases the muscle will deplete its stored fuel at an accelerating rate. In addition, the level of lactic acid will increase substantially. Depletion of muscle energy and lactic acid accumulation will lead to muscle pain.

The above discussion supports the following recommendations for repetitive jobs:

a) Avoid static load
b) Avoid extreme posture
c) Avoid extreme force
d) Avoid concentration of job stress (that is, using few muscles)

These recommendations can be implemented through the adoption of a program that encompasses the following elements: workplace improvement, method improvement, monitoring, rehabilitation and education (Ayoub 1982).

6) *Predetermined Time Systems*
Predetermined time systems, such as MTM, are based on the

assumption that a task, any task, can be broken down into a set of some fundamental motion elements. The list of the principal elements varies among the different systems. However, all the systems cover some common elements, such as *reach, grasp* and *position*.

Total task time (standard) is estimated by selecting time values from tables and charts provided for each system. The time values are based on the distance of motion. Qualifiers such as the degree of precision required in performing the motion and the body segment involved in its execution are used to create different categories (classes) for each element.

In assigning the time values to various elements, no attempt was made by any of the systems to take into consideration the degree of muscular stress that accompanies the performance of various motions. Reach, for example, varies as the distance travelled. Plane and direction of reach are considered to have no effect on the motion execution. The basis for this assumption is not very clear and runs contrary to how the muscles execute reach motions. Reaches which involve the shoulder joint (or the upper arm) rely heavily on the deltoid muscle (both anterior and middle parts). In turn, the force developed by the deltoid depends on the direction and plane of motion as well as the distance moved.

Figure 11 shows the results of an experiment in which EMG was used to assess the deltoid force (action potential) while performing different reaches. All reaches were carried out in three planes and in several directions within each plane. The three planes were defined to simulate horizontal, upward, and downward reaches. In each plane, reaches were made to a point located in the front (0° angle), to the side (90° angle) and diagonally (45° angle). The activity of both middle and anterior parts of the deltoid were monitored.

Results of the experiment show that the load on the deltoid (as assessed by the EMG) does vary with the direction of motion as well as with the plane of motion. The difference in muscle loading among various reaches is statistically significant. However, all the reaches would be assigned the same time value in accordance with MTM protocol. Some may argue that "fatigue allowances" are intended to compensate for factors such as excessive muscular loading. This is simply not so, for the allowances assigned to jobs are a mixture of time for personal needs and compensation for job difficulty or workplace conditions. And they definitely do not address problems associated with muscle fatigue or excessive muscular loading.

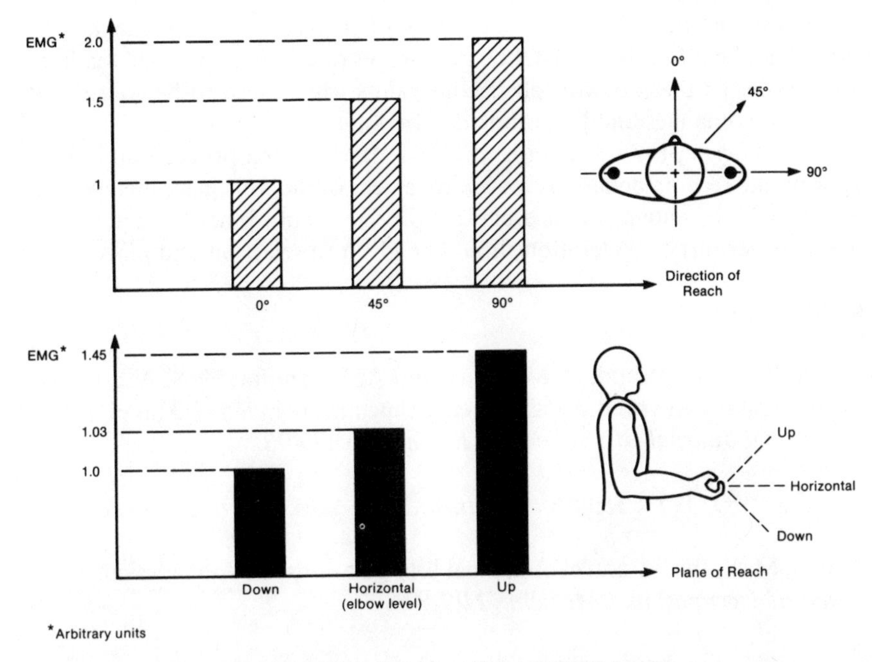

Fig. 11 Effect of reach pattern on EMG levels

There is a real need for revising and updating predetermined time systems to account for muscular loading that accompanies different motions and tasks. Until this is done, some of the criticisms usually levied at the use of predetermined systems will continue to have merit.

Excessive Physical Loading

Workload and the corresponding body responses depend on several specific and measurable parameters which include force, distance, time and individual degree of fitness. Jobs that encompass the extreme of these parameters are usually billed as too demanding. There are many contributing factors which, individually or collectively, have to be present for the level of demand to be excessive. For example, the occurrence of high force on the job may be the result of poor workplace design, using improper methods or poorly planned and organized jobs. All of these, as well as others, are considered as the source of ergonomic deficiencies.

Recognition and analysis of ergonomic deficiencies should be the first step in the process of job evaluation/redesign. For the process to be effective, the workplace, method, job, etc., should be surveyed and assessed in a systematic and orderly manner.

Following the tabulation and review of the recognized deficiencies, it should not be difficult to (a) define the sources of excessive physical loading, and (b) define the job/workplace constraints which need to be considered before any changes/modifications can be made.

Considering (a) and (b) together, the IE can then proceed and make appropriate recommendations for improvement of the workplace method and the overall job content. In the event that outright improvements are not feasible, then serious consideration should be given to selection and placement.

References

Aberg, V., K. Elgstrand, P. Margnus, and A. Lindholm. 1968. Analysis of components and prediction of energy expenditure in manual tasks. *International Journal of Production Research* 6:189-96.

Astrand, P.O. 1977. *Health and fitness*. New York: Barron's/Woodbury.

Ayoub, M.A. 1982. Control of manual lifting hazards: II. Job redesign. *Journal of Occupational Medicine* 24(9):668-76.

——. 1982. Occupational tendinitis control for the apparel industry. *Proceedings of IEA Conference*. Tokyo, Japan:162-3

Basmajian, J.V. 1978. *Muscles alive: Their functions revealed by electromyography*. Baltimore: Williams and Wilkins.

Brouha, L. 1960. *Physiology in industry*. New York: Pergamon Press.

Caldwell, L.S., and R.S. Smith. 1966. Pain and endurance of isometric muscle contractions. *Journal of Engineering Psychology* 5(1):25-32.

Calfin, D.B., and G. Anderson. 1984. *Occupational Biomechanics*. New York: Wiley Interscience.

Corlett, E.N., S.J. Madeley, and I. Manenica. 1979. Postural targetting: A technique for recording working posture. *Ergonomics* 22(3):357-66.

Grandjean, E. 1982. *Fitting the task to the man: An ergonomic approach*. London: Taylor & Francis, Ltd.

Laubach, L.L. 1978. Human muscular strength. In *Anthropometric source book, NASA No. 1024*. National Aeronautics and Space Administration, Washington, D.C.

Plagenhoef, S. 1971. *Patterns of human motion*. Englewood Cliffs, N.J.: Prentice-Hall.

Roebuck, J.A., K.H.E. Kroemer, and W.G. Thompson. 1975. *Engineering anthropometry methods*. New York: Wiley-Interscience.

***Mahmoud A. Ayoub** is a professor in the Department of Industrial Engineering, North Carolina State University, Raleigh.*

3

Mental Work

Barry H. Kantowitz, Ph.D.

As levels of technology have improved in the workplace, physical effort has been replaced by mental effort. At the lowest level of technology, the worker provides power and control for a simple system, for example, operating a shovel. The first improvement had machines provide power while the human still provided control, for example, operating a lathe. Newer and more complex systems provide power and information, although the human still remains in control, for example, operating a power plant. The highest level of technology removes the human from the control loop so that the machine provides power, information, and control, for example, an autopilot in a modern jet plane. The human acts as a system monitor and supervisor, intervening only rarely if at all.

As levels of technology and automation move from the factory floor to the office, the practicing industrial engineer will have to keep abreast by learning more about mental work. This does not imply that lessons learned about physical work will become irrelevant. The office worker who spends his working day entering data at a CRT (cathode ray tube) terminal cannot perform efficiently if physical ergonomic standards—chair and desk height, illumination and contrast, etc.—are not met. But it is clear that the physical effort required to work at a keyboard is only a small proportion of the entire job. Most of the job calls for mental rather than physical effort.

Experimental psychologists have compiled a vast literature that describes and explains human mental life. An overwhelming array of postulated mental processes and stages has been formulated and tested. Alas, almost none of this literature can be put to immediate use by the practicing engineer. The naive engineer who seeks solutions in the pages of the *Journal of Experimental Psychology* will find only frustration and jargon.

This puzzles engineers who do not know that experimental psychology is more concerned with formulating theoretical issues than in using the theory to solve practical problems. Out of sheer necessity, some engineers have begun to do their own psychological research. However, the human is an extremely complex system, and what appears to be a straightforward engineering approach to the problem is often fraught with methodological pitfalls. Doing effective research on mental work requires special training that most engineers lack.

But all is not lost. There are some engineers who have learned about psychology and some psychologists who have learned about engineering. Together, these people practice a profession that has been variously called engineering psychology, human factors, and/or ergonomics. You can use their findings to improve systems that require people to be interfaced to technology.

This chapter is intended to help practicing engineers, especially those without much training in ergonomics, understand the fundamental issues in mental work. Special emphasis is given to the limitations of the human as an information processor. Good system design requires that these limitations be taken into account. Topics covered include cognitive skills, errors and reliability, and simple ways to measure mental workload. An Appendix provides sources for additional information.

Cognitive Skills

The human boasts an impressive array of mental skills that allow him to function well in an uncertain world. He can detect faint stimuli, such as the flame of a single candle thirty miles away on a clear, dark night. The same transducer can function over a wide range of input values; for example, your ear can function to allow you to hear both the ticking of a watch twenty feet away as well as the takeoff of a jet plane. Indeed, because of this wide range, it is customary to use logarithmic scales to measure human sensory performance. The human can control a complex series of motor outputs—observe a gymnast or a typist at work. The human can easily recognize patterns embedded in noise; until recently, no computer program could recognize fingerprints, so this operation was performed manually by people. The human can develop heuristics to solve problems when algorithms are too costly or do not exist; many artificial intelligence techniques for playing games like chess are derived in part from human problem-solving techniques. The human can make incomensurables comensurable by taking a multivariate decision space, such as deciding what job to take which combines the dimensions of salary, location, type of work, etc., and mentally collapsing it to form a single decision axis. The human is adaptive and can generate solutions to problems that have not been anticipated by system designers. Finally, when the human is so overloaded that failure cannot be avoided, the human fades away gracefully under stress, whereas machines fail suddenly in all-or-none fashion. For all these reasons (and more), humans will be a vital part of industry for the forseeable future.

Despite this impressive panoply of cognitive skills, there are chinks in the armor and some kinds of human mental failures are more likely than others. The human has limited processing resources and, so, can be overwhelmed by unfriendly mental environments. In particular, the areas of memory and attention stand out as potential sources of human mental error. The following two subsections illustrate typical problems in these areas.

Memory

Although experimental psychologists have studied memory for more than a century, the resulting theoretical controversies hardly inspire confidence in the practitioner who wishes to minimize human memory error in some existing real-life system. Nonetheless, it is possible to make some general statements about memory that the engineer can use.

First, at the risk of considerably oversimplifying the theoretical debate within experimental psychology about the number of internal memory systems, we can limit discussion to only two kinds of human memory. We distinguish between the kind of memory used to hold very recent events versus memory for information that is acquired days, weeks, or even years earlier. *Working memory* contains recent events, such as the information that a warning signal occurred ten seconds ago. *Long-term memory* contains all kinds of older information such as your telephone number and operating procedures for some particular system. While long-term memory holds a tremendous amount of information, working memory can hold only a few items at one time. (There is debate as to exactly how many items, but we will probably be safe if we assume it to be less than a dozen and perhaps as few as three or four.)

One obvious implication of these relative capacities is that long-term memory should be substituted for working memory whenever possible. However, information cannot be withdrawn from long-term memory without invoking working memory in most instances. So this obvious strategy will not work. We must instead try to minimize demands upon working memory.

Information is maintained in working memory by a process called *rehearsal*. Rehearsal is a non-automatic process that requires effort and attention in ordinary circumstances. So the need to rehearse information diminishes one's capacity for handling other stimuli and events. When rehearsal is interrupted, information will be lost from working memory. For example, imagine a situation where you are required to look up a computer password in a code book that is located away from the computer console. On your way back to the console, you rehearse the password by covertly repeating it to yourself over and over again. If a co-worker interrupts you before you can enter the password, perhaps by asking a question, there is a good chance that you will forget the password. (Incidentally, this chance is increased if the password is a random combination of digits and letters. A meaningful word is easiest to remember. A non-word that you can pronounce, for example, PONAT, is also better than a random combination, but not quite as good as a real word.)

It is crucial to minimize the load placed on working memory by selecting appropriate hardware and procedures. At one time, air-traffic controllers had to remember which dots on their scopes corresponded to particular flights. Often, the controller had to request a particular plane to make some maneuver (for instance, turn right 360°) merely to confirm that his identification of the plane was correct. A grease pencil was some help but required frequent erasure and updating of the screen. Now this task has been allocated to the machine, which has a far more reliable working memory than does the human controller. Flight names are automatically displayed on the oscilloscope and additional information, such as altitude, can also be displayed. The net result is to make work much easier for the controller by minimizing demands on working memory. Many other examples could be cited to demonstrate this principle. If human performance is unreliable, the engineer must check that working memory has not been overloaded.

Attention

As with memory, there are several varieties of attention studies by psychologists, and we shall again limit discussion to only two. *Selective attention* allows us to focus our efforts upon one particular portion of the environment, despite other potential distractions. *Divided attention* refers to our ability apparently to perform more than one task simultaneously. Your ability to conduct a conversation at a cocktail party despite the babel surrounding you is an instance of selective attention. Your ability to read this book while simultaneously listening to a baseball game illustrates divided attention.

One traditional technique for improving selective attention requires coding of displays and controls in person-machine systems. A simple example would be having a display turn red to indicate a fault. A single red signal in a bank of green signals is easy to notice. Of course, if all the signals turned red, we would again have a problem in selecting the key display that highlights the fault at hand. Similarly, shape coding of controls in an airplane cockpit aids the pilot in selecting one particular control from the set of all controls. Sometimes in stressful situations selective attention can be locked into a narrow range so that other important events are neglected. A tragic example of this narrowing of attention accounted for the crash of an airliner over the Florida Everglades. Eastern Flight 401 was diverted from a night landing at Miami International Airport because the instrument panel did not show a positive lock for the nose gear. The crew set the autopilot to maintain 2,000 feet while they concentrated upon this problem. No one noticed when the autopilot was accidently disengaged and the plane entered a gradual descent. Attention that normally would have been given to the altimeter, a crucial instrument, had been diverted to the nose gear. The plane crashed, killing ninety-nine of the 176 people aboard.

A worker whose job calls for divided attention cannot simply ignore part of the environment in order to focus upon one aspect or task. In this situation, nearly all inputs must be processed. People have a limited capacity to attend to several tasks simultaneously. While a job may not overtax this ability during average working conditions, it is quite common for peak loads to induce failures of divided attention. One helpful hint for the engineer who must redesign the person-machine interface is to divide the human's task into input (perceptual) and output (response selection and control) requirements. Studies of divided attention have shown that people can process incoming information in parallel, whereas output in most common situations is serial. Hence the mental bottleneck is more likely to be in generating control outputs than in assimilating incoming information. So, if it is not possible to slow down both input and output rates, the human will benefit more if output demands are decreased.

Mental Workload

It is relatively easy to get a clear index of physical workload based upon objective task measures (for example, lift a 100-pound pallet 4 feet) or physiological indexes of human performance such as oxygen consumption. Hence, reasoning by analogy, it seems at first that some comparable index of mental workload should also be available. Unfortunately, such is not the case. There is no single number that scales mental workload and it appears that researchers will never agree upon a single best method for evaluating mental workload. There is even a lack of agreement concerning the proper definition of mental workload. While we all have an intuitive understanding of what is meant by mental workload, precise technical definitions are difficult to come by. Mental workload is most often defined in terms of the operations used to measure it.

Three common techniques have been applied to measuring mental workload: subjective ratings, behavioral timesharing, and psychophysiological indexes. Subjective ratings are obtained simply by asking workers to rate their internal experience of workload by stating a number. Behavioral timesharing requires the simultaneous performance of a side (or secondary) task, along with the primary task of interest. The degree of decrement on the side task is considered an index of mental workload. Psychophysiological techniques require simultaneous measurement of heart rate or brain waves, which are then interpreted as indexes of mental workload. While the last two techniques have the considerable advantage of being related to theoretical models, making data easier to interpret, they require sophisticated equipment and data-collection techniques. Thus, the practicing engineer has little recourse but to make do with subjective ratings, even though their interpretation can be obscure at times.

The easiest way to get a subjective rating of mental workload is simply to ask an operator to estimate workload in a specific task by giving a number on some arbitrary scale. Scales of 1 to 7 and of 0 to 100 have been most common. Often, verbal descriptions are attached to the ends of the scale so that, for example, 1 might mean extremely little mental work and 7 might mean extremely heavy mental work. While the exact meaning of a particular rating, say 4.2, is unclear, one can still compare a set of two or more specific tasks to determine which task gets the highest rating. It is important to obtain ratings from experienced workers either who are doing the task as the ratings are obtained (preferred method) or who have done the task previously and are giving ratings based upon their memory.

A better, but also more expensive, way involves using several sub-scales that refer to different mental components of the task at hand. These sub-scales can be combined statistically to create a single number representing overall calculated mental workload. The following table summarizes this technique as used by researchers in the Human Performance Group, NASA-Ames Research Center. To calculate an overall workload score, each sub-scale is multiplied by an appropriate weight. In general, the weights are different for different people. For any one person, the weights are obtained by asking people to select which of a pair of sub-scales is more important as a contributor to overall mental workload. All possible pairs of sub-scales are compared in this manner. The number of times a particular sub-scale was preferred to other sub-scales is its weight. (Sometimes this weight is normalized by dividing by the total number of paired comparisons to make the weights less than 1.) The overall workload rating is calculated as the weighted sum of each sub-scale rating, that is, each person's rating on a sub-scale is multiplied by the weight of that sub-scale and all these products are added together.

Rating Scale Descriptions

Title	Endpoints	Description
Overall Workload	Low, high	The total workload associated with the task, considering all sources and components.
Task Difficulty	Low, high	Whether the task was easy or demanding, simple or complex, exacting or forgiving.
Time Pressure	None, rushed	The amount of pressure you felt due to the rate at which the task elements occurred. Was the task slow and leisurely or rapid and frantic?
Performance	Failure, perfect	How successful you think you were in doing what you were asked and how satisfied you were with what you accomplished.
Mental/ Sensory Effort	None, impossible	The amount of mental and/or perceptual activity that was required (for example, thinking, deciding, calculating, remembering, looking, searching).
Physical Effort	None, impossible	The amount of physical activity that was required (pushing, pulling, turning, controlling, activating, etc.).
Frustration Level	Fulfilled, exasperated	How insecure, discouraged, irritated, and annoyed versus secure, gratified, content, and complacent you felt.
Stress Level	Relaxed, tense	How anxious, worried, uptight and harassed or calm tranquil, placid, and relaxed you felt.
Fatigue	Exhausted, alert	How tired, weary, worn out, and exhausted or fresh, vigorous, and energetic you felt.
Activity Type	Skill based, rule based, knowledge based	The degree to which the task required mindless reaction to well-learned routines, required the application of known rules, or required problem-solving and decision-making.

Appendix

The first place to look for more information would be a human factors textbook. I recommend Kantowitz, B.H., and Sorkin, R.D., 1983, *Human Factors*, New York: John Wiley & Sons. Next would be journals. *Ergonomics Abstracts*, published by Taylor & Francis Ltd. (London, England) is the single best place to look. This journal is available in large libraries. It classifies abstracts both by topic and by industry. You can browse through the major journals in the field, *Human Factors, Ergonomics,* and *Applied Ergonomics*, but this is usually much less efficient than using the abstracts. If this fails, you are in over your head and need to obtain expert assistance. Many companies have human factors sections who can be sources of expert help. A NATO conference on mental workload is available as a book: Moray, N., ed., 1977, *Mental workload*, New York: Plenum Press, but its information is becoming dated.

Barry H. Kantowitz *is professor of psychology with the Department of Psychological Sciences, Purdue University, West Lafayette, Indiana.*

Foundations of Ergonomic Job Design

Stephan Konz, Ph.D.

There are eight foundations of ergonomic job design, table 1. The eight foundations lead to five ergonomic design principles (see table 2). Then sixteen work station design principles are given.

Eight Foundations

1. People vary. Some people are tall, others short. Some are strong, others weak. Some are dexterous, others clumsy. Some read well, others read poorly. Some can see well, others see poorly. There is not just an average person; there is variability about that average. In addition, the person who can read well is not necessarily strong or tall. And the person who is dexterous may not have good vision. Not only does the population vary about an average characteristic, but also specific individuals have specific strong and weak points.

2. People are more educated. Figure 1 shows how a high school education (and even more) has become the norm. Thus, ordinary workers should be considered as sources of information about their jobs, not as unthinking

TABLE 1
Foundations of Ergonomic Job Design

1.	People vary.
2.	People are more educated.
3.	People want a say.
4.	Safety and health are more important.
5.	The world is becoming smaller.
6.	Machines are becoming more capable.
7.	Job specialization is changing.
8.	Jobs are more interrelated.

TABLE 2
Ergonomic Design Principles

1.	Make the machine adjust to the man.
2.	Minimize the percentage excluded by the design.
3.	Design jobs to be more cognitive and social and less physical and procedural.
4.	Emphasize communication.
5.	Use machines to extend human performance.

assemblies of muscle and bone. Unfortunately, many of our management concepts date from the time when a grade school education was typical.

3. People want a say. Our society is becoming more and more democratic. There are still pockets of authoritarianism ("Don't ask questions; do it because I say so") but, over the years, we have become, more and more, a participative society. Increasing participation probably is related to increasing education. This increasing participation by informed workers on the design of their job may not only furnish the engineer with additional information, but also increase the acceptance of the ideas. In contrast, the authoritarian exhibition of expertise probably will lead to poor designs that will not be implemented. Note the popularity of the Quality of Working Life (QWL) activities that the Quality Circles now operate in over 2,500 American firms.

4. Safety and health are more important. Table 3 gives the historical progress of occupational safety and health in the United States. Society now has greater expectations from a designer and from management. Attention to just the bottom line of productivity no longer is sufficient.

5. The world is becoming smaller. It's not becoming physically smaller, but improved communication and transportation have reduced the effect of distance. If a manufacturing job has a high total labor content (the product of number of units times labor hours/unit), it probably will be done in Third

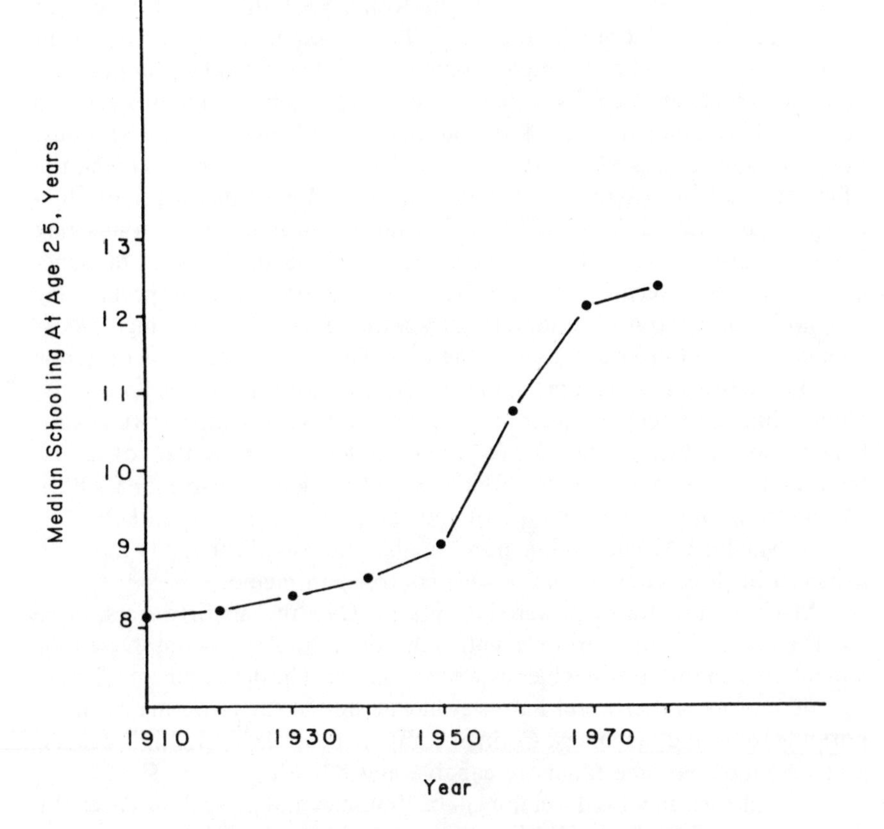

Fig. 1 High school education (and more) has become the norm

TABLE 3

Both safety and health are receiving more emphasis. An index of safety is the annual occupational death rate. An index of the interest in occupational health is membership in the American Industrial Hygiene Association.

Year	Deaths, Rate/ 1000,000 workers	Membership in AIHA
1933	37	
1940	38	160
1950	27	621
1960	21	1165
1970	17	1649
1980	13	5003
1981	12	
1984		6264

World countries (Brazil, Taiwan, Hong Kong, Sri Lanka, etc.) instead of the United States, since their labor costs/hour often are less than 10 percent of those in the U.S. For example, assume a task has a production quantity of 100,000 units and requires one hour/unit. Then labor content is 100,000 hours. If U.S. labor costs are $10/hour and Hong Kong costs are $1/hour, the U.S. labor cost is $1,000,000 and the Hong Kong cost is $100,000; the Third World labor savings is $900,000. Even if Hong Kong labor productivity is half that of the U.S. (that is, it takes two hours/unit), the Hong Kong cost rises to $200,000 and the saving still is $800,000. Since management can communicate with these distant locations easily (especially by telephone) and air transportation is quicker than formerly, many high-labor-content jobs no longer are done in the U.S. The relative slowness of goods transported by ship doesn't make much difference for standardized products. High-value items such as electronics come by air. Our comparative advantage in manufacturing is moving to goods that have a high content of *skilled* labor and a high content of research and development. These changes have had a strong impact on the type of jobs done by American workers.

6. Machines are becoming more capable. Increased capability has been achieved in three dimensions: power, control and memory.

Machines usually are powered by motors. Over the last fifty years, there has been considerable improvement in motor technology—compressed air and internal combustion engines as well as electric. The development of small electric motors and efficient batteries has permitted the powering of many portable tools and machines. Control components (relays, circuit breakers, switches) have become far more capable and reliable.

Complementing this development of "muscles and nerves" has been the development of the "brain"—the computer. Initially, machine memory was primitive, with information being stored in groups of relays. Approximately fifty years ago, the stored program computer was developed. Since then, a large variety of storage media have been developed—providing more memory at lower cost and with quicker access. Table 4 shows the decreasing cost of computers—decreasing not only in absolute terms but, more importantly, versus the cost of human labor. Computers also have become smaller and more reliable with the switch from vacuum tubes to transistors to integrated circuits.

TABLE 4
Relation of Labor and Computer Costs in the USA

Year	Unit labor costs	Computer price, instructions/s	Ratio
1970	100	100	100/100 = 1.00
1975	135	35	35/135 = 0.26
1980	196	8	8/196 = 0.04

These improvements in machine power, control, and memory have many effects. Computers can substitute for human control of machine power. For example, an automatically guided vehicle (AGV) can replace the human driver of an industrial truck. A numerical-controlled (NC) machine tool can move a drill bit to a predetermined location and begin drilling. Improved sensors and circuits permit feedback control rather than open loop control. For example, the AGV can stop if there is an obstacle in its path; the NC machine tool can substitute a new drill bit if the drilling torque gets too high (as when a tool is dull). Machine memory permits quick and flexible access to large amounts of data. Examples are airline ticket reservations, production control and scheduling, payrolls, and word processors.

7. Job specialization is changing. Examples abound. Consider the situations in 1835, 1885, 1935, and 1985. In 1835, we had a military engineer. Then, specializations were added for civil engineering, mining, mechanical, aerospace, industrial, etc. Will an ergonomics engineer be next? Teachers had the "one-room schoolhouse." Then teachers began teaching by grades and then by topics within a grade. In these cognitive and social jobs, specialization increased.

Yet for other American jobs there has been a decrease in specialization. There are many examples. A gandy dancer on a railroad spent the entire day driving spikes into railroad ties; an assembly operator spent the entire year adding three components to an assembly; a store clerk spent the entire year in one department. Now, the railway maintenance worker does a variety of tasks, the assembly operator works on a variety of products (often multiple products within a day), and the clerk works in different departments and does different tasks on different days. In these physical and procedural jobs, specialization decreased.

8. Jobs are more interrelated. At one time individual incentive plans were popular. The worker was told to produce X units. If a worker produced 10 percent more, the worker was paid 10 percent more. Now there are not many simple repetitive jobs left in the United States in which the output is controlled by one individual. More and more "everything touches." Very few jobs stand alone. The assembler's work is influenced by a multitude of other workers, the dentist has several assistants, the truck driver depends on the mechanic and the dispatcher, the waitress depends on the hostess and the cook and the busboy.

These eight foundations lead to five ergonomic design principles.

Five Design Principles

Ergonomic Principle 1: Make the machine adjust to the man. Personnel selection, in contrast, means finding a person who can adapt to the machine. Adjusting the machine to the man involves not just physical adjustment of the machine controls and displays so people can use them, but also conceptual design so the machine is user-friendly. That is, the machine is designed so it can be operated with minimum error and effort by a wide range of potential users. Make procedures easy for people. The key concept is that if the man/machine system does not function well, the system should be redesigned rather than blame being placed on the operator.

Ergonomic Principle 2: Minimize the percentage excluded by the design. Use of any machine or procedure requires certain human capabilities (strength, education, dexterity, reach distance, visual acuity, etc.). The goal is to permit "everyone" to use the machine or procedure. In practice, a few potential users can be excluded. For example, for an industrial material handling task, children and adults over seventy can be excluded. Or, for operation of a word processor, people with less than one hour of training may be excluded. However, our society wants the percentage of people excluded to be small. For example, confinement to a wheelchair no longer should prevent access to buildings; being female no longer should prevent doing various jobs.

Ergonomic Principle 3: Design jobs to be more cognitive and social and less physical and procedural. Physical work now tends to be done by machines (such as a power hand saw, nailing gun, lift truck, backhoe, hoist, and conveyor). The operator *controls* the power instead of *furnishing* the power. Procedural work in manufacturing in the U.S. is being replaced by the same work done in low-wage economies. In addition, the procedural work remaining in the U.S. in both manufacturing and service industries is being replaced by cams, circuits, and computers. Thus, by elimination, the jobs that remain are more cognitive and social. If there is physical or procedural work, it probably will be highly varied and intermittent. By 1980, over 50 percent of the jobs in the USA were in the office.

Ergonomic Principle 4: Emphasize communication. Communication can be from the man to the machine, the machine to the man, and from person to person. People communicate to machines through controls; machines communicate to people through displays. People can communicate with each other through a number of senses but the primary mode is visual. Within visual, there again are many alternatives (such as by direct vision, video, and even the old standby, the printed word). Improved communication not only improves speed of information transfer but, more important, reduces errors. Reduced errors improve productivity by requiring less time to do a task and gives a high-quality product (which is easier to sell).

Ergonomic Principle 5: Use machines to extend human performance. Machines are not only becoming more capable, but also more economical than U.S. labor. Machine cost tends to be relatively low. Machine cost has three basic components: capital, maintenance, and power.

Power is usually furnished by electricity, either through electric motors or compressed air. (The cost of compressed air is strongly influenced by the electricity cost for compressing the air.) At present, industrial power costs are 3 to 10 cents/kwh. Although there are a few large machine tools which use over one kw in an hour, most machines use far less (especially in offices, where over 50 percent of the population works). A word processor might use power at the rate of 0.5 kw or less. Thus, for most machines, power cost is less than 10 cents/hour.

Maintenance cost depends upon the machine. In a year of 2,000 hours (50 weeks × 40 hours/wk), a typewriter might require $100 of maintenance, or 5 cents/hour. A word processor might cost $500 a year, or 25 cents/hour. An automobile might require $500, or 25 cents/hour. A machine tool might required $1,000, or 50 cents/hour. Thus, for most machines maintenance requires less than 25 cents/hour.

Capital cost is the third cost. A $4,000 word processor which lasts ten years would be $4000/20,000 hours = 20 cents/hour. A $10,000 car which lasts five years would be 10,000/10,000 hours = 100 cents/hour. A $20,000 machine tool or lift truck which lasts ten years would be $20,000/20,000 hours = 100 cents/hour. Thus most machines have capital costs of less than a dollar. (I have made a number of simplifying assumptions such as purchase cost = installed cost and zero salvage value.)

When capital, maintenance, and power costs are added together, most machines cost less than a dollar or two per hour; with smaller machines (for example, typewriters, word processors, nailing guns) cost often is less than a quarter.

What is labor cost? It's higher—much higher. In 1985, the minimum *wage* is $3.35/hour, but many industrial workers are paid $8, $10, or more per hour. To this must be added the cost of fringe benefits (Social Security, holidays, vacations, medical benefits, etc.). Fringes tend to run from 20 percent to 50 percent of wages. Thus labor *costs* probably run from a minimum of $4/hour to over $20/hour. Table 5 summarizes the comparison.

Thus it is important to maximize the utilization and capability of the expensive portion of the system—the human. To do this, extend the human's performance with the support of machines.

Workstation Design

The previous section gave the big picture; this section will give a summary of the detailed picture. Table 6 gives the sixteen principles concerning the design of a work station. For more details and examples of the detailed picture, see *Work Design: Industrial Ergonomics* (Konz 1983) and *Facility Design* (Konz 1985).

1. *Avoid static loads and fixed work postures.* Our bodies work better when they have a dynamic load instead of a static load. Figure 2 shows how a static load can be changed by work station design.

2. *Set the work height at 2 in. below the elbow.* The optimum work height, the same for sitting and standing, is based on the elbow. Since the height of the elbow varies with sitting and standing, and people come in

TABLE 5
Cost/Hour for Machines and People

Machine Costs	**Example of a Word Processor**	
Capital		**$/hour**
Capital cost/hour of machine life	$4000/(10 yr × 2000 hours/yr	= 0.20
Maintenance		
Annual cost/annual hours	$500/2000 hours	= 0.25
Power		
KWH (cost/kwh)	0.5 kw (0.06 $/kwh)	= 0.03
		0.48
Labor Cost		
Wage rate (1 + fringe percent)	$6 (1 + 0.3)	= 7.80
or	$10 (1 + 0.3)	13.00

TABLE 6
Principles Concerning Physical Design of the Work Station (Konz 1983)

1. Avoid static loads and fixed work postures.
2. Set the work height at 2 inches below the elbow.
3. Furnish every employee with an adjustable chair.
4. Support limbs.
5. Use the feet as well as the hands.
6. Use gravity; don't oppose it.
7. Conserve momentum.
8. Use two-handed motions rather than one-handed motions.
9. Use parallel motions for eye control of two-handed motions.
10. Use rowing motions for two-hand motions.
11. Pivot movements about the elbow.
12. Use the preferred hand.
13. Keep arm motions in the normal work area.
14. Let the small woman reach; let the large man fit.
15. Locate all materials, tools, and controls in a fixed place.
16. View large objects for a long time.

various sizes, any work station that puts the work a fixed distance from the floor, whether the person is sitting or standing or is big or little, is bad design.

Fig. 2 Reduce static loading and twisting of the neck and torso during typing by putting source documents on an adjustable arm ahead of the eyes (left), not to the side (right). Making the distance of the document holder easily adjustable permits the operator to set the holder at the operator's own focus distance (Konz, 1985)

Although for most work the optimum work height is 2 in. below the elbow, for keying work (computers, typing) it is slightly above the elbow. Note that work height is not table height—most items have a thickness of 1 to 5 in.

There are three design approaches: change machine height, change elbow height, and change work height. Changing machine height is most useful if one operator uses the machine for a month or more. It is relatively easy to modify the height of many benches and tables. A two-level typing desk is a common office example. Figure 3 shows how conveyors and pallets should be adjusted so the move (whether loading or unloading the conveyor) is always downhill. Changing elbow height is most commonly done with adjustable-height chairs, although standing operators can stand on platforms. Changing work height can be done by lowering container bottoms (grocery sack on shelf), tipping parts containers on their side (so you need not reach over the box side), or even cutting away the box side.

3. *Furnish every employee with an adjustable chair*. The cost of an adjustable industrial chair is very low. Cost is capital cost, as maintenance and power costs are zero. Assuming a price of $200/chair, a life of ten years, and 2,000 working hours/year, cost/hour is $200/20,000 = 1 cent/hour. Assume a typical labor cost (wages + fringe) is $10/hour. Thus, if output improved only 0.1 percent, this is worth 1 cent/hour. In an eight hour day, 0.1 percent is 0.001 (480 min) = 0.5 min = 30 seconds. Will a good chair improve productivity by 30 seconds/day? If you think yes, get the chair.

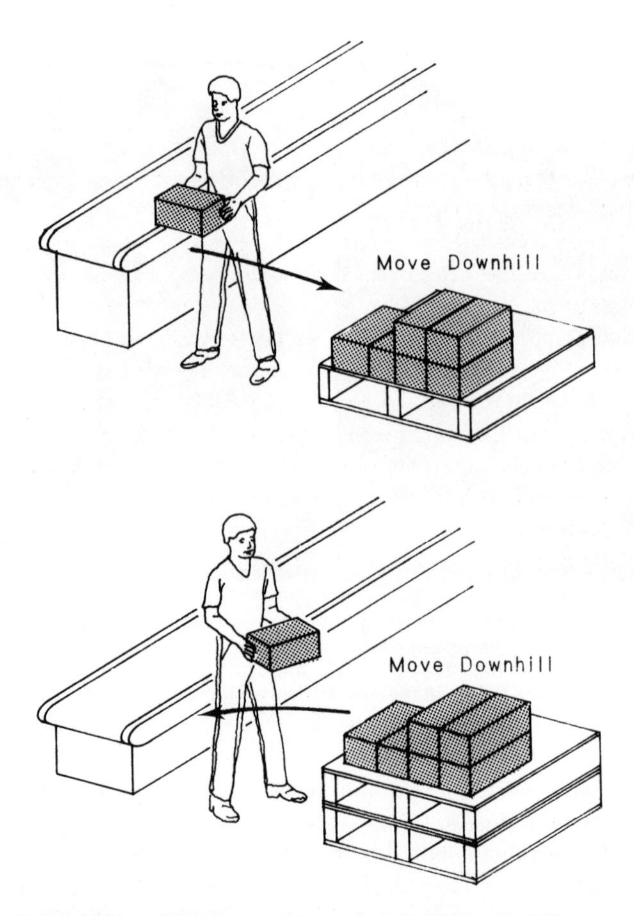

Fig. 3 Move downhill whether from a conveyor to a pallet or a pallet to a conveyor. When loading a conveyor from the pallet, adjust the conveyor to be low; raise the pallet by having the lift truck driver place it on a platform (such as an empty pallet). When loading a pallet from a conveyor, have the conveyor higher and the pallet on the floor (Konz, 1985)

A well-designed chair permits elbow height to be adjusted to the work, that is, the seat height is adjustable. If the adjustment is awkward or difficult, it tends not to be made. If the underside of the table or desk is thick, then the top of the thighs hit it when the seat is raised; therefore specify thin work-surface thicknesses and avoid center drawers and panels. The back support should adjust up and down as well as in and out. The seat should be padded, covered with a breathable fabric, be as wide as possible, and not too deep ($\leq$ 16 inches). Seats that swivel tend to be more comfortable. Armrests normally are not needed. Casters give mobility but take away stability; for chairs with casters, use five supports instead of four.

4. *Support limbs*. The head is about 7 percent of body weight, the trunk about 51 percent, each hand and arm about 5 percent, and each leg and foot about 16 percent.

For the head, poor VDT design may cause the screen to be too high so the head cannot maintain its normal 20° downward tilt and the neck muscles must support the head weight. Supporting the arm not only reduces fatigue, but also reduces tremor and thus improves hand accuracy. Thus arm support is especially necessary for fine work such as with micromanipulators. Chairs support the legs. A footrest may be needed for the feet.

5. *Use the feet as well as the hands.* Since the foot can react as quickly as the hand, it is suitable when discrete action is required. However, the foot is not suitable for manipulative controls due to the construction of the ankle (versus the wrist) and the weight of the leg (versus the arm). Use pedals only for seated operators, since use of pedals while standing causes unnecessary strain on the body. If the pedal is used repeatedly, use a wide pedal so the operator can have the option of using either foot. Generally it is preferable to depress the toe rather than depressing the heel or moving the entire foot and knee. Knee switches should use a lateral motion of the knee; the advantage is that the leg weight isn't moved.

6. *Use gravity; don't oppose it.* Figure 3 showed proper use of gravity when loading and unloading conveyors. Examples of using gravity to move material being worked on include paint from a paintbrush, welding beads from a welding rod, and solder on a solder joint. Use fixtures that permit the item to rotate and the operator to use a downhand position.

7. *Conserve momentum.* Avoid unnecessary acceleration and deceleration since it takes time and energy to accelerate/decelerate an arm, leg or the body. As in sports, follow through to give maximum velocity and accuracy. For hand motions, make movements curved rather than requiring sharp reversals. Replace sharp objects in the hand's path as they cause the operator to be concerned with injury and thus use sharp decelerations.

8. *Use two-handed motions rather than one-handed motions.* This principle is based on physiological cost to the worker, speed of movement, accuracy of movement and total output. Work output is greater with two hands than with one hand. Physiological cost to the worker is greater with two hands than with one hand but the increase is not as much as the increase in output. Speed and accuracy of hand-arm motions can be combined into one index, bits/second, from:

$$I = \log_2 A/(W/2)$$

where

I = Information/move, bits
A = Amplitude of move
W = Width of target in movement direction

For example, an 8-in. move to a 0.5-in.-diameter target gives $I = \log_2 32 = 5$ bits. Typical speed with the preferred hand is 12.9 bits/second, for the non-preferred hand is 11.7 bits/second, and for both hands working at the same time is 21.2 bits/second. (It has been reported that the fingers can process 38 bits/second, the wrists twenty-three, and the arms only ten.)

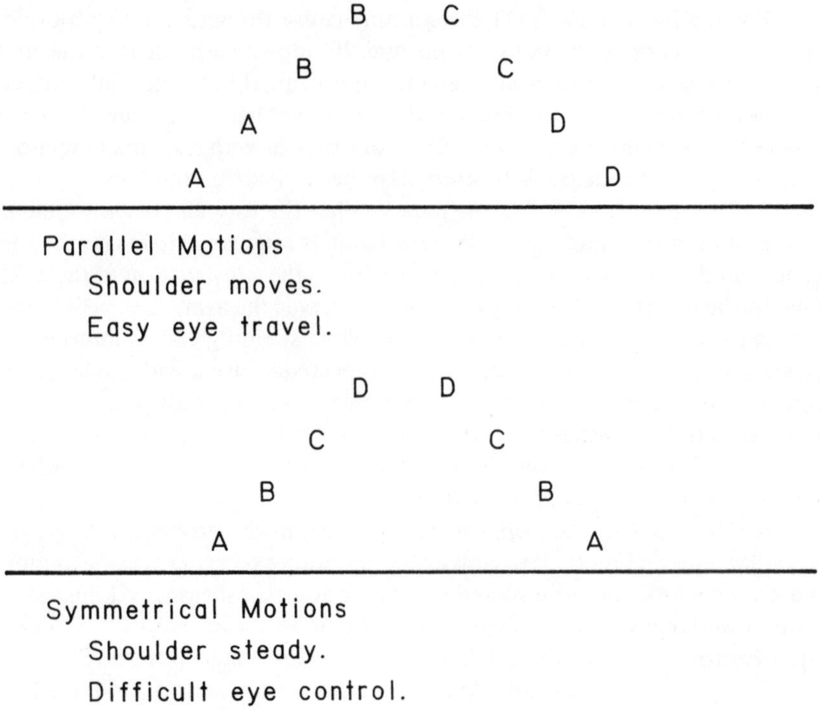

B C

B C

A D

A D

Parallel Motions

Shoulder moves.

Easy eye travel.

D D

C C

B B

A A

Symmetrical Motions

Shoulder steady.

Difficult eye control.

Fig. 4 Parallel motions (top) should be used instead of symmetrical motions (below) unless eye control is not needed (Konz, 1985)

9. *Use parallel motions for eye control of two-handed motions*. Figure 4 shows the two alternatives. When eye control is needed, the general principle, using both time/unit and physiological cost/unit as criteria, is to minimize the degree of spread between the hands. Use symmetrical motions only when the motions are highly practiced and eye control is not needed.

10. *Use rowing motions for two-handed motions*. Two hands can be used in an alternating manner (such as bike pedalling with the feet) or in a rowing motion (both hands moving out and back together). Alternation uses more shoulder motion and torso twisting than rowing. Thus rowing is the preferred technique.

11. *Pivot movements about the elbow*. Direction of horizontal motion affects speed, accuracy, and physiological cost of the motion. If 0° is defined as three o'clock, the optimum move angle for the right hand is 30°. It takes 5 percent longer to move straight ahead (90°) and 15 percent longer to move cross-body (120°). Physiological cost also is lower for pivoting (30°) than cross-body (120°). Somewhat surprisingly, motions are more accurate when they are cross-body. For best efficiency, put bins ahead of the shoulder, not the nose (the arm is pivoted from the shoulder, not the nose).

12. *Use the preferred hand.* As mentioned above, the preferred hand is about 10 percent faster for reach-type motions. If the hand uses a tool, the use time advantage of the preferred hand is much greater—20 to 30 percent is a reasonable estimate. The preferred hand also is more accurate in movement and is 5 to 10 percent stronger. About 10 percent of the population is left-handed. In general, have work come into a work station from the operator's preferred side and leave from the non-preferred side. The reason is that reach and grasp are more difficult than dispose and release. However, if the new item is obtained on the same side as the disposal, a body turn is eliminated.

13. *Keep arm motions in the normal work area.* Because of the pivoting of the lower arm about the elbow, the normal work area is windshield-wiper shaped. See figure 5 for males and figure 6 for females. Figure 7 shows how extra distance can be avoided by proper orientation of pallets and bins.

14. *Let the small woman reach; let the large man fit.* Because women generally are smaller than men, design so that women can reach objects and controls while at the same time permitting men to fit within the workspace. The goal is to design so that most of the user population can use the design. Most can be 95, 99, or 99.9 percent of the user population (that is, exclude 5, 1, or 0.1 percent). The excluded people can be at the upper end of the distribution, split between the upper and lower, or at the lower end. Although

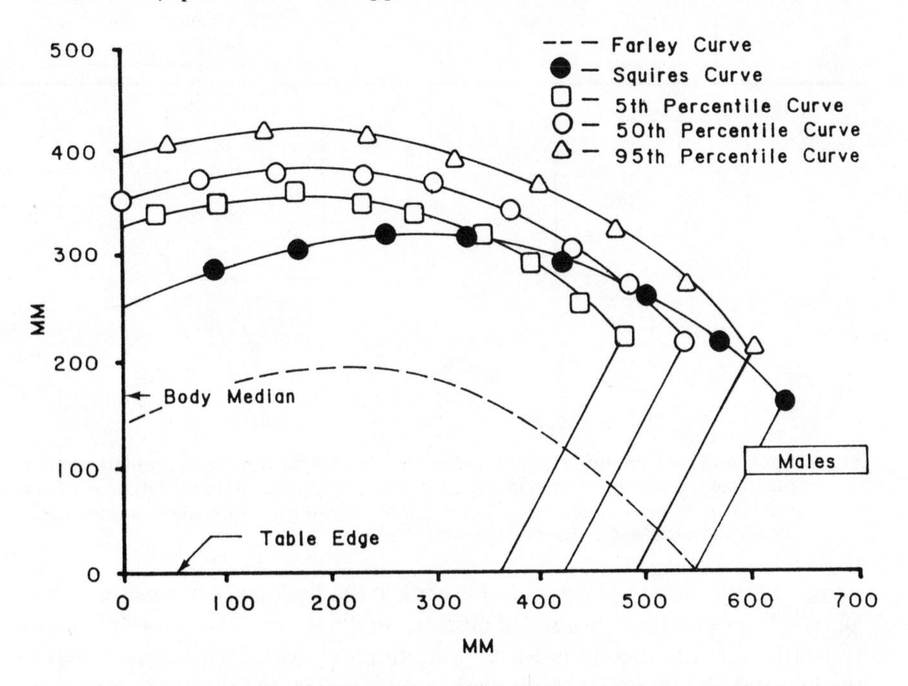

Fig. 5 Normal male work area (right hand) is "windshield wiper" shaped. The early curve by Farley was too simplified; Squires did not consider differences in body size. The left hand area is mirrored (Konz, 1985)

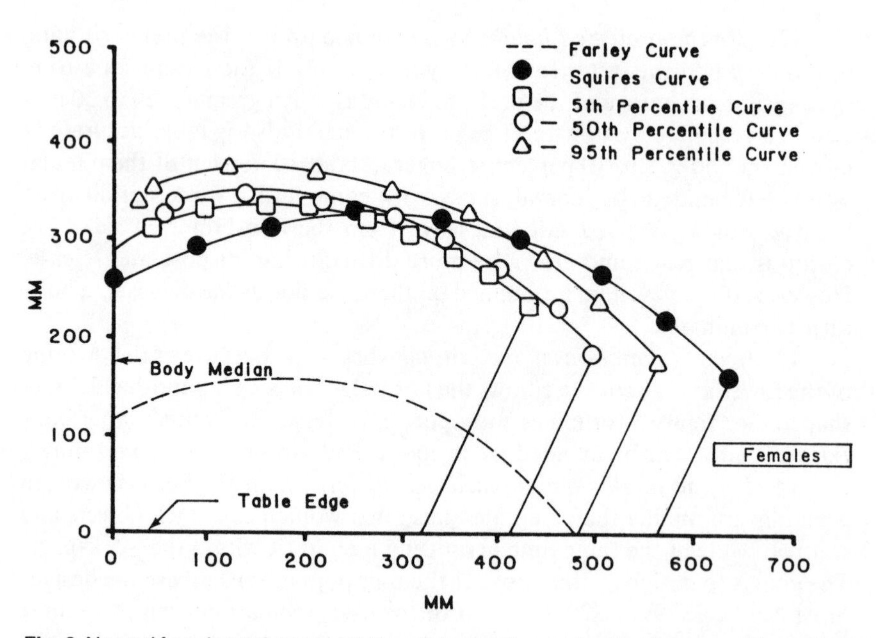

Fig. 6 Normal female work area (right hand) is slightly smaller than for males (Konz, 1985)

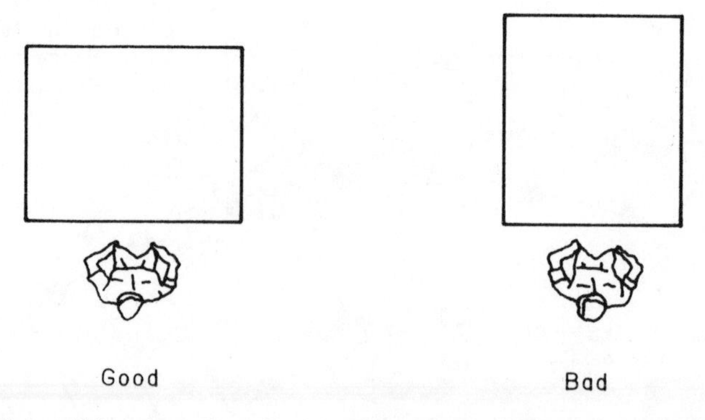

Fig. 7 Pallet and bin orientation affects reach and move distances. In addition to original pallet (bin) orientation, consider a turntable under the pallet (bin). After half of the load is completed, rotate it 90°. Long reaches and moves severely stress the back as well as decrease productivity (Konz, 1985)

designing out part of the population makes the designer's job easier, laws against discrimination and social customs make it more and more difficult to justify a design that excludes anyone. In most situations you must make the jobs adjust (use hoists for weaker people, adjustable chairs for different sizes of people, move bin locations, use power tools, etc.). Note also that just because 90 percent of the workforce can lift a specific weight or reach a specific distance does not make it necessary to use this maximum weight or distance; less may be better. Note also that redesigning the job to make it easier benefits the entire population, not just the extremes.

User population also is becoming more broadly defined. The primary change is the changing sex/occupation stereotypes. Thus the designer must design for a range from small women to large men instead of having female jobs (with a range from small woman to large woman) and male jobs (with a range from small man to large man).

15. *Locate all materials, tools and controls in a fixed place*. Performance of any task requires (1) planning, and (2) doing. Locating items in a fixed place reduces the planning (information processing) time.

16. *View large objects for a long time*. The object can be made large by bringing it close to the eyes. Bringing the head down, however, causes neck and shoulder strain. Raising the object generally means the hands and arms must be higher; if so, support them. Another alternative is to bring the object close optically through use of 2X or 4X magnification. In this case the magnification tends to put the operator in a straightjacket as movement becomes very limited. Change postures during working rests by having the operator get supplies and components, take completed units away, etc.

Long time concerns inspection and machine-paced work. For inspection, "shoot sitting ducks"—that is, inspect stationary objects, not moving objects. During machine-paced work, for some cycles there is excess work (in relation to time available). The operator cannot complete the task before the object is taken away. If the average machine cycle is increased so all the long cycles are included, the idle time on the average cycles becomes quite high. Thus for high productivity and high quality, use operator-paced work, not machine-paced work.

Effect of Repetition

Effect on time/unit. Practice makes perfect. This principle has been known for a long time. The amount of improvement that can be expected as a function of time was quantified during the 1930's and was a well-known technology by World War II. Briefly, learning is given as a rate:

$$\text{LCRATE} = \text{2XTIME}/\text{XTIME}$$

where

LCRATE = learning curve rate, %
2XTIME = time/unit at quantity 2X
XTIME = time/unit at quantity X

Thus, if time/unit at unit 50 was 1.0 and time/unit at unit 100 was 0.9, then the learning curve rate is 90 percent. Typical learning curve rates are 90 to 95 percent—that is, when the quantity doubles, the time at the doubled unit is 90 percent of the time at the original unit. (See Konz 1983, Chapter 24, for more detail, including the learning rate for various processes.)

A key implication is that production and the labor force cannot both remain constant. That is, if the facility is producing a constant 500 units/period for month after month, then the work-hours and thus employment should decrease. If the labor force is constant, then output should increase.

Effect on health. A large number of repetitions will stress any machine—especially if the load on the machine is high. The human body, like any machine, will be stressed by many repetitions. A particular problem is the wrist.

Figure 8 is a cross section of the wrist. Most of the muscles which move the fingers are in the forearm. The fingers are connected to these muscles through tendons which run through narrow channels of the bones of the wrist. More specifically, the flexor tendons run through the carpal tunnel (*carpal* is Latin for wrist). Synovial membranes lubricate movements of the tendons. Finger movements with a flexed or extended wrist cause the tendons to be displaced past and against the adjacent walls of the carpal tunnel (much like a belt sliding on a pulley). Contact between the tendons and the adjacent surfaces causes irritation of the synovial membranes (synovitis). Synovitis results in thickening of the synovial membrane, which in turn causes compression of the median nerve (which also passes through the carpal tunnel). This compression is called carpal tunnel syndrome (Armstrong 1983). Dequervain's disease is a kind of tenosynovitis associated with the thumb.

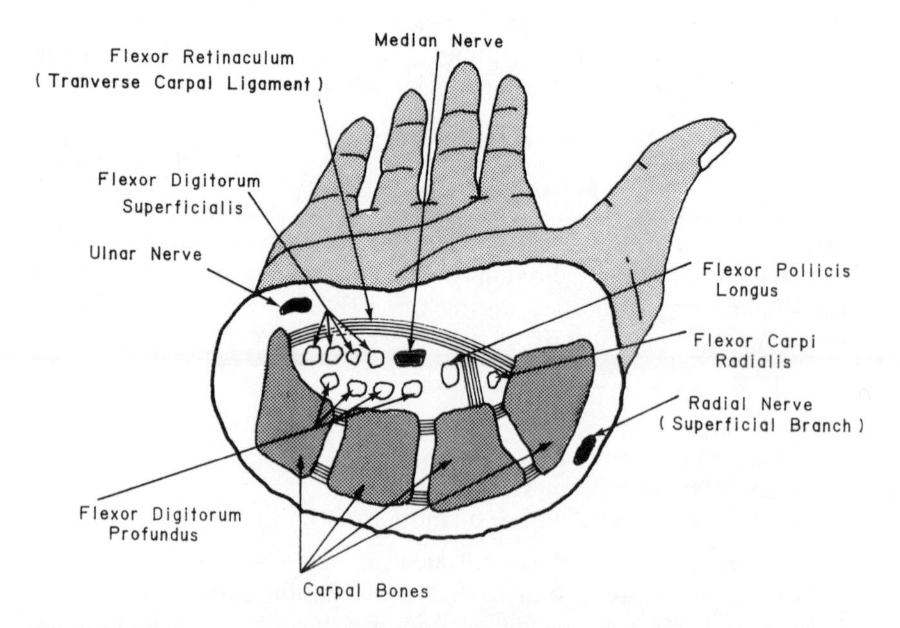

Fig. 8 The median nerve and tendons pass through the carpal (wrist) tunnel. Reduce wrist problems by (a) reducing repetitions on a specific wrist, (b) reducing the force exerted, and (c) exerting the force with a more favorable wrist orientation

As with any machine, the problems can be reduced by making the machine stronger or the stress less. Selecting strong wrists is not a feasible solution as (a) there are no reliable tests indicating a predisposition to synovitis (although women seem more susceptible than men), and (b) discrimination laws would make it difficult to implement any such test, even if it could be developed. Thus the solutions favor lessening the stress. (See Tichauer and Gage [1977] and Armstrong et al. [1982] for some suggestions.) The general strategy is to reduce repetitions on a wrist (for example, use the left and right hand alternately, or alternate tasks among workers), to reduce force required (for example, sharpen knife blades if using a knife, use machine power instead of human muscles), and to exert the force with a more favorable wrist orientation (the handshake position) instead of a contorted position (for example, by using a redesigned handle).

References

Armstrong, T., et al. 1982. Investigation of cumulative trauma disorders in a poultry processing plant. *American Industrial Hygiene Association Journal* 43(2):103-16.

——. 1983. *An ergonomics guide to carpal tunnel syndrome.* Akron, Ohio: American Industrial Hygiene Association.

Konz, S. 1983. *Work design: Industrial ergonomics.* New York: Wiley.

——. 1985. *Facility design.* New York: Wiley.

Tichauer, E., and H. Gage. 1977. Ergonomics principles basic to hand tool design. *American Industrial Hygiene Association Journal* 38(11):622-34.

***Stephan Konz** is professor of industrial engineering at Kansas State University, Manhattan.*

5

Work Station Design

Tarald O. Kvålseth, Ph.D.

The general aim of ergonomics or human factors engineering when designing work stations is to achieve an appropriate matching between the work requirements and the operator capabilities, so as to maximize the performance of the operator and of the total system and the physical and mental well-being, satisfaction and safety of the human operator. Ergonomics research has produced extensive data, theories, principles and methods relevant to such design objectives. It is the purpose of this chapter to present, in a concise and practical way, sets of generally accepted design guidelines that are based on such ergonomics knowledge. The list of guidelines is by no means exhaustive. Instead, the objective has been to give those guidelines that are judged to be the more important and that may be applicable to a wide variety of work stations. The chosen format of this chapter is also such that it may serve as a convenient checklist.

The chapter starts with a set of general work station design principles relevant to the physical arrangement of a work station and the posture and motion patterns of the operator. Subsequent sections deal with guidelines for proper control devices and displays, including VDT displays. A section concerning anthropometry is also included. For additional explanations and underlying theories and empirical evidence, the reader can refer to such recent general texts as Grandjean (1980), Kantowitz and Sorkin (1983), Konz (1983), McCormick and Sanders (1982), Oborne (1982) and Shackel (1974).

General Principles

1. *Minimize static loads.* Loads on body members due to static work components may cause strain on muscles, tendons, ligaments and spinal discs. The resulting physical pains may be reversible and vanish after the static load is removed, but some ailments may be of a persistent nature. Examples of static loads to be avoided are (a) holding, lifting or carrying objects with the hands, especially when arms are outstretched, (b) standing in one position for extended periods of time, (c) manipulative hand operations with outstretched or raised arms, (d) sitting without back support, (e) pushing or pulling heavy objects, (f) bending the back forward or sideways excessively, (g) using hand tools with unnatural hand grasps and (h) excessively inclining the head either backward or forward.
2. Every employee should be provided with an adjustable and properly designed chair, meeting the following requirements:
   a) The height of the seat and backrest should both be adjustable.
   b) Back support is particularly required for the lower back (lumbar region).
   c) The seat should be cushioned and give way about 2.5 cm (1 in.).
   d) Fabric rather than plastic should be used as a cover material for the seat and backrest.
   e) The recommended depth and width of the seat are, respectively, about 38 to 40 cm (15 to 16 in.) and 40 to 45 cm (16 to 18 in.). With arm rests, a distance of at least 48 cm (19 in.) between the arms is recommended.
   f) An angle of about 100° between the backrest and the seat is a common recommendation. There is less of a consensus regarding the desired angle of the seat, although the majority opinion among ergonomists seems to be that the seat should slope backward slightly (about 1° to 5°).
   g) Arm rests are not generally recommended for industrial chairs since they are liable to restrict movement. In some circumstances, arm rests may be appropriate as arm support for reducing tremor, for example, during fine manipulative tasks. The recommended distance between the top of the arm rest and the compressed seat is about 20 cm (8 in.), although this distance should ideally be adjustable.

   h) Casters provide mobility; however, for industrial chairs, casters may also represent a safety hazard caused by inadvertent chair movement.
   i) Foot rests may be necessary for comfortable posture with approximately horizontal thighs and feet and vertical lower legs.

3. The work surface should be about 5 cm (2 in.) below the elbow for both sitting and standing postures.
4. The worker should be able to, at his or her discretion, alternate between a sitting and standing posture. This may require that the work surface be of adjustable height.
5. Both arm and foot movements should be used, while considering the following points:
   a) Movement speed and accuracy tend to favor arm movements, especially for complex tasks.
   b) When arm and foot movements require considerable attention, such simultaneous movements should be avoided since the attention requirement may exceed human capability and lead to potential safety hazards.
   c) Foot movements tend to reduce the speed and accuracy of arm movements.
   d) Avoid having both feet move simultaneously.
6. Both arms should move simultaneously and in such a way that the two movements are (a) symmetrical and opposite in direction (away from and toward the center of the body) if visual attention is not required during or at the end of each movement or (b) parallel if visual control is required.
7. Arm movements should be continuous and curved. Straight movements with sudden changes in direction and velocity are inefficient and fatiguing.
8. Keep arm movements within the normal work area. The normal work area in the horizontal plane may be defined as the area determined by the two arcs drawn by the hands when the forearms are moved about relaxed upper arms (with the angle between upper arm and the horizontal plane being approximately 65°). The normal work area in the vertical plane may be similarly determined by the arcs drawn by the hands during vertical sweeps of the lower arms while pivoting about the elbows and with the upper arms remaining relaxed.
9. Arm movements should pivot about the elbow rather than the shoulder (that is, rather than using cross-body movements of the entire arm).
10. The preferred hand should be used since it is generally faster, stronger and capable of more accurate manipulations than the nonpreferred hand.
11. Twisting motions should be performed with the elbow bent to prevent overstressing of muscles and tendons.

12. For work stations requiring highly repetitive hand/arm movements, careful analysis needs to be made as to potential cumulative trauma disorders such as tendinitis, tenosynovitis, tennis elbow, DeQuervain's disease and carpal tunnel syndrome (see Armstrong 1983 and Tichauer 1978).
13. Fixed locations should be used for tools, materials and controls. This principle eliminates the need for such ineffective task elements (therbligs) as search and select.
14. A work station should be so designed that it is compatible with the physical dimensions and strengths of the individual user or potential user population. Anthropometric data should be used for determining user population characteristics.
15. Sufficient friction between shoe soles and floor is necessary to avoid slip and fall accidents.
16. Each hand-operated tool and device should be made to fit the hand and in such a way that it (a) can be used with the hand in the neutral position (that is, in line with the forearm), (b) can be used by either hand, (c) has properly designed hand grip (at least 10 cm (4 in.) in length and approximately 5 cm (2 in.) in diameter for good power grip) and (d) utilizes the appropriate muscle groups and avoids single-finger repetitive action (thumb action is less undesirable than index-finger action).
17. Eliminate or minimize the effects of undesirable work environmental conditions such as excessive noise, poor illumination and excessive heat or cold.

Several of these principles may be easily accommodated when using a flexible work station such as that shown in figure 1. Nearly every component of this complete work station is adjustable. Components such as arm rests, carousel and parts tray may also be removed. The table has continuous up and down and tilt adjustment.

Sitting Versus Standing

During work station design, an early decision is generally required as to whether the operator should be sitting or standing, or possibly a combination of the two postures. Being seated has a number of advantages over standing, one such major advantage being the lower physiological load on the operator when sitting. Reduced static muscular load required to maintain body posture and improved blood circulation results if the operator is allowed to sit. When the operator is standing for extended periods of time, especially in the absence of leg movements, the blood as well as tissue fluids tend to accumulate in the legs, with the result that the so-called venous pool-

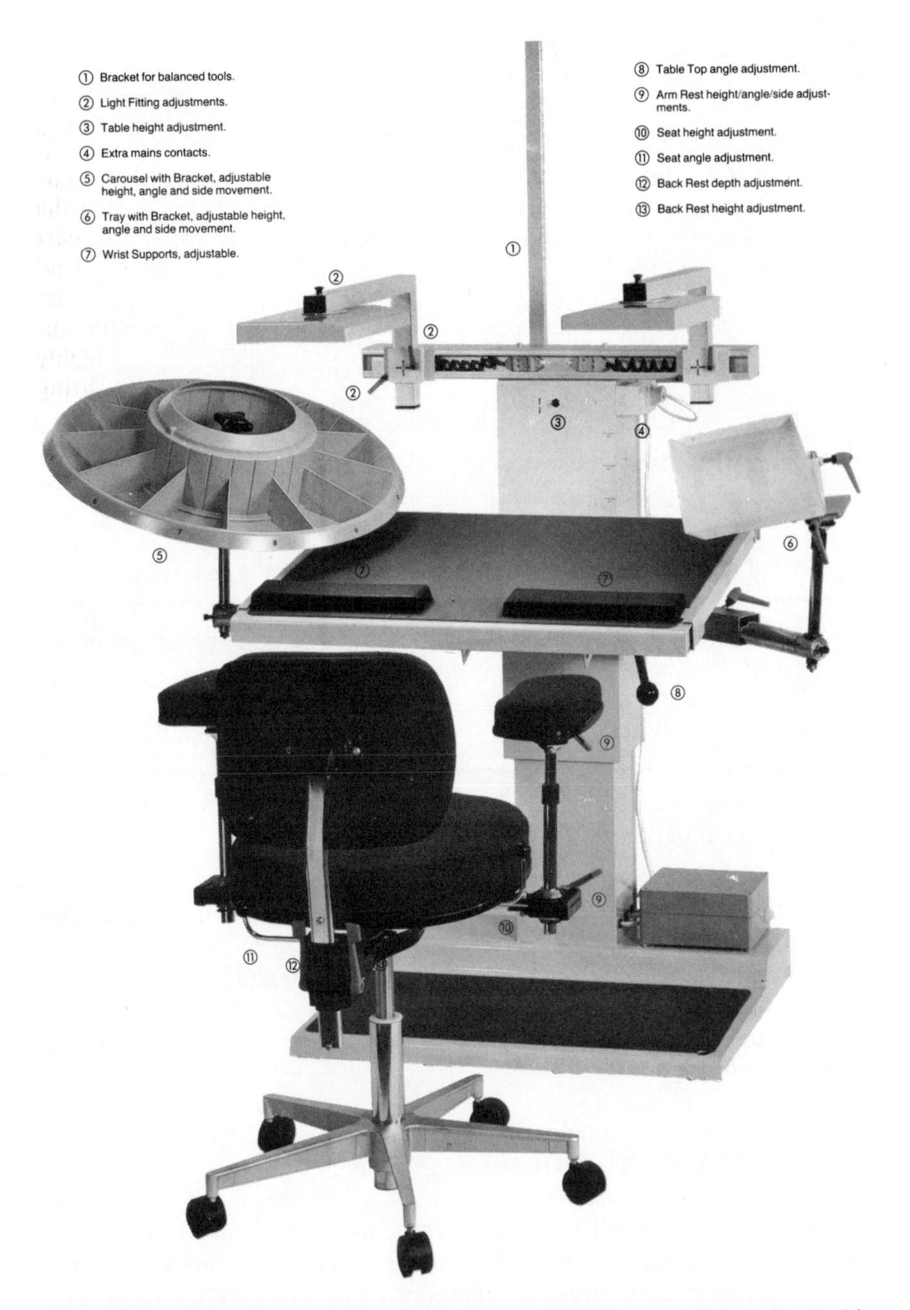

Fig. 1 Complete workstation with a high degree of flexibility, especially well suited for light assembly work. Operator can adjust the various table and chair dimensions, providing for a good fit of the workstation to the operator. Table can also be raised sufficiently for the operator to work in a standing position. (Courtesy of Dr. Arne Aaras.)

ing may cause swelling of the legs and varicose veins. Such a potential problem for the standing operator may be reduced if the operator is able to move the legs so that the leg muscle actions help move the blood.

Prolonged sitting may also have some health disadvantages. In particular, backaches and pains may result involving the spine and the muscles of the back, especially when inappropriate sitting posture and poorly designed chairs are used. Grandjean (1980) also points out that prolonged sitting may lead to (a) curvature of the spine, which in turn may impair the function of the internal organs of breathing and digestion, and (b) slackening of the abdominal muscles. From a physiological and orthopedic point of view, a highly desirable situation is one in which the operator can alternate between sitting and standing at his/her discretion (see figure 2).

In order to provide some specific design guidelines, it is suggested that workplaces with sitting operators are preferable in the following situations:

1. Where tasks requiring fine manipulative hand movements are predominant.
2. A high degree of body stability and equilibrium is required.
3. Precise foot control actions are required.
4. All materials and tools required for the task can be located within the seated workspace.
5. No heavy material handling tasks are required.
6. The task requires relatively fixed body posture for extended time periods.

By comparison, workplaces with standing operators are preferable in the following situations:

1. Frequent handling of heavy objects is required.
2. Mobility is required as the operator has to move around in the workplace.
3. Extended reaches and moves of substantial magnitude are frequently required.
4. Manual downward forces of substantial magnitude are frequently required.

Man-Machine Interface

The interaction between the human operator and the machine or equipment occurs via control devices (knobs, levers, pedals, keyboards, etc.) and information sources or displays (dials, counters, lights, charts, CRT, etc.). The proper design of this interface has important implications for the performance of the total system and for the safety and well-being of the operator. While detailed design guidelines and underlying data are available in various publica-

Fig. 2 Workstations permitting the operator to alternate between sitting and standing. The work piece can be lowered, raised, and tilted. In the upper two figures, such continuous adjustments are accomplished by mechanical means, while a hydraulic cylinder is used for the vertical adjustment in the workstation to the left. (Courtesy of Dr. Arne Aaras.)

tions (Kvalseth 1982, McCormick and Sanders 1982, Shackel 1974), the purpose of this section is to outline briefly some of the more important principles.

Displays

1. A display with a moving pointer and fixed scale is generally preferable to one with a fixed pointer and movable scale.
2. A circular or semicircular scale is better in most situations than vertical or horizontal straight scales.
3. The scale numbering should increase in a clockwise direction on a circular or semicircular scale, upward on a vertical straight scale and to the right on a horizontal straight scale.
4. Number sequences of major scale markers should be 1, 2, 3, etc.; 5, 10, 15, etc.; 10, 20, 30, etc; rather than, for example, 3, 6, 9, etc., or 4, 8, 12, etc.
5. If possible, multi-scale, multi-pointer and nonlinear (for example, logarithmic) scale displays should be avoided.
6. The size of scale markers, separation between markers and the size of alphanumeric characters should comply with established recommendations (see Kvalseth 1982).
7. Digital displays are particularly good for making quick and accurate readings when the displayed value does not change too quickly.
8. Displays, including representational displays (graphs, wiring diagrams, process flow diagrams, maps, histograms), should be as simple as possible and omit irrelevant information and details.

Controls

1. Since no single control device can be rated as good with respect to all of the operational criteria (that is, speed and accuracy with which it can be operated, its range of movement and amount of force that the operator can exert on it), some compromise and subjective judgment need to be used when selecting controls.
2. Both hand and foot controls ought to be used, keeping in mind the points raised above under General Principle 5.
3. Particular care must be used when selecting foot controls to avoid the possibility of accidental activation that may lead to potential hazards. Guarding of foot controls may be necessary.
4. The most suitable type of control resistance (spring loading, friction, viscous damping and inertia) needs to be considered for each control device. Each type of control resistance reduces the possibility of accidental activation and provides feedback that may aid the operator.
5. To enable the operator to identify each control quickly and correctly, appropriate methods of control coding should be used. The most common coding methods are color, shape, labelling, texture, size and loca-

tion. Using more than one method of coding, that is, providing coding redundancy, may be advantageous in some situations.

Interface Layout

1. The most important (in terms of the total system performance) and most frequently used displays should ideally be located in an area that is within 30° below the horizontal line of sight and 15° to each side when the operator is seated. For a standing operator, this optimal area is to be shifted upwards by some 5°.
2. The most important and most frequently used hand controls should ideally be located within an area that extends approximately from 25 cm (10 in.) to 75 cm (30 in.) above the seat reference point and 38 cm (15 in.) to each side.
3. When displays or controls are used in a fixed sequence, they should be laid out accordingly.
4. Displays or controls having related functions ought to be grouped together.
5. Control-display compatibility should be such that each associated control and display are located near each other.
6. The clearances between neighboring controls must be sufficient to prevent accidental activation.
7. Population stereotypes must be considered so that the relationships between controls and displays as well as the operational modes of controls and displays are compatible with natural operator expectations. For example, the motion of a control and of the associated display should be in compatible directions; turning a steering wheel to the right should cause the vehicle to turn right; moving a hand lever forward, upward, or sideward to the right should cause an increase in the display readings (or in the associated machine or equipment response).

VDTs

While some of the guidelines given above are also relevant to visual display terminals (VDTs) or visual display units (VDUs) associated with computerized systems, some important recommendations specific to VDTs are offered subsequently. For additional information, reference is made to Bailey (1982), Cakir et al. (1980), and Shackel (1979).

1. In order to permit adjustability of the work station layout, the keyboard should be separate from the display housing.
2. The recommended luminance for symbols on the VDT screen (that is, the amount of light emitted by the symbols per unit area) is about 50 ml (millilamberts).
3. The regeneration rate of the screen should exceed the flicker-fusion frequency of the eye to avoid the sensation of disturbing flicker. A

regeneration rate of at least 60 Hz, which is that of home TV receivers, is recommended.

4. A contrast of about 94 percent for the background versus the symbols has been recommended as preferred, with 88 percent being acceptable (Gould 1968).
5. For black and white VDT display, it appears preferable to use dark symbols against a light background.
6. Since color VDT displays are a recent advance, very limited research data are available regarding the appropriate use of colors. Color can be used to improve the legibility of displays and to structure and emphasize parts of the displayed information, but overuse of color may be detrimental to operator performance.
7. Good legibility requires a character resolution of at least ten raster lines per character.
8. The user's normal line of sight should be perpendicular to the VDT screen.
9. The potential problem of glare from ambient lights may be minimized by using (a) a VDT screen that is deeply recessed, (b) a hood or shield, (c) an etched-glass screen or (d) optical coatings on the screen. Direct glare from the sun or sky or indirect glare reflected from the screen can be avoided by orienting the operator in such a way that the windows are to his or her side rather than front or rear.

It is important to remember that since VDTs tend to be used relatively continuously, even minor design deficiencies may cause considerable user discomfort. In order to reduce such discomfort, it is recommended that the VDT operator be given relatively frequent breaks during which the operator may perform non-VDT type of work. A fifteen-minute break after two hours of continuous VDT work may serve as a reasonable recommendation, with even more frequent breaks if the visual demands of the task are very high.

An example of a well-designed VDT work station is shown in figure 3. The chair and various table components are easily adjustable. The keyboard table can be adjusted vertically and horizontally. The display (CRT) table can be moved up and down as well as tilted and swiveled.

Anthropometry

Studies of the dimensions, weights and strengths of various members of the human body, an area of study referred to as anthropometry, have produced voluminous data having a wide range of potential applications for the design of equipment and work stations. Such anthropometric data have been tabulated for both sexes, for different ages, and for people from different regions of the world. These types of data may be consulted if, for example,

Fig. 3 A well-designed VDT workstation. (Courtesy of IBM Corporation.)

a manufacturer of a VDT work station wants to make some of its dimensions adjustable so as to accommodate 95 percent of its potential user population. Similarly, anthropometric data for hand strength may be used to determine if a hand-operated device is appropriate for 99 percent of its potential users. The list of potential applications of anthropometric data is virtually endless, and the designer should utilize this rich data source to ensure, quite literally, that the machine or work station fits the human operator.

In order to appreciate the interpretation and basis of anthropometric data, some simple probability distribution concepts are helpful. Let the quantity (random variable) X denote some specific human characteristic such as the height (without shoes) of adult females in the United States. The pth percentile of X, symbolized by x_p, is then defined by the probability statement

$$P\,(X \leq x_p) = p$$

That is, 100p percent of the U.S. females are of heights x_p or less. It may be reasonable to assume that X has an approximately normal probability distribution over its range of potential values, with μ and σ denoting its mean and standard deviation, respectively. Since $Z = (X - \mu)/\sigma$ becomes a standard normal variate, the above probability statement may be expressed as

$$P(Z) \leq \frac{x_p - \mu}{\sigma}) = P(Z \leq z_p) = p$$

where z_p is given in standard normal probability tables for different p values. By replacing the population parameters μ and σ by their sample values (estimates) $\bar{x}$ and s, it follows from the last expression that x_p can be estimated from the equation

$$x_p = \bar{x} + z_p s$$

Commonly used values of p are 0.90, 0.95, 0.99 for which $z_p = 1.28$, 1.64 and 2.33, respectively, with the same z_p values, but with a negative sign, for $p = 0.10$, 0.05 and 0.01, respectively.

Thus, for example, based on a random sample of 2000 adult females in the U.S. whose mean height and standard deviation are $\bar{x} = 161.0$ cm (63.4 in.) and $s = 6.0$ cm (2.4 in.), it follows from the preceding equation that the 95th percentile of height is $x_{.95} = 161.0 + 1.64\ (6.0) = 170.8$ cm (67.2 in.). Similarly, 10 percent of the U.S. adult females are of heights less than or equal to $x_{.10} = 161.0 - 1.28\ (6.0) = 153.3$ cm (60.4 in.). Additional examples are given below.

Subsequent sections provide some values of average measurements $\bar{x}$ and the standard deviations s for dimensions and strengths of different parts of the human body. The reader is warned against being caught in the trap of designing for the so-called average person. First, there is no average person, other than as a statistical expression. Some people may be average in a few dimensions, but no one is average in all dimensions. Second, by designing for the average person using the 50th percentiles (that is, $x_{.50}$ values), the result may be such that the design is unsuitable for 50 percent of the potential users.

Body Dimensions

Table 1 gives the $\bar{x}$ and s of various dimensions of the nude adult male and female body for the components identified in figure 4. These data have been adapted from Bailey (1982), who in turn used data reported by Daniels et al. (1953), Dreyfuss (1967), Garrett and Kennedy (1971), and Woodson and Conover (1964). Additional measurements and references are available in

Damon et al. (1966), Das and Grady (1983), Hertzberg (1972), Kvalseth (1983), Oborne (1982), and Roebuck et al. (1975).

The data in table 1, which are based on the U.S. population, are referred to as structural (static) measurements. That is, the measurements are taken when the body components are stationary in the positions illustrated in figure 4. A second type of data referred to as functional (dynamic) measurements are concerned with compound measurements of the body in common movement positions such as arm-reach envelopes and angular movement ranges of different joints. Such functional anthropometric data are available in some of the references listed above.

As an example of the use of the data in table 1, consider the case of a designer concerned with the layout of a vertical instrument panel on which a pushbutton control has to be located so that about 95 percent of the potential male operators can reach the control while standing. The designer needs to know the fifth percentile of vertical arm reach for males. From (a) standard normal tables with $z_{.05} = -1.64$, (b) the $\bar{x}$ and s values in table 1 (Characteristic A1) and (c) the x_p expression given above, it follows that $x_{.05} = 209.6 - 1.64\,(8.5) = 195.7$ cm (77.0 in.). That is, the control button should be located no higher than about 196 cm above the floor. If the design were to accommodate at least 95 percent of both the male and female populations, then the location of the control should be no higher than 185 cm $= 199.1 - 1.64\,(8.6)$ where $\bar{x} = 199.1$ cm and $s = 8.6$ cm from table 1 for females. Of course, a slight height increment of approximately 2.5 cm (1 in.) may be applied to the preceding dimensions to account for the likely fact that the operators will be wearing shoes. While the data in table 1 refer to nude people, approximate increments to be added to these data to account for both light and heavy clothing are given in several of the references listed previously.

As another example of the use of the anthropometric data in table 1, consider the problem of determining the appropriate height between the seat and the inside of the roof of automobiles designed to fit the lower 90 percent of the U.S. male population. Since $z_p = 1.28$ for $p = 0.90$ from normal tables, it follows from the above x_p expression that the seat-to-roof distance has to be at least $x_{90} = 90.7 + 1.28\,(3.7) = 95.4$ cm (37.6 in.) where the data 90.7 and 3.7 correspond to Characteristic D1 in table 1.

Muscle Strength

When designing a piece of equipment or a work station, information about the strength of different muscle groups of the human operator may be as important as knowing about body dimensions. Muscular strength depends on a wide variety of factors, age being perhaps the most obvious one. Strength increases rapidly during the teens, reaches its maximum during the mid to late twenties, and remains at that level for the next five to ten years, beyond

TABLE 1
Mean $\bar{x}$ and Standard Deviation s of Body Dimensions Representative of U.S. Male and Female Workers of Age Range 18 to 45 (See Figure 4 for Identification of the Characteristics)*

		Males		Females	
		$\bar{x}$(cm)	s(cm)	$\bar{x}$(cm)	s(cm)
A1.	Vertical reach	209.6	8.5	199.1	8.6
A2.	Stature	174.5	6.6	162.1	6.1
A3.	Eye height	163.3	6.9	149.9	6.4
A4.	Crotch to floor	83.1	4.7	74.4	4.1
A5.	Waist breadth	27.2	2.4	23.9	2.0
A6.	Hip breadth	33.3	2.0	34.8	2.3
B1.	Head width	15.2	0.6	14.5	0.5
B2.	Interpupillary distance	6.1	0.4	6.4	0.5
B3.	Head circumference	56.1	1.6	54.9	0.4
B4.	Neck circumference	37.3	2.1	33.8	1.8
B5.	Head length	19.6	0.7	18.5	0.8
B6.	Head height	22.1	1.4	21.8	1.3
B7.	Ear to tip of lip length	9.4	0.02	9.1	1.8
B8.	Ear to top of head	13.2	0.8	12.7	0.8
B9.	Ear breadth	3.6	0.3	3.0	0.3
	Ear length	6.4	0.4	5.1	0.5
C1.	Thumb-tip reach	82.6	4.9	73.9	3.8
C2.	Chest circumference	93.7	6.7	88.9	5.6
	Chest depth	23.1	2.0	23.4	2.0
C3.	Waist circumference	80.3	8.2	66.3	5.3
	Waist height to floor	106.4	5.4	100.1	4.6
	Waist depth	20.1	2.3	16.8	1.8
C4.	Hip circumference	94.2	6.2	95.0	5.8
	Hip depth	22.4	2.0	21.1	1.8
C5.	Upper thigh circumference	55.4	4.8	55.4	4.3
	Gluteal furrow height	80.3	4.1	72.6	4.1
C6.	Calf circumference	36.6	2.7	34.3	2.3
C7.	Ankle circumference	26.4	1.4	21.1	1.3
	Ankle height	6.9	0.7	6.9	0.5
C8.	Foot length	26.7	1.1	24.1	1.0
	Foot width	9.7	0.5	8.9	0.5
C9.	Shoulder height	143.8	6.2	131.8	5.6
C10.	Forearm circumference (flexed)	29.5	2.2	24.9	1.5
	Biceps circumference (flexed)	32.3	2.7	26.4	2.5
D1.	Head to seat height	90.7	3.7	85.6	3.2
D2.	Eye to seat height	78.7	3.6	73.7	3.0
D3.	Shoulder breadth	45.5	2.5	41.7	2.3
D4.	Hip breadth sitting	34.0	2.4	38.1	2.9
E1.	Hand length	19.1	1.0	18.3	1.0
E2.	Head breadth	8.9	0.5	7.6	0.5
E3.	Wrist circumference	17.0	0.9	15.0	0.8
E4.	Hand circumference	21.6	1.1	18.3	1.0
E5.	Hand thickness	3.3	0.2	2.5	0.3
F1.	Knee height	54.1	2.7	49.8	2.3
F2.	Popliteal height	43.7	2.5	41.1	1.8
F3.	Buttock to popliteal length	48.8	2.5	47.5	2.8
F4.	Buttock to knee length	59.4	2.8	57.4	2.5
F5.	Elbow to wrist length	28.7	2.1	23.4	1.3
F6.	Thigh clearance	16.8	0.9	12.4	1.3
F7.	Shoulder to elbow height	36.8	1.9	31.0	1.5
F8.	Elbow rest height	23.1	2.6	22.9	2.5
F9.	Mid-shoulder to seat height	62.5	3.2	57.9	2.8

*Adapted from Bailey (1982).

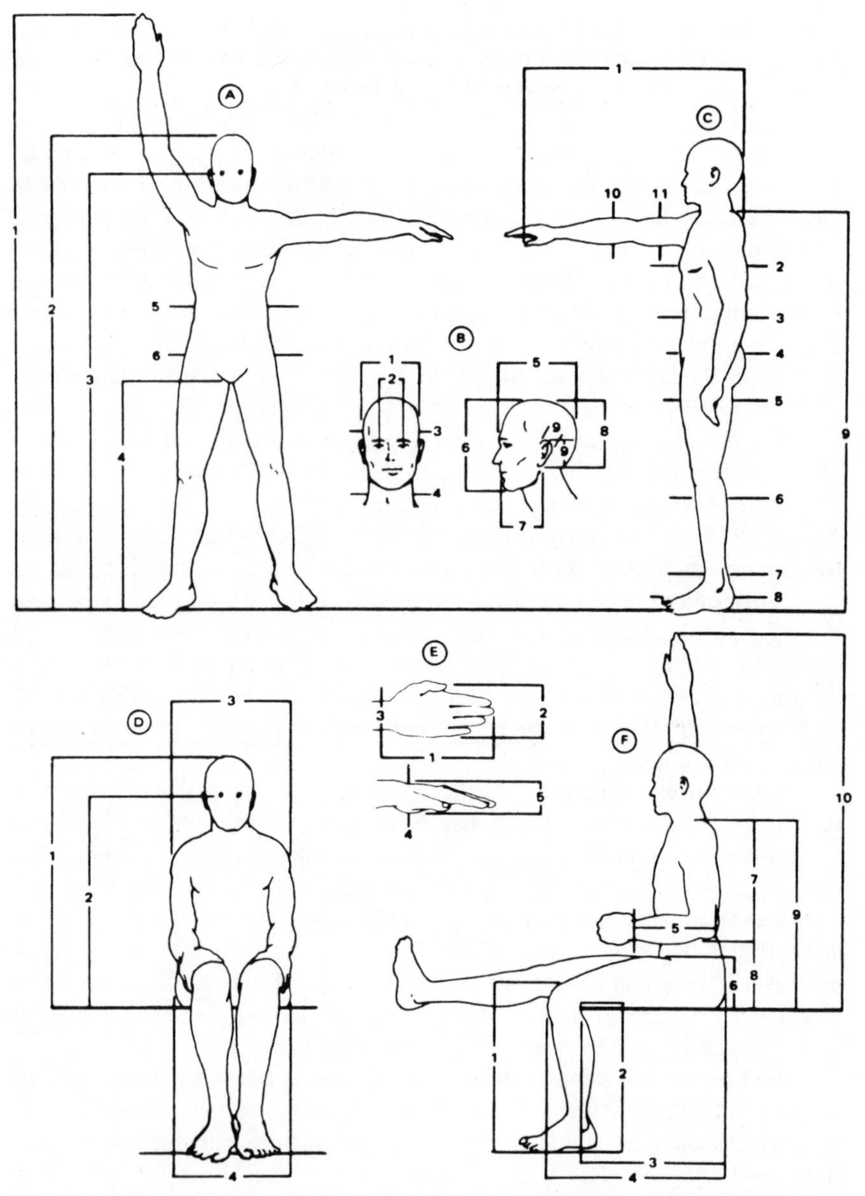

Fig. 4 Identification of body dimensions and characteristics given in Table 1. (Courtesy of R.W. Bailey.)

which it experiences a continuous decline. Sex is another factor influencing strength, with women generally considered to have very approximately two-thirds the strength of men of the same age. Additional factors include build (height, weight), general health, physical fitness, diet, environmental factors, body position, occupational factors (for example, backrests on seats increase pushing strength) and motivation.

A substantial amount of anthropometric data have been collected for the strength of muscle groups associated with various body components. These data are primarily based on the maximal forces exertable by muscles and muscle groups for short periods of time (of the order of a few seconds) and while the muscles are stationary, that is, the data are given in terms of isometric (static) forces or loads. Relatively little research has been conducted to determine levels of isotomic (dynamic) work while the muscles are moving. A small sample of isometric strength data is given in table 2. These data may be some of the most relevant to industrial ergonomics, while additional data are available in the anthropometric data sources listed previously.

Based on the $\bar{x}$ and s values in table 2, various percentiles of strength may be computed from the x_p formula given above. For example, the fifth percentile for hand-rotation torque is found to be $x_{.05} = 8.4 - 1.64\ (2.6) = 4.1$ cm-kg (3.6 in.-lb) when turning a knob of 2.5-cm (1-in.) diameter. This information may clearly be useful for a designer when choosing the resistance to be used for a rotary control device. Similarly, a designer may need to choose a pushbutton control that should require some force to guard against accidental activation, although the force requirements should not exceed the capability of 95 percent of the male population for activating this control by pressing with the index finger. It follows from table 2 that this activation force should not exceed 3.8 kg $= 5.9 - 1.64\ (1.3)$.

It should be noted that for the types of muscular actions that are of interest to ergonomists it is likely that the integrated exertion of several muscle groups has to be considered. In such cases, the weakest link in the muscular chain concerned becomes the determining factor for the maximal force that can be exerted. It is also important to remember that the types of isometric strength data given in table 2 refer to maximum strength for instantaneous exertion. If maximum force has to be maintained for some time, the force becomes a decreasing function of time with a decreasing rate of change, that is, the decrease in maximum force is more rapid early on.

Anthropometric data for maximum lifting strength in different positions are also available in several of the references listed previously. However, the industrial ergonomist should be more concerned with permissible weight limits that can be lifted safely without undue risk of back injury. Such lifting guidelines have been prepared by the National Institute of Occupational Safety and Health (1983). Simple-to-use guidelines for safe lifting are also available in Davis and Stubbs (1980), which gives acceptable levels of forces that can be lifted safely by males of different age groups and for different lifting conditions or positions (standing, sitting, squatting, kneeling, two

TABLE 2
Mean $\bar{x}$ and Standard Deviation s of the Maximum Static Strength of Some Body Components*

Characteristic	$\bar{x}$	s
Hand grip (squeeze, kg)		
Industrial workers: Preferred hand, males	53.1	7.0
Preferred hand, females	33.6	4.7
Average for both hands, females		
College students: Right hand, males	49.0	9.5
Left hand, males	43.1	8.2
Hand rotation torque (cm-kg) on knobs with knurled edges (males)		
Knob diameter (cm): 0.6	1.4	0.4
1.3	3.3	1.0
1.9	6.7	2.4
2.5	8.4	2.6
3.8	10.6	2.7
5.1	15.1	3.5
7.6	34.4	9.8
10.2	50.3	12.5
12.7	70.1	18.9
Finger force (kg) of right hand, males		
Thumb versus object	7.3	1.7
Index finger versus object	5.9	1.3
Middle finger versus object	6.4	2.0
Ring finger versus object	5.0	1.7
Little finger versus object	3.2	1.1
Thumb versus tip of index finger	9.6	2.3
Thumb versus side of index finger	10.5	2.2
Right arm pull (kg), horizontal, seated operator, males		
Elbow angle 180° (straight arm)	54.9	16.8
150°	55.3	16.3
120°	47.2	14.1
90°	39.9	13.6
60°	28.6	10.0
Right arm push (kg), horizontal, seated operator, males		
Elbow angle 180° (straight arm)	62.6	22.2
150°	55.8	20.4
120°	46.7	19.5
90°	39.5	15.0
60°	41.7	17.2

*Adapted from Hertzberg (1972), Konz (1983) and Woodson (1981).

handed and one handed). Safe limits for pushing, pulling and palmar thrusting are also given. Their data may also be used as guidance for determining safe force limits for females by using the rule of thumb that female strength is roughly two-thirds that of males.

Center of Gravity

In some design situations, it may be of practical value to have some reasonably accurate idea of where the center of gravity (mass) CG of the human body is located. While the CG varies with body weight, stature and build, it tends to be slightly above half the height dimension A2 in table 1 and is independent of age. Woodson and Conover (1964, 5-23) present the whole-body CG for different positions of the body and its extremities. Some of the more important average ball-park figures of CG locations for adult males may be given as follows (rounded off to the nearest centimeter). When a person is standing erect with the arms hanging down, the CG is about 10 cm (3.9 in.) forward of and 15 cm (5.9 in.) above the seat reference point (SRP), where SRP is defined as the midpoint of the intersection of the plane of the seat surface with the plane of the backrest surface of the seat. When seated with vertical back, the arms hanging straight down and a 90° knee angle, the CG is about 22 cm (8.7 in.) ahead of and 24 cm (9.5 in.) above the SRP. For the same seated position, but with the arms stretched forward horizontally, the distance between the SRP and the CG is about 25 cm (9.8 in.) horizontally and 28 cm (11 in.) vertically; with the arms stretched upward vertically, these respective dimensions become 23 cm (9.1 in.) and 30 cm (11.8 in.).

The locations of the CG of individual body components are also available in the anthropometric literature. Some such data are reported by Konz (1983, 271).

This chapter has outlined sets of guidelines for the ergonomic design of work stations in general, aimed at fitting the work station to the operator (instead of vice versa). Some design recommendations for work stations containing control devices and displays, including VDTs, have also been outlined. Many of the design guidelines and principles may appear to be common sense, but judging by real work stations as they exist in most industrial firms, it would seem that common sense is not all that common. The final sections of the chapter have dealt with anthropometry, a useful data source for achieving appropriate matching between the operator and his or her work station.

References

Armstrong, T.J. 1983. An ergonomics guide to carpal tunnel syndrome. *Ergonomics guide series*. Akron, Ohio: American Industrial Hygiene Association.

Bailey, R.W. 1982. *Human performance engineering: A guide for system designers*. Englewood Cliffs, N.J.: Prentice-Hall.

Cakir, A., D.J. Hart, and T.F.M. Stewart. 1980. *Visual display terminals*. New York: Wiley.

Damon, A., H.W. Stoudt, and R.A. McFarland. 1966. *The human body in equipment design*. Cambridge: Harvard University Press.

Daniels, G.S., H.C. Meyers, and S.H. Worrall. 1953. *Anthropometry of WAF basic trainees*. WADC-TR-53-12.

Das, B., and R.M. Grady. 1983. Industrial workplace layout and engineering anthropology. In *Ergonomics of workstation design*. T.O. Kvalseth, ed. London: Butterworths.

Davis, P.R., and D.A. Stubbs, 1980. *Force limits in manual work*. Guildford, Surrey, U.K.: IPC Science and Technology Press.

Dreyfuss, M. 1967. *The measure of man: Human factors in design*. 2nd ed. New York: Whitney Library of Design.

Garrett, J.W., and K.W. Kennedy. 1971. *A collation of anthropometry*. Vol. I and II. AMRL-TR-68-1, AD723630.

Gould, J.D. 1968. Visual factors in the design of computer controlled CRT displays. *Human Factors* 10:359-76.

Grandjean, E. 1980. *Fitting the task to the man*. London: Taylor & Francis, Ltd.

Hertzberg, G.T.E. 1972. Engineering anthropology. In *Human engineering guide to equipment design*. H.P. Van Cott and R.G. Kinkade, eds., 467-584. Washington, D.C.: U.S. Government Printing Office.

Kantowitz, B.H., and R.D. Sorkin. 1983. *Human factors: Understanding people-system relationships*. New York: Wiley.

Kvalseth, T.O. 1983. Sources of ergonomics information for industrial job design. In *Ergonomics of workstation design*. London: Butterworths.

McCormick, E.J., and M.S. Sanders. 1982. *Human factors in engineering and design*. 5th ed. New York: McGraw-Hill Book Co.

National Institute of Occupational Safety and Health. 1983. *Work practices guide for manual lifting*. No. 81-122. Reprinted by the American Industrial Hygiene Association, Akron, Ohio.

Oborne, D.J. 1982. *Ergonomics at work*. Chichester, U.K.: Wiley.

Roebuck, J.A., K.H.E. Kroemer, and W.G. Thomson. 1975. *Engineering anthropometry methods*. New York: Wiley.

Shackel, B., ed. 1979. *Applied ergonomics handbook*. Guildford, Surrey, U.K.: IPC Press.

——. 1979. *Man-computer communication*. Vol. 1 and 2. Maidenhead, Berkshire, U.K.: Infotech International.

Tichauer, E.R. 1978. *The biomechanical basis of ergonomics*. New York: McGraw-Hill Book Co.

Woodson, W.E. 1981. *Human factors design handbook*. New York: McGraw-Hill Book Co.

Woodson, W.E., and D.W. Conover. 1964. *Human engineering guide for equipment designers*. 2nd ed. Berkeley, Calif: University of California Press.

Tarald O. Kvålseth *is professor of mechanical engineering, University of Minnesota, Minneapolis.*

6

Product Design

Donald V. Zurwelle

Overview

Ergonomics is playing an ever-increasing role in the design of products worldwide. However, in the United States today, relatively few manufacturing companies employ full-time ergonomics professionals. The issues of ergonomics or human factors are addressed by ergonomics practitioners — development engineers and industrial designers. Consultants in ergonomics are used to analyze new designs and to solve particularly involved problems and as expert witnesses in litigation. Integrated ergonomics/industrial design groups are rare in industry at this time, though they represent the best organizational approach to excellence in human factors.

The practitioner system is a workable one if the combination of simple guidelines, applicable ergonomics data and use testing is followed. A documented methodology to analyze how a product will be used and misused is especially helpful, though not mandatory. Informal analysis can also be quite effective. The more complex the product-use pattern, the more rigorous must be the ergonomics investigation.

Data covering anthropometrics and biomechanics are a particularly important foundation for good product design. Anthropometrics is simply the physical measurement of humans, and biomechanics is the study of the human body's capabilities. Currently available data in these disciplines are at times non-realistic, inappropriate, or just difficult to find. Much anthropometric information presently in the literature was derived from studies of military personnel — a select and more homogenous group. This must be borne in mind and accounted for when designing for a non-military population. Good anthropometric and biomechanics data relating to females and especially to children is far less available. Information concerning the physically impaired is quite narrow.

All data must be interpreted in relation to the known conditions of use. A simple example would be the sizing of a panel access hole through which a hand must pass to turn a crank handle. Known conditions might be: predominantly male users often wearing work gloves; rotating a handle 90° with ten pounds of force; the handle being located several inches behind the panel face. The access hole size and shape then should accommodate a 90-percentile male hand expanded by a firm grasping position plus allowance for thickness of a work glove. Further, rotation and flexing of the wrist must be taken into consideration. Complete ergonomic analysis is often less obvious than it appears, although common sense may be applied to many aspects.

Product design quality depends upon an understanding of the user-product interface in terms of the user's characteristics. These are not readily redesigned or modified. Ergonomic principles when properly applied result in safer products, more easily understood and effectively employed by the user.

Design for safety has obvious benefits for the user and also, less obviously, the manufacturer when anticipating liability litigation. Analysis of use patterns to discover possible or likely misuse is important. Misuse which can be reasonably foreseen and avoided through design or warnings provides fertile ground for future litigation, if it is not addressed during the product development cycle. Behavioral modification to control unsafe acts is not a widely understood or applied discipline in the home or workplace. Therefore, product design for safety remains the best approach to accident reduction.

A sound methodology to ensure attention to safety in design includes a safety committee charged with reviewing the product on at least two milestone dates. The first date is the completion of the design on paper and the second is the assembly of pilot lot units. A standard safety checklist should be used for evaluation. It is important for the design team and safety committee to identify and agree upon potential mechanical, electrical and task hazards. Since real-time observation of accident experiments with human subjects is not possible, the analysis of accident reports compiled by attorneys can be a valuable exercise.

So-called fail-safe design should be considered for those products which are inherently hazardous, such as power saws, power mowers, and explosive cartridge nailers.

Finally, safe design, to be effective, must not impair the use of the product for its intended purpose. Users so encumbered will find ways to defeat the most clever of safety features.

Design for reliability should be an on-going process of design and testing using prototype units. Clearly, there is a close relationship between product reliability, durability, and safety.

A product's reliability in use may be tested in the laboratory and in the field. Generally, the more meaningful data come from field-testing with intended users. Laboratory tests often fail to uncover real world use/misuse patterns which affect product reliability.

The user-product interface must be seen as a dynamic relationship. This input-decision/output-feedback system is basic to understanding the interaction of the user and product. To reliably perform its function, a product should supply the user with visual and auditory feedback. Without feedback, human beings cannot modify actions taken and forces applied during a use cycle.

Adjustments and controls should be understandable, consistent with, and appropriate to a product's use envelope. In addition, they must be repeatable and positive.

When designing adjustments or controls, one should account for a wide range of user experience and also areas of fairly universal learned behavior and expectation. Several years ago a line of portable power tools was introduced with detachable cordsets. Despite several obvious advantages, the line met increasing user resistance and was eventually discontinued. The cord latch held securely but its operation was fundamentally flawed. A simple, rotating device, the latch moved *counterclockwise* to lock the cord in place, Yet, there is very strong learned behavior associating locking, tightening or securing with clockwise rotation. Further, there was no auditory or tactile feedback as the latch was moved to the locked position. The user could not feel positive that indeed the cord was fully locked in place. Visual inspection of the operating lugs on the power tools was also not helpful. Locked and unlocked positions were not clearly identified. A basically useful feature lost acceptance in the marketplace because the ergonomic issues were ignored.

Repeatability can be important when a control is regularly reset during normal use. Examples are variable motor speed dials, drill/hammer mode selectors on power tools used for drilling and setting concrete anchors, and cut depth and bevel adjustments on circular saws. Legible markings, intermediate stops, correct operating forces, smooth movement and proportioned gripping surfaces all contribute to positive and repeatable controls.

The use of well-designed symbols to mark adjustments and controls is almost mandatory for products to be marketed internationally. Symbols and pictographs are also helpful within national boundaries in areas where there is limited literacy.

Design for durability under conditions of normally expected use and reasonably foreseen misuse should be another area of focus. The lack of adequate durability may have safety implications.

Premature or constant product failure can be aggravating to a home user but disastrous for a professional user. In the latter case, business success or contractual obligations may be at stake.

Testing for durability may be performed in laboratory simulations and field trials. Generally, prototype units do not serve well for this type of testing. Methods and materials used to construct prototype units often do not correspond to production parts. This difference is especially true of plastic, injection-molded parts. Those made of a given plastic from experimental molds rarely exhibit the same characteristics as those from production molds. Field trials using pilot lot units have the best chance to uncover design flaws. Forces applied by humans can be difficult to duplicate on mechanical test rigs.

Design for usability is closely dependent upon a solid understanding of a product's intended purpose and use environment. New product designs with new applications require careful analysis of the use sequence and potential patterns of misuse. Product configuration must be based upon this analysis as well as traditional configurations of similar devices. The less new a product, the more importance that must be placed upon any long-established forms. Successful product designs must not only work right but be perceived as being right by the user. Again, the emphasis must be on the resolving of points of friction between the user and the product. Preliminary modeling (figure 1) and prototype fabrication (figure 2) are invaluable for analyzing product configuration.

Design for comfort is the area most controversial and difficult to define. The concept of "feel" is hard for the average person to understand and evaluate. Nevertheless, most people will decide intuitively upon the rightness or wrongness of a product's feel. More objectively, feel can be stated as the sum of weight, center of gravity and moment of inertia. To a lesser degree, visual mass and shape can influence feel.

Hand grip size and shape are most critical. Anthropometric data, comparisons with similar grips, forces to be controlled or applied, and space for any internal components all provide a basis to begin design. Modeling of designs for evaluation by a range of hand sizes is almost mandatory (figure 3). Areas of focus should also include avoidance of localized pressure points, isolation from excess vibration, and the tactility of the grip surface.

Poor grip design leads to lack of force control, work strain and eventual muscle or tendon trauma.

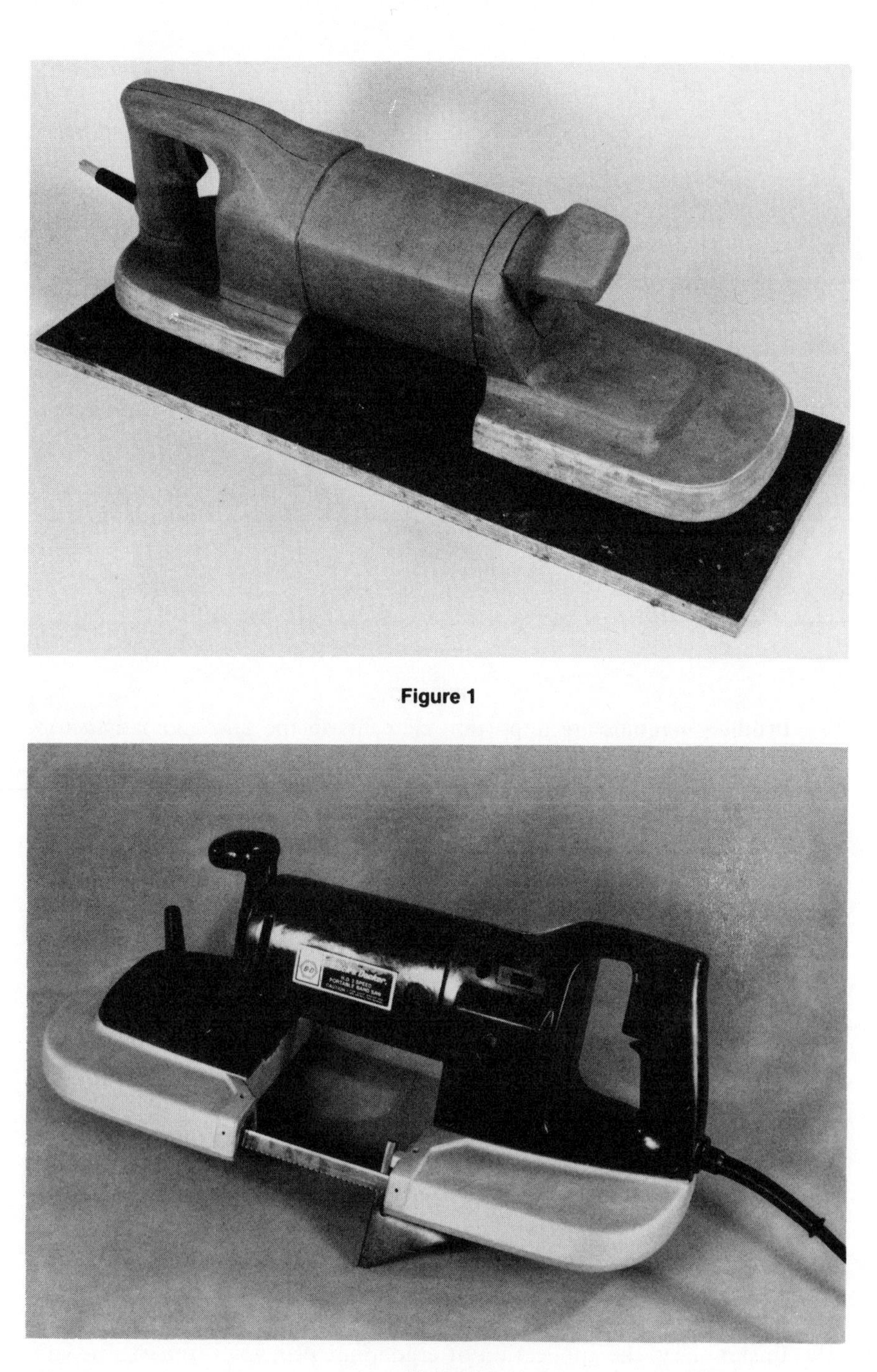

Figure 1

Figure 2

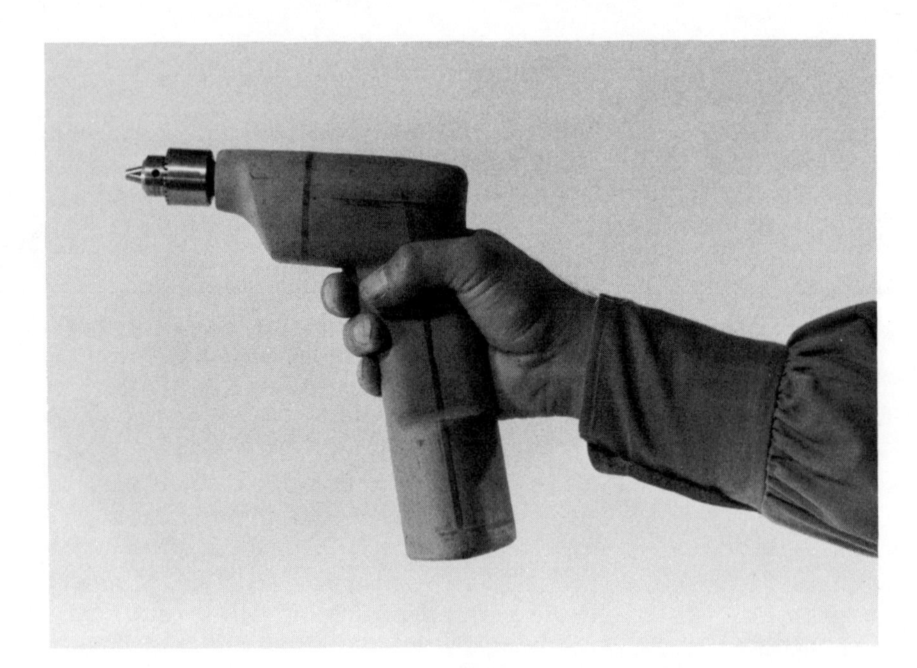

Figure 3

Product manuals are important elements in the safe and satisfactory utilization of products. Customer surveys in the power-tool industry have shown that about 70 percent of those interviewed utilized the instruction manuals packed with the products. General safety information, specific product safety data, applications, operating instructions, cleaning and maintenance guidelines, service locations, approved accessories, warranty statement and assembly instructions, if any, are all mandatory items for a good manual. The text should be straightforward, without technical jargon. Clear and accurate illustrations are a must. In addition, a multilingual format should be considered.

Increasingly, larger corporations must be world marketers in order to compete effectively. Black and Decker, for example, markets the same model of professional tools throughout the Western Hemisphere. The products, cartons and manuals use three languages: English, Canadian French, and Latin American Spanish (figure 4). In several areas of the United States, Spanish is spoken almost as frequently as English, and, consequently, multilingual markings have national as well as international implications.

While well-written manuals are never substitutes for well-designed products, they do enhance the user's general satisfaction, safe product use and understanding of all product capabilities.

In summary, the application of ergonomic principles to design is vital to the success of all products in today's highly competitive marketplace. Those products which optimize the user-product interface ultimately provide greater user satisfaction.

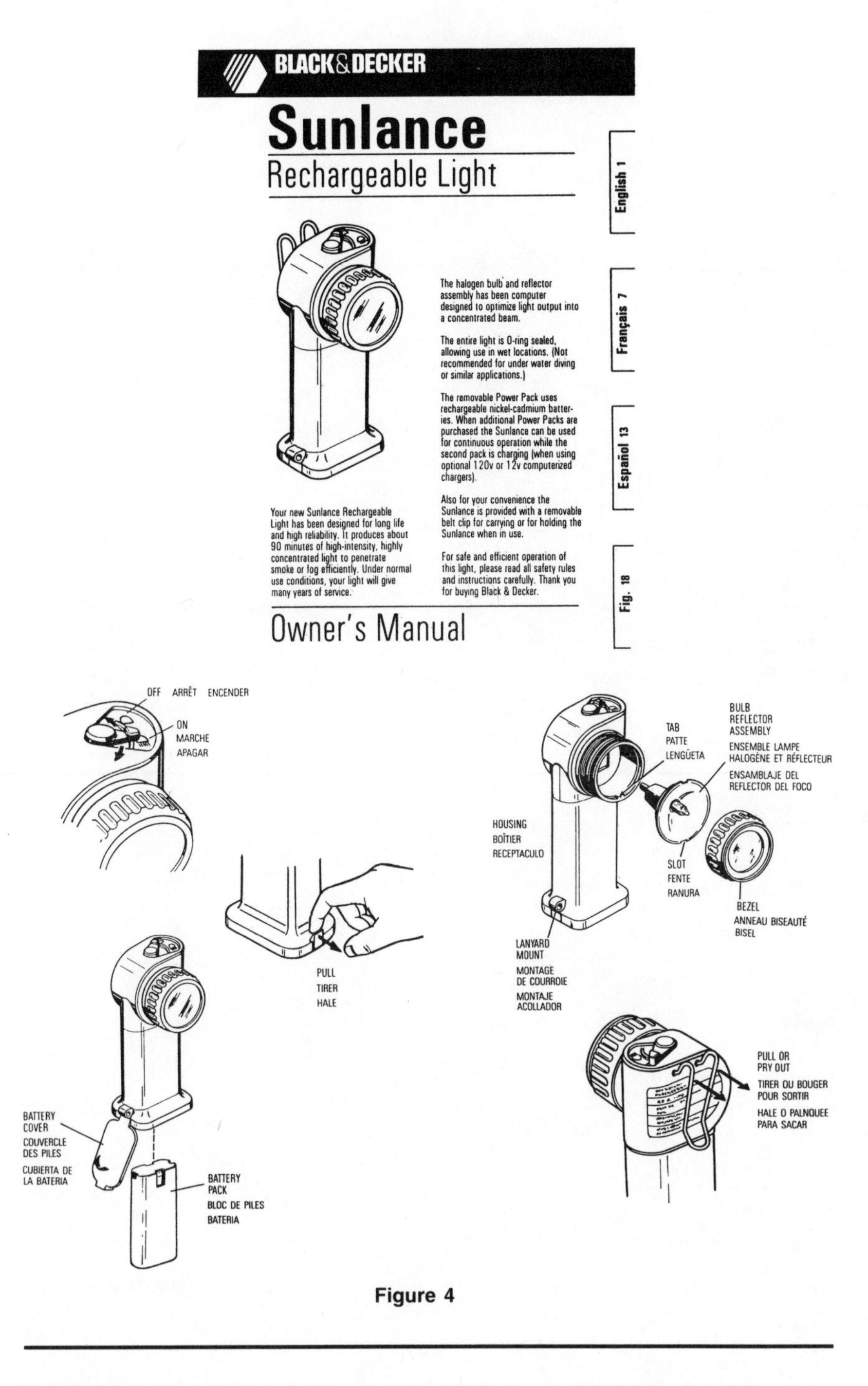

Figure 4

***Donald W. Zurwelle** is manager/industrial design at the Professional Products Division of Black & Decker (U.S.), Inc., Hampstead, Maryland.*

7

Environmental Factors

Jerry D. Ramsey, Ph.D., P.E.

Noise

Noise in an occupational environment can create problems of several types. There is the potential of permanent hearing loss associated with exposure to loud noises over long periods of time, or exposure to extremely loud noises for brief periods. Noise has also been demonstrated to create an annoyance effect which has implications to worker safety and to work performance or output. There is some evidence, although contradictory, that noise can create physiological responses that have long-term health implications and that are contributors to stress at the workplace.

Components and measurements. The important physical components of noise are represented by the frequency and the intensity of the sound energy or sound pressure. Differences in frequency, measured in cycles per second, or Hertz, are sensed as a different tone or pitch. The intensity of noise is normally measured in decibels and is sensed by the human ear in terms of loudness or volume. Intensity is represented by a logarithm scale ranging from approximately 0 decibels, which is the threshold of hearing perception, to the threshold of pain, which occurs in the 120-130 decibel range. Human hearing is not equally sensitive to sound pressure at all frequencies, figure 1. Low-frequency noises typically require more sound energy to be perceived at any level of loudness, except at very high levels of intensity. Also depicted in figure 1 are the frequency and intensity levels associated with normal speech.

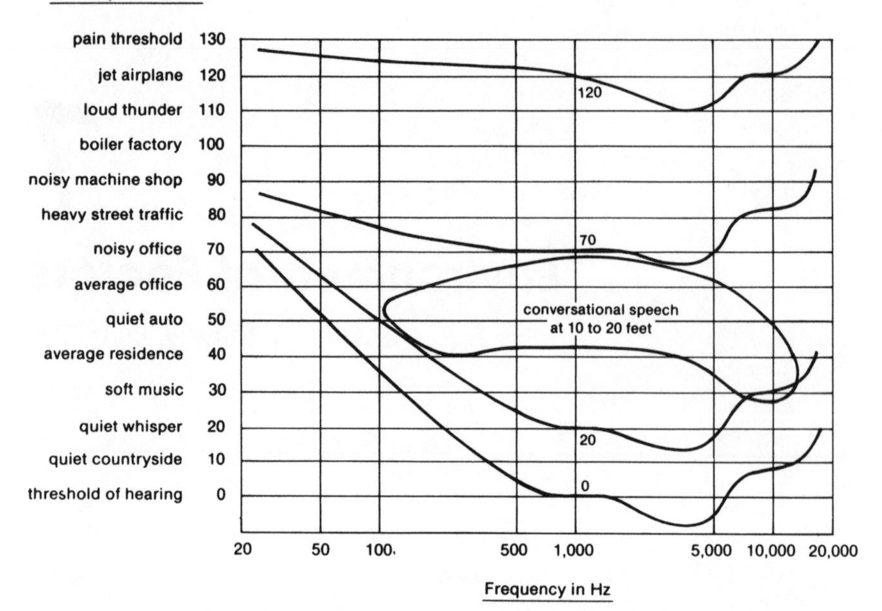

Fig. 1 Equal loudness and typical sounds

Noise intensity or loudness is measured with a sound-level meter. It is common for the meter to be calibrated in a dbA scale, which filters the composite noise in a manner similar to the way the human perceives sound energy. Sound energy is also measured by means of a dosimeter which is attached to an individual worker and which measures the cumulative noise impact on the worker during a given period of time. Noise frequency is generally determined by the use of octave-band filters attached to the sound-level meter. Such filters allow the measurement of sound energy within a given noise band spectrum.

Human responses. The hearing process is initiated by means of the external ear, ear canal, eardrum, and the connecting ossicles (hammer, anvil, and stirrup), which collect and transmit mechanical vibratory energy. Next, this energy is transferred to the fluid of the cochlea and, thus, to the organ of Corti, the auditory nerve, and then to the brain, which interprets the sound energy signals. Hearing problems which occur in the mechanical transmission portion of the ear can often be corrected with surgery or with bone-conduction hearing aids. Excessive noise, however, impairs the nerve-conduction portion of the hearing process and results in permanent and irreparable damage to hearing.

It is generally accepted that continuous long-term occupational exposure to noises above 85-90 dbA creates a risk of permanent hearing loss. As the intensity level increases above this range, increasing hearing loss will occur. Similarly, longer exposures result in more hearing loss. Hearing loss also increases with age, since the normal mechanisms of bone and nerve conduction tend to deteriorate as part of the normal aging process. Hearing loss can be assessed quite accurately by means of an audiometer which records a person's response to signals presented at a series of frequency and intensity combinations. Periodic audiograms throughout a person's employment history can be reviewed to determine if hearing loss is in excess of what would be expected due to normal aging loss (NIOSH 1973).

Recommendations and controls. Federal regulations of the Occupational Safety and Health Administration (OSHA) require that work environments with noise levels above 85 dbA be regularly monitored and that audiograms of exposed workers be made and maintained. The time-weighted average noise level for a workplace can be determined by prorating the noise level over the periods of exposure in order to determine if noise represents an excessively high level. This time-weighted average schema defines acceptable noise level as 90 dbA for eight hours, 95 dbA for four hours, 100 dbA for two hours, etc. Thus, four hours at 90 dbA represents four-eighths or one-half of an acceptable noise exposure. Any combination of noise level and exposure time is acceptable if the sum of these fractional doses does not exceed unity — that is, a full day's noise exposure.

If noise is determined to be excessive, the first approach to correction should be through engineering controls. These include the selective use of acoustic materials, barriers, shock absorbers, mufflers, enclosures, and isolations. If these methods are not adequate, then the limiting of pesonnel exposure through work shift changes or the use of personal protection devices (for example, earplugs or earmuffs) may be possible.

Vibration

Occupational vibration in the working environment can be of two general forms: whole body vibration, which tends to produce overall fatigue or loss of productivity, and localized vibration in body segments, which can result, when accompanied by long-term exposure, in a chronic trauma known as Raynaud's phenomenon. Raynaud's phenomenon, sometimes called white finger, can cause degeneration to a point where a worker who normally uses vibrating tools (for example, chain saw, jackhammer, disk grinder) can no longer work at these tasks due to the pain and loss of sensitivity in the hands.

Components and measurements. The measurement of occupational vibration involves, as with noise, the measurement of frequency and intensity.

Frequency is normally measured in Hertz, but intensity in vibration can most easily be reflected as units of acceleration. Since one G represents the normal acceleration due to gravity, it is common to refer to acceleration in terms of relative G units. In the case of a rotating or reciprocating motion, intensity can also be expressed in terms of revolutions per minute and a magnitude of displacement. Many of the sound-level meters which are usable to measure noise can also be used, with the addition of an accelerometer for low frequencies, to measure vibration energy as well.

Human responses. The human under whole-body vibration tends to react as a complex system of component masses, springs and dampers. The body components themselves, including trunk, arms, head, and eyeballs, each tend to have a resonant frequency. Resonance occurs at the frequency that generates the most displacement for a specific mass. The actions of the muscle, ligament, and cartilage at the joint provide the spring and attenuation characteristics. The human body vibrating as a unit reaches resonance around 3-6 Hertz. Research from the literature has indicated that, for brief-duration exposures, the human body can tolerate and function effectively at G levels in the range of 3.0 G, except for that subset which also involves a 3-6 Hertz frequency, and there the limit would be more normally 1.0 G. For exposures of less than an hour, levels around 0.3 G are reasonable. For prolonged exposure a level of 0.05 G across most frequencies appears to be safe (Ramsey 1975).

Limits on segmental vibration occur due to interference with the blood flow and, thus, the oxygen supply to the body segment (for example, hand or arm). Here again, limits tend to be specific to the segment, since each has its own resonant frequency. However, symptoms of Raynaud's phenomenon are most likely to occur with vibrations between 25-150 Hertz and amplitudes of at least 100 microns.

Recommendations and controls. Although international standards have been proposed concerning whole-body vibration limits, no regulations exist for the United States. Control for whole-body vibration can be in several forms: using vibration damping mounts or shock absorbers for heavy equipment, interfering with vibration through buildings by separating the floors or walls in order to break the transmission link, using auxiliary slings or seating which have been specially designed to ameliorate the transmission of vehicle vibration to the driver or occupant, balancing and proper maintenance of reciprocating and rotary equipment, etc.

Localized vibration problems can often be remedied through a change in tool type or vendor, proper tool maintenance, or the use of auxiliary support straps or handles which can help share the vibratory energy and provide cushioning against direct energy transmission to the arms or hands.

Lighting

Lighting is an important element of the occupational environment in that lighting levels which are too low, have improper color balance, or produce glare can create the potential for eye fatigue, increased safety hazards, and decreased productivity due to interference, errors or fatigue.

Components and measurements. The most important measurable components of occupational lighting are illumination, measured in foot-candles (fc), and brightness, measured in foot-lamberts (fl). The foot-candle is a measure of the luminous flux which arrives at a given location. It is a function of the nature and intensity of the light source and the distance over which the light is transmitted. It can easily be measured by the use of a light meter, such as in a camera, or by other more sophisticated photometers. The loss of luminous intensity follows the inverse-square law. Although the design of luminaires in a plant or workplace layout will be concerned primarily with the foot-candles at the workplace, the real measure of ability to see a work object is more properly defined in terms of brightness (fl). This measure includes the fc which arrive at a workplace and are modified based upon the reflectance of the object which the light is striking. Light, shiny surfaces have a reflectance near 1.0, whereas black matte surfaces have a reflectance near 0.0, and little if any of the incident light would be available for seeing. The same fc meter can be used to measure fl by simply pointing the meter toward the reflecting surface and thus determining the amount of light reflected toward the eye.

Human responses. The lighted image of an object enters the eye through the pupil and lens, is presented to the retina as an inverted image, and is transmitted by the optic nerve to the brain for proper interpretation. Farsightedness and nearsightedness are vision problems that result when the lens fails to focus clearly on the retina (that is, focuses behind or in front of the retina, respectively). These problems are normally correctable by means of an external lens, either eyeglasses or contact lenses. The ability to discriminate focused detail, that is, visual acuity, is measured in terms of the visual angle an object imparts to the eye.

Daylight vision which utilizes color reception depends upon visual focus on the cones within the retina, whereas vision at low levels of illumination and in the periphery depends more upon the rods of the retina. The rods do not perceive color and are located in the area beyond the principal focus region (fovea). Thus, vision at night is enhanced by looking at the general area rather than focusing on a small object or area. Defective cones result in color defects or color blindness and these can have serious safety implications (for example, the normal acceptance of red and green representing stop and go signals).

Recommendations and controls. The brightness level at the work site represents only a part of the consideration needed for good vision. As shown in figure 2, the ability to see an object is much more dependent on the visual angle or apparent size of that object, and the contrast the object makes with its background, than it is on either the brightness level or the amount of time which is provided for viewing. The object which is large enough to see, and has adequate contrast, can be seen under extremely low levels of illumination. There are recommendations, however, concerning general lighting levels at the workplace and these are expressed in terms of foot-candles (fc). They indicate that 100 fc is adequate for most desk and bench work where normal seeing is required. Extremely detailed work may require supplemental lighting of several hundred additional foot-candles, but storage rooms, hallways, and stairs required only 20-50 fc if the only concern is general vision within the area. Glare has a strong negative impact on the ability to see.

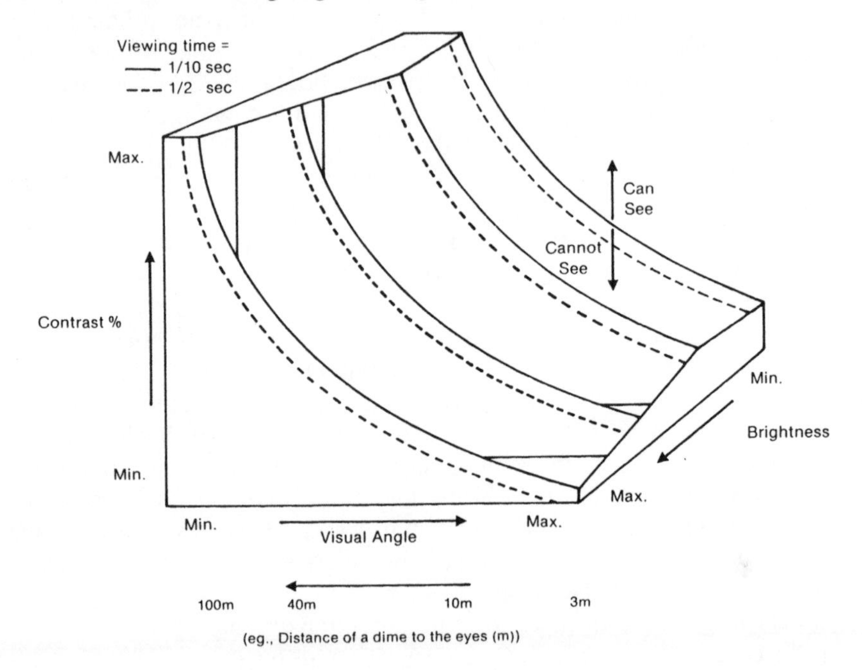

Fig. 2. Factors relating to ability to see

Different luminaires generate different electromagnetic spectra and, thus, differences in perceived color. Fluorescent lighting is typically nearer "white light" and outdoor color balance than is incandescent lighting, which tends to have more red and orange wavelengths. Lighting which is adequate but not excessive, is free of glare, is from the proper direction, and is of appropriate color balance can reduce eye fatigue, provide a more enjoyable and acceptable work environment, and minimize some possible negative effects on productivity and safety (Ayoub and Ramsey 1975).

Heat and Cold

The hot occupational environment is possibly the most commonly encountered of all environments. The human, as a homeothermic animal, is able to adapt well to most hot environments. Combinations of work and environmental temperature which yield an increase in the heat stored within the body, however, can yield conditions which pose serious risks to worker health, as well as significant losses in worker productivity. The worker in the cold environment is typically protected with increased layers of clothing, but the combination of low temperature and clothing creates substantial negative impact on a person's motor abilities. Extremely cold environments also present risks to workers' health, especially to the hands, arms, toes, and feet, which tend to be the most vulnerable body parts during exposure to low temperatures.

Components and measurements. There are four basic components necessary to provide a complete definition of the thermal environment. The first is the air (or dry bulb) temperature, which is commonly measured by a mercury-in-glass thermometer. This measurement is available at most private and public worksites and from the National Weather Service on a daily basis. The relative humidity of the air is the second important variable, and it relates to human comfort and the ability of the human body to lose heat to its environment. It is determined by means of a psychrometric chart and a measurement of wet bulb or dewpoint temperature. Wet bulb temperature is obtained by exposing the thermometer, which has a wet wick over the sensing element, to a forced convective air flow (for example, use of a sling psychrometer). The third component of importance is the air velocity or wind speed; this is normally measured by means of an anemometer of a vane or hot-wire type. The fourth component, mean radiant temperature, is that thermal energy which is transferred as electromagnetic energy between a hot (radiating) body and an object. The sun outdoors or the high-temperature furnace inside can transmit high levels of radiant heat energy which will add to the total heat gain at an object. In the occupational environment, this is commonly obtained as a measure of globe temperature, that is, from a thermometer placed in the center of a black, copper sphere (Ramsey 1983).

Human responses. The human follows some well-defined relationships concerning heat transfer with an environment. Heat storage S will be zero when the body is in thermal equilibrium. Heat loss from the body is primarily accomplished through the evaporation E of perspiration from the body surface (skin). Heat is always added to the human body to the extent that work is being performed and generating metabolic heat M. Even the quietly seated human will generate metabolic heat, although at a much lower level than when that same person is involved in moderate or vigorous activity. The human will also respond to either heat loss or gain from the convective C, or radiative R, heat transfer of an environment. Thus, the equation $S =$

$M - E \pm R \pm C$ summarizes very nicely the human response to work in a thermal environment (Ramsey and Ayoub 1975).

The occurrence of heat exhaustion, during which feelings of serious fatigue and various feelings of illness or discomfort may be present, requires that the individual be moved to a cool location, given plenty of water to drink, and be allowed to rest. The occurrence of heat stroke is much more serious, and, although it involves many of the same symptoms as heat exhaustion, it is typically characterized by an extremely hot, dry skin and a dangerously high deep body temperature. When these symptoms occur, the individual should be cooled immediately with a bath, shower, hose, or wet towels in order to promptly lower the body temperature. The other actions indicated above for heat exhaustion should also be taken.

The blood vessel system of the body is automatically and effectively involved in the thermal-regulation process. With the onset of high temperature, vasodilation (vessel opening) occurs, and the blood is shunted nearer the surface of the skin so that more body heat will be removed through evaporation. The presence of cold temperature creates the opposite response of vasoconstriction (vessel closing), and warm blood is shunted away from the periphery and into the body core to maintain the temperature for vital body functions. This process puts in jeopardy the fingers, toes, ears, hands, and feet, which have a high ability to lose heat due to their large relative surface area and the lack of normal warm blood flow during cold exposure.

Recommendations and controls. When the storage of body heat (deep body temperature) stays below a level of approximately 101.4°F (99.6°F oral temperature), research has shown that the typical worker will be able to continue without increased risk of heat stress. There has developed, over the last dozen years, consensus concerning the threshold or entry levels of environmental and work conditions which present a safe working environment for most workers in the heat (Ramsey 1975). This relationship, which is depicted in figure 3, uses wet bulb globe temperature (WBGT) as a composite measure of the thermal environment. The figure shows that as the intensity of the work increases, and thus the metabolic workload associated with that task gets higher, the threshold value in WBGT units gets progressively lower. For example, the worker at a light work task (for example, working seated at an assembly task) would have a threshold limit of 86°F WBGT, whereas the worker at heavy work (for example, continuous lifting of cartons) would have a corresponding limit of 79°F (Smith and Ramsey 1982). Also shown in figure 3 are the threshold limits reflected as readings from the Botsball. This device, which measures wet globe temperature (WGT) directly from a small, wet, black globe, is generally simpler to use and less expensive than the WBGT. For conditions of moderate relative humidity and radiant heat, the difference between the two indexes is about 4-5°F; when the relative humidity is high and the radiant conditions are low, the difference is only 1-2°F.

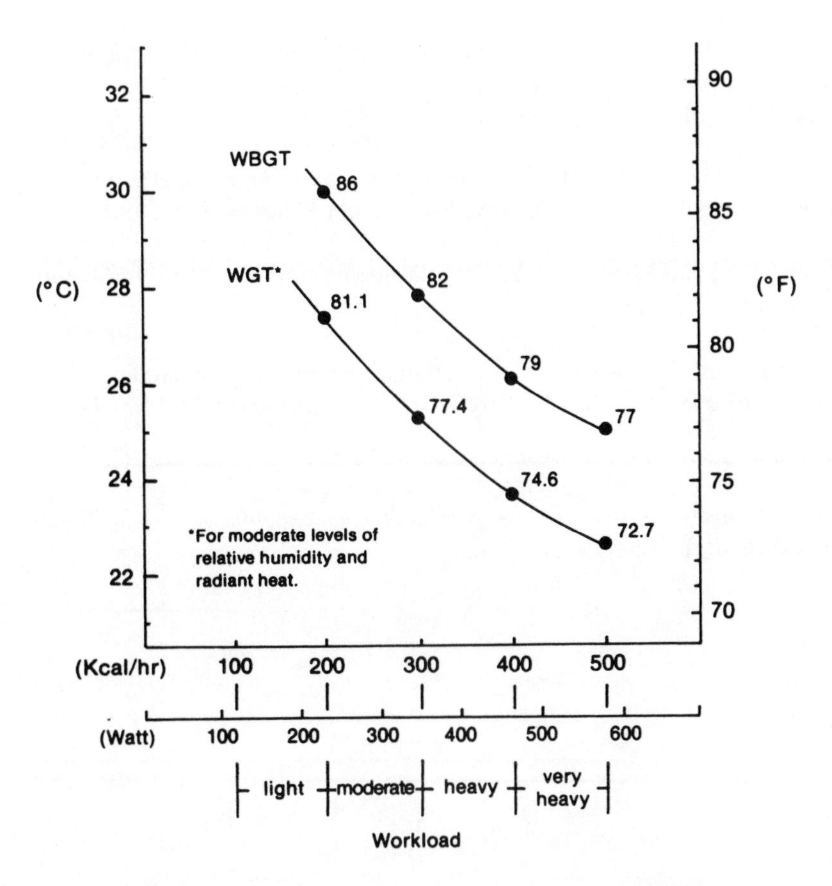

Fig. 3. Threshold limits for combinations of workload and heat

The most useful thermal index for the cold environment is the windchill index. This index depicts the combined effects of air velocity and temperature on both the sensation of coldness and on the extreme conditions where exposed flesh freezes and severe problems may occur. Most cold occupational environments avoid extreme levels by providing adequate clothing and/or warmer areas which provide escape from the continuous cold.

References

Ayoub, M.M., and J.D. Ramsey. 1975. The hazards of vibration and light. *Industrial Engineering* 7(11):40-4.

National Institute for Occupational Safety and Health. 1973. *The industrial environment, its evaluation and control*. Washington, D.C.: U.S. Government Printing Office.

Ramsey, J.D. 1975. Occupational vibration. In *Occupational Medicine: Principles and practical applications*. Carl Zenz, ed., 553-62. Chicago, Ill.: Year Book Medical Publishers.

——. 1983. Heat and cold. In *Stress and fatigue in human performance*. G.R.J. Hockey, ed., 33-60. New York: John Wiley & Sons, Ltd.

Ramsey, J.D., and M.M. Ayoub. 1975. Occupational heat stress. *Industrial Engineering* 7(9):38-42.

Smith, J.L., and J.D. Ramsey. 1982. Designing physically demanding tasks to minimize levels of worker stress. *Industrial Engineering* 14(5):44-50.

Jerry D. Ramsey *is associate vice president for academic affairs at Texas Tech University, Lubbock.*

8

Summary

B. Mustafa Pulat, Ph.D.

The previous six chapters covered topics which have attracted most attention in industrial ergonomics. The effects of physical and mental demands of tasks have been summarized in the first two chapters, along with design suggestions to keep such demands within capability ranges. It is important to note that humans always need some stress to function effectively. Neither too little (underload) nor too much (overload) stress is good. Boredom, central nervous system (CNS) fatigue, and atrophy are natural results of extended periods of underload. In such cases we use strategies to either increase the load or enrich the job. Short periods of overload are acceptable. Continued overload eliminates reserve capacity; thus one cannot respond to emergency conditions, and leads to exhaustion. In such cases, we use strategies to redesign the working conditions (task, work station, procedures, etc.) to thin the overall load.

The work methods and work station design chapters are very much interrelated. Again, the objective is to keep stress due to job elements (including their sequence) and workplace components (chair, workbench, parts, equipment, machine, etc.) including component arrangement within acceptable limits, preferably at optimal levels. Naturally, a corollary of this statement is that work station components and required job elements should not pose health risks. Poor performance occurs when human capabilities are exceeded or underutilized. Work stations must be designed for ranges of sizes of people.

The principles given in the product design chapter aim at developing products which can be used effectively without undue stress on the user. Product liability considerations are also important. We must design for real users and real use conditions.

The environmental factors section outlines basics, human responses, and recommended controls for the five most common environment-related stressors in industry. If not controlled, these will add on to stress due to task, work station design and job organization to create overload, and may impose health risks.

Ergonomics is most effective if applied during the design stage. However, audits of jobs effectively bring into light creeping changes since design and are effective in identifying those that need ergonomics attention. Table 1 gives several symptoms of problems. "Yes" answers to the questions posed indicate the need for attention. Once a job is selected for further investigation, then the checklist given in table 2 may be used in order to identify the specific problems for correction.

TABLE 1
Symptoms of Ergonomics Problems

1. Are there too many rejects on this operation?
2. Are the operators making frequent mistakes?
3. Is there high material waste?
4. Is labor turnover unacceptable?
5. Do the employees have complaints?
6. Is production output unacceptably low?
7. Is absenteeism unacceptably high?
8. Are there accidents on the job?
9. Do employees visit the infirmary frequently?
10. Is product quality too low?
11. Is training time unacceptable?
12. Do employees take frequent rests?
13. Do personal and fatigue allowances seem too much?
14. Is operator assignment limited by size, age, sex, physique, etc?

Extensive ergonomic study is warranted if:

1. Employees are being injured.
2. Operation volume is high.
3. Labor turnover is high.
4. The workplace is utilized for several shifts.

TABLE 2
Ergonomic Survey of Workplaces

Workplace Characteristics

- There are extended lateral or forward reaches, beyond normal arm reach.
- There is inadequate clearance for handling or maintenance tasks.
- There are inaccessible workplaces for using handling equipment.
- There are poor chairs, which are difficult to adjust, with inadequate back support and no footrest.
- Dials and displays are difficult to read or reach.
- There are inefficient work motions because of workplace layout.
- Awkward postures are required.
- There is inadequate space for temporary storage at the workplace.
- No adjustability is built into the workplace.
- The work surface appears to be too high or too low.
- Workers frequently sit on the front edge of their chairs.
- There is continuous foot pedal operation while the worker is standing.
- Workers frequently adjust their chairs by adding cushions or pads.
- Workers are required to hold their arms or hands without the assistance of armrests.
- The workplace appears to be unnecessarily cluttered.
- The worker is frquently engaged in static holding work.
- There is no room to move about.

Perceptual Load

- Auditory signals are difficult to hear or excessively loud.
- There are small and difficult-to-see defects.
- Fine color differences are to be discriminated.
- Critical distance judgments are necessary.
- There is an excessive or unacceptable need to discriminate parts by touch.
- Excessive eye-movement demands exist.
- Numbers, words, symbols and scale divisions are of a size inadequate to suit the reading distance.
- Critical displays are not within ± 15° of NLS (normal line of sight).
- Instruments, components and labels are not within visual field.
- Display-control compatibility is violated.
- There are inconsistencies as to on-off positions of controls.
- There are insufficient target-background contrasts.
- Vigilance is impaired by noise and other peoples' activities.
- The worker has insufficient time to sense and respond to signals.

Mental Load

- There is a need to keep track of multiple factors simultaneously, especially in the case of operating multiple machines.
- The task is highly repetitive and monotonous.
- Critical task elements exist where errors are not tolerated.
- High demand exists for short-term memory, such as working with nine-digit codes.

Environment

- There is excessive noise that is annoying and distracting and that interferes with speech intelligibility.
- Process noise is loud enough to cause hearing loss.
- There are direct or reflected glare sources in the work area.
- The amount of illumination is not sufficient for the task.
- Lights shine on moving elements of machinery to produce distracting flashes.
- Excessive contrasts are present in the visual field.
- Eyes have to move periodically from light to dark areas.
- The thermal environment is uncomfortable.
- There is vibration that is annoying and hazardous to health.
- Ventilation is not adequate.
- The worker is exposed to unacceptable thermal or visual environmental changes.
- Floors are not even.
- Floors are slippery.
- Housekeeping is poor.
- Hot surfaces present burn hazards.
- Air in the room contains toxic, flammable, explosive substances.
- There is a dermatitis hazard.
- Process dust settles on equipment and displays, impairing visual performance.

Specific Equipment

- Dials and controls are poorly labeled.
- Displays are not adequately lit.
- Pinch points are not adequately guarded.
- Electrical equipment is not properly grounded.
- Excessive strength requirements exist for operating equipment.
- Hand tools present injury potential.
- Maintenance manuals are missing or not up to date.
- Sharp edges exist in the work area.
- Warning signs and labels are not very apparent.
- Protection against accidental activation of control switches does not exist.
- Trip hazards exist in the work area.

Physical Demands

- There is frequent heavy lifting.
- There is occasional very heavy lifting.
- There is constant handling of materials, with little variety.
- The task requires handling difficult-to-grasp items.
- The task requires exertion of forces in awkward positions (body bent, twisted, etc.).
- The task requires constant standing.
- The task requires frequent daily stair or ladder climbing.
- There is static muscle loading.
- There is high pressure on hands from thin edges.
- There is short-duration heavy effort.

- The worker is required to push or pull carts, boxes, etc., that involve large break-away forces to get started.
- Workers complain that fatigue allowances are insufficient.
- Heart rate and oxygen consumption values are above the recommended maximum.

Work Methods

- The range of movements is anatomically incorrect.
- High-precision movements exist.
- Sudden movements are necessary during manual handling.
- Machine pacing is not compatible with capabilities.
- One motion pattern is repeated at a high frequency.
- Hand tools are used at incorrect hand positions.
- Visual control of manual movements is necessary.
- There are unnecessary moves.
- There are straight-line motions involving sudden and sharp changes in direction.
- There are nonsymmetrical motions.
- There are twisting motions with elbows straight.
- Work between body members is not balanced.
- Muscle groups involved are not adequate for the job.

Other

- Work hours and breaks are not properly organized.
- Job performance aids are inadequate.
- Motivation is lacking.
- There is poor supervision.
- Supplies are inadequate.
- Feedback (knowledge of results) is inadequate or nonexistent.
- Skill demands are incompatible.

ERGONOMICS GROUP ORGANIZATION

9

Selling the Idea to Management

Leo A. Smith, Ph.D., P.E.

There was a time, quite recently actually, when the great majority of individuals in management positions had never seen nor heard the word *ergonomics*. If by chance some industrial engineer mentioned it in conversation, the manager most likely thought the engineer was trying to make some inane comment on "economics" and, rather than listen to what followed, let his mind wander to thoughts about the obviously sad state of affairs in engineering education.

The terms *human factors* and *human engineering* were somewhat more familiar, particularly in management circles associated with the defense and/or aerospace industries, but they were not typically thought of as referring to production management tools. In the last few years, the term *ergonomics* has become more widely recognized, due largely to its use in video and print advertising and particularly in association with automobiles, hand tools, and computer-related products. In addition, articles in business publications have mentioned the term in product liability and workmen's compensation contexts. As a result of this recent exposure to the term, it seems fair to conclude that the typical manager may now at least recognize the word ergonomics and may indeed have some understanding of its important role in the product-design process. Unfortunately, it also appears that most managers still fail to recognize the potential of ergonomics to benefit the day-to-day production process.

Management can be sold on the idea that ergonomics activities can make a significant positive contribution to all aspects of the firm's operation, but the selling job is not necessarily simple. It is certainly appropriate for management groups to have a healthy skepticism about all proposed demands on the manpower and financial resources of the corporation, and ergonomics proposals are not immune from such skepticism.

Management's foremost concern is to facilitate the production of goods and services, and ergonomics activities often appear on the surface to be unnecessary frills that are not only costly but may also get in the way of other work which is more obviously related to getting the product or service out the door. Additionally, many ergonomics activities require multidisciplinary involvement, drawing on the expertise of several professional groups within the firm, that is, engineering, medical, personnel. Multidisciplinary projects often present special problems to management since there is always the prospect that someone's professional feelings might get bruised unintentionally and the question of whose budget will be assessed and who will have overall control of the project must be resolved to everyone's satisfaction. Management can avoid such problems by simply not doing the project in the first place. Thus, proposals for ergonomics activities must convince management that they are worth the effort and expense they will require.

Three Approaches to Justification

Smith and Smith (1982) identified three basic approaches that one may take when attempting to convince management that a program of ergonomics activities should be undertaken. It is doubtful that any one of these would be used in isolation, but it is instructive to consider each separately. The approaches are:

1. Justification on the basis of increased productivity
2. Justification on the basis of reduced nonproductive time and reduced overhead expenses
3. Justification on the basis of social responsibility or legal requirement (called the "You really ought to (gotta) want to do it" approach by Smith and Smith).

Justification Based on Increased Productivity

This approach should receive first consideration since it is the easiest to argue and the one most commonly emphasized by management. Under this approach, one attempts to prove that the costs of performing the proposed activity are more than offset by direct productivity increases resulting from the project. Productivity records before or without the accomplishment of the proposed activity are compared with projections of the productivity level resulting after or with the project. One should be very careful not to overstate the anticipated productivity increase, since more future benefit can be obtained from an after-the-fact evaluation that concludes "We did better than we anticipated" than from one that indicates "We almost reached our anticipated improvement."

Justification on the basis of direct increases in productivity appears to be easiest to document in situations where the manufacturing process and/or the product itself have been initially hastily designed in an attempt to respond quickly to opportune market conditions. In these circumstances, tasks have often been designed in a so-called quick-and-dirty manner and it has more or less been assumed that the process man-machine compatibility will be improved upon later when time permits. Productivity benefits often accrue with the compatibility improvements. Smith and Smith suggest that justification on the basis of increased productivity is most appropriate when:

1. The firm is relatively new or has recently become involved in a new product line
2. Technological change frequently impacts the product or the production process
3. The firm has devoted limited time and resources to classical-methods engineering activities
4. The firm does not have engineered labor standards

Justification Based on Reduced Nonproductive Time and Overhead Expense

In this context nonproductive time refers to time spent away from one's primary activity for whatever reason, and overhead costs refer to those due to personnel-related administrative expenses. An example of nonproductive time is excessive time spent away from one's work station in an effort to relieve workplace-design-induced postural stress such as compression ischemia. Examples of overhead expense are the cost of training activities resulting from excessive turnover on a poorly designed task and the costs associated with excessive instances of goods being returned due to quality-inspector errors. Reduced nonproductive time may be a subpart of an increased productivity justification and should be so presented when possible.

Smith and Smith (1982) present the following discussion of the circumstances under which this approach is appropriate:

"Justification on the basis of reduced nonproductive costs and overhead is effective when:

1. the firm is experiencing an unusually high accident or injury frequency;
2. the firm has a high percentage of highly skilled labor;

3. the firm is experiencing high rates of absenteeism, turnover, or trips to the medical department;
4. employees are observed to take a disproportionately large number of breaks, or to frequently be away from their assigned work stations."

It is obvious that these conditions contribute to employees spending their time in nonproductive activities. The only condition that might need explanation is the second. If a highly skilled employee is away from his work station, productivity will likely suffer due to an inferior performance by a substitute. Thus, the justification argument becomes one of minimizing unnecessary time away from the work station.

> "Ergonomics analysis of these situations usually substantiates that the nonproductive time and excessive overhead costs are due to poor work place design and associated postural stress, incompatible display-response relationships, or inadequate tools and job aids which singularly or in combination render the employee's job unnecessarily difficult to master and uncomfortable to perform. Ergonomics projects designed to eliminate these difficulties will reduce the undesirable nonproductive time."

Justification Based on Social Responsibility or Legal Requirement

The first two approaches are typically put in monetary terms, although the first is easier in this regard than the second. This third approach can also be given a monetary aspect since failure to act in certain areas may carry financial penalties, but its central thrust is not financial. It appeals not so much to the pocketbook as it does to the moral and ethical responsibilities of the firm to its employees. The justification argument is based on the obligation of the firm, as a responsible member of society, to seek to improve the quality of its employees' work life and to manufacture a high-quality, user-friendly product. It is argued that ergonomics is an effective tool for accomplishing this goal since its application provides enhanced man-machine compatibility, enlarges the population of potential job incumbents, and reduces the possibility of events which can give rise to product liability litigation. The fact that there are laws that encourage the firm to fulfill its responsibilities to society is certainly a motivating factor, but it is not the driving force behind the argument.

Smith and Smith (1982) suggest that justification on the basis of social responsibility is perhaps most applicable when:

1. The firm employs non-unionized labor and/or wishes to avoid any potential for employee dissatisfaction.

2. The firm has been in existence for a long time and/or is the principal employer in a particular area.
3. The firm must compete actively for labor with surrounding companies and/or wishes to demonstrate its desire to comply with equal employment opportunity guidelines.
4. The firm produces products for a highly competitive market and the product line is technologically stable with respect to product design and manufacturing methods.
5. The firm's product line — for example, power tools — has a high product-liability potential.

The rationale for using the social-responsibility approach in the first two situations is that ergonomics activities will demonstrate the firm's concern for its employees' quality of work life and thus enhance its labor relations and public image. Under the third situation, any ergonomics job-design activities that increase the percentage of the population (including the various minority groups such as older and handicapped individuals) that could potentially be employed would increase the flexibility of the personnel department in job placement and demonstrate the firm's commitment to providing equal employment opportunity. Under the conditions outlined in item 4, the social responsibility argument is really the only viable one since previous industrial engineering efforts have most likely already capitalized on all available productivity-improvement opportunities. The fifth situation needs no elaboration.

Presenting the Case for Ergonomics

How one goes about presenting the case for ergonomics to management is greatly influenced by the personalities of the individuals involved, the political power structure in the firm, the history of previous attempts to perform ergonomics activities, and the accepted way of doing things in the company. One method that has proved successful in situations where ergonomics efforts are being initially attempted is the development and presentation of an ergonomics "show and tell" seminar to selected individuals (Lucas 1974, Smith and Smith 1982). The staging of such a seminar consists of four steps:

1. Selection of the target audience
2. Development of the presentation material
3. The presentation
4. Follow-up

Selection of the Target Audience

The target audience most likely will consist of several groups of individuals representing different interests. The individual who has the final approval authority must be present. Lower levels of management responsible for the day-to-day planning and supervision in those areas where ergonomics activities are anticipated immediately should also attend. Additionally, representatives of staff areas whose functions relate to ergonomics such as medical, safety, hygiene, training, and personnel should be included. The group needs to be small enough to facilitate discussion but broad enough so that all interests are represented. In such a group, people should feel comfortable enough to be able to express their ideas both pro and con, but they should also feel forced into being considerate of the desires of the other interests represented.

Development of the Presentation Material

Two types of presentation materials need to be utilized. The first consists of general information introducing the attendees to the definition, purpose, and scope of ergonomics. The types of ergonomics activities that are being performed in competing firms or firms that are known to be considered as trend setters by the attendees should be mentioned. One or two examples of ergonomics success stories might be developed into a handout for distribution. For examples, refer to Teel (1971), Chaffin (1975), and Khalil (1976). The advantages to be derived from providing ergonomics training to first line supervisors and others in the organization might be discussed (Smith and Smith 1984).

The second type of presentation material should be specific to the local situation. Statistics and photographs should be prepared. The statistics should document the firm's recent experience in the areas of lost-time injuries, medical visits, employee complaints relative to working conditions, absenteeism, extra training costs due to excessive turnover, employee performance quality, and other data typically positively impacted by ergonomics activities. The photographs should be candid shots of the firm's work areas, illustrating those situations where ergonomics improvements are needed and the need for improvement is easy to understand. For example, pictures can be shown of improper seating causing poor work posture or display-control incompatibilities that could easily lead to errors of operation. The pictures must not constitute a witch hunt that could embarrass any of the attendees. They should, rather, seek to encourage the attendees to look at the situations in question from the viewpoint of ergonomics, a view they most likely have not taken previously.

While planning the statistics and pictures to be presented, keep the audience in mind. Younger individuals who are striving hard to work their way up the management ladder typically are most responsive to situations that show some promise of productivity improvements or reductions in nonproductive time. Usually, these people are evaluated on the basis of how much they produce, so appeals to the first two justification bases should be directed to them. Older managers (and usually the final decision-maker falls in this category) are more sensitive to the firm's social responsibilities and its public image. Sociological studies suggest that middle- to late-middle-aged persons are more likely than others to be at that stage in adult life where they want to "Do something good for our people." These individuals are certainly cost-conscious, but they also respond very positively to justification on the basis of social responsibility. Photographs of situations where work life quality can be improved by ergonomic analysis and redesign, especially if the investment cost per work day is reasonably low, often convince older managers to approve a project.

The presentation — The presentation should last no longer than two hours; the purpose is to orient the attendees to the need for ergonomics activities and the justifications for them, not to teach a short course on ergonomics. The views of all attendees should be solicited during the presentation. This is especially true for those persons (for example, safety and medical personnel) whose views are expected to be supportive. The presentation should gently move the final decision-maker into a position where he feels he not only wants to say yes, but more or less has to say yes or be seen as unsupportive of efforts that would not only benefit the firm but also improve the employees' work lives.

Followup — The followup depends on the seminar's outcome. A memorandum to all attendees summarizing the discussion, the decisions made, and the action to follow may be all that is necessary. If questions were raised by some attendees that had to be left unanswered, an effort must be made to provide the answers as soon as possible. If requests were made for more information on ergonomics, then these should be honored. It is hoped permission to begin one or more ergonomics projects would have been obtained and work can start immediately.

Summary

Ergonomics can be sold to management. Contrary to the view sometimes presented by the public media and novelists, the great majority of managers are motivated to provide the best possible work environment for their employees while producing a high-quality product or service at a reasonable cost. With a little guidance, they will quickly recognize that ergonomics can significantly contribute to the accomplishment of this goal.

References

Chaffin, D.B. 1975. Ergonomic considerations can improve productivity—A case in point. *AIIE News—Ergonomics* 9(2):2-3.

Khalil, T.M. 1976. The role of ergonomics in increasing productivity. *AIIE Spring Annual Conference Proceedings* (May):57-64.

Lucas, R.L. 1974. Human factors in industry—Getting the point across. *Human Factors Society Annual Conference Proceedings* (October):404-5.

Smith, L.A., and J.L. Smith. 1982. How can an IE justify a human factors activities program to management? *Industrial Engineering* 14(2):38-43.

———. 1984. Observations on in-house ergonomics training for first-line supervisors. *Applied Ergonomics* 15(1):11-4.

Teel, K.S. 1971. Is human factors engineering worth the investment? *Human Factors* 13(1):17-21.

Leo A. Smith *is professor of industrial engineering, Auburn University, Auburn, Alabama.*

10

The Fisher Body Division — General Motors Corporation Ergonomics Organization

Klaus M. Blache, Ph.D.

Selling Ergonomics To Management

Implementation of an effective ergnomics program requires the support of management. The job of the ergonomist is to explain and demonstrate the benefits of human factors engineering to obtain that support. Six steps which were followed at Fisher Body are:

1. Explain the purpose of ergonomics in a terminology that management can relate to.
2. Show success stories from similar industries.
3. Using historical records as a basis, ask the questions:
   - — Is absenteeism on specific jobs too high?
   - — Is turnover on specific jobs too high?
   - — Are certain age/gender/size groups only performing specific jobs?

- Is productivity too low?
- Do employees frequently complain on specific jobs?
- Is product quality too low?
- Is medical-visit frequency per employee high, compared to similar plants?
- Are there frequent accidents of a specific type?
- Are accidents per employee of a specific type increasing over time?
- Is there too much scrap or rework?
- Is the worker frequently away from his or her workplace?

Transform the success stories from other locations into potential benefits at your location. Be realistic; point out that an ergonomics program will not remove all of these problems or always result in success stories. Most of the changes, however, will bring positive results.

4. Again using historical records, calculate and present projected savings and benefits over time from:
   - Decreased occupational medical visits (direct labor costs)
   - Decreased workers' compensation payments
   - Decreased sickness and accident costs
   - Using placement coordinators (persons responsible for placing restricted employees on jobs they can perform)
   - Using transitional work centers (specific areas set up to accommodate restricted employees)
   - Improved employee attitudes (can check with periodic survey of impacted areas)
   - Those more difficult to measure benefits such as improved productivity, better quality, and less absenteeism. These benefits can be monitored but the direct impact from ergonomic changes is not as easily ascertained.
5. Pick a pilot project to demonstrate that ergonomics can work. Use conservative cost savings, since you want to start with a success. Once management gains confidence in ergonomics, riskier changes can be attempted.
6. Once a program has been implemented, provide periodic feedback on successes and failures. This can be done through presentations, written reports or a progress tracking system.

How Fisher Body Is Organized

In Fisher Body manufacturing, there is a Human Factors Divisional Committee that is mainly concerned with worker-workplace interactions. The organization of this committee is shown in figure 1. It should be noted that the only full-time ergonomics engineers on this organization chart are from Industrial Engineering.

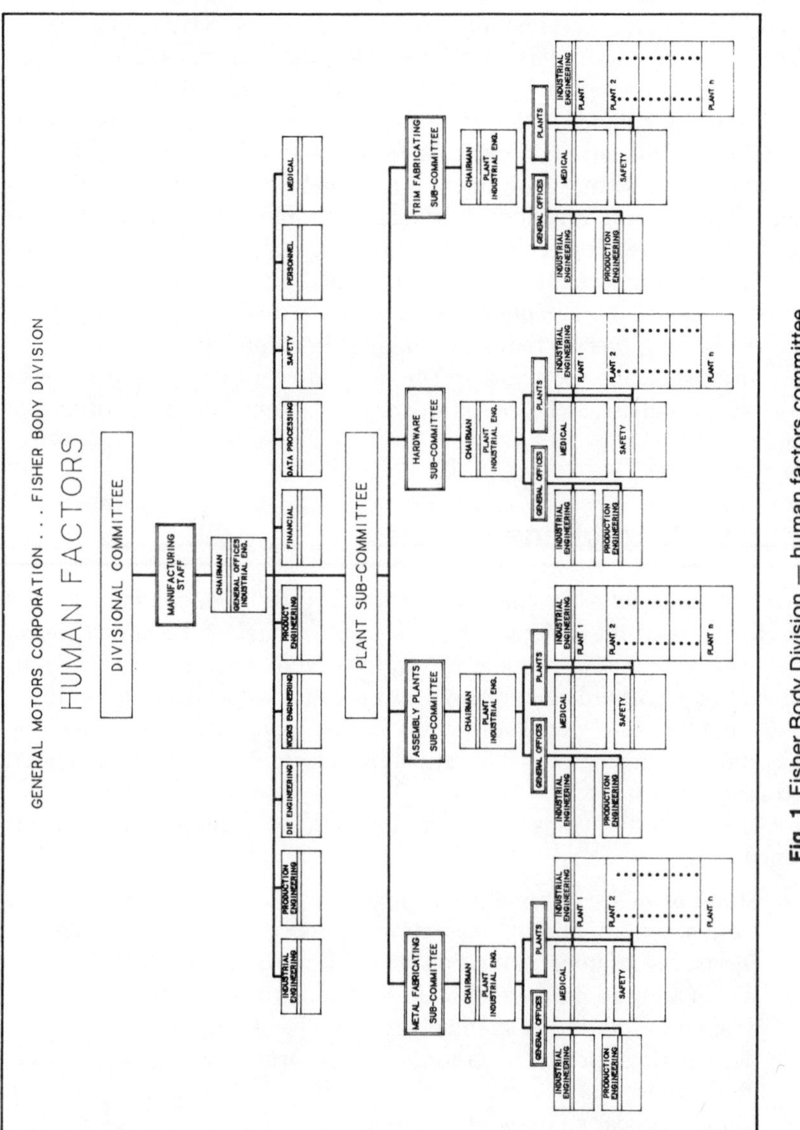

Fig. 1 Fisher Body Division — human factors committee

The first level comprises manufacturing engineering representatives from ten departments. The chairman of the committee is from Industrial Engineering, reporting to the manufacturing staff. The second level contains four plant subcommittees, one for each of the different types of plants. Each subcommittee has a chairman, who is from one of these plants. These subcommittees contain engineering representatives from each plant and Central Engineering, as well as plant representatives from Medical and Safety. On specific projects, outside consultants from companies and colleges are employed.

In addition, each plant has its local group that discusses ergonomic concerns. Typically included in this group are representatives from departments of benefits, industrial engineering, medical, placement/transitional work center and safety. Plant involvement is extremely important for implementation of an ongoing ergonomics program. Employees at the plant must understand the reasoning behind the ergonomic concepts, so that future situations of a similar nature can be quickly corrected. In addition, their involvement will increase the acceptance of any required workplace changes.

Furthermore, there is Industrial Engineering representation on the corporate Human Factors Committee. This committee provides an opportunity for the various divisions to share information and maintain a coordinated effort.

Fisher Body Implementation

Depending on the financial and human resources available, one should determine the scope of the program. Keep it small enough to be both efficient and effective. Training others at the various required levels of ergonomic understanding is key to gaining momentum and assistance in one's efforts. This could include regional awareness programs, specific topic/problem classes aimed at target groups, educational articles in the company newsletter, video tapes, and more.

At Fisher Body, typical Industrial Engineering ergonomic assignments included:

- Study of office automation equipment
- Design of an industrial inspection station
- Electromyographic evaluation of work movements
- Responding to daily ergonomic questions received from the plants
- Training program on manual materials handling
- Distributing practical ergonomics information to appropriate individuals
- Biomechanical analysis of a shipping dock operation
- Training on ergonomic considerations in quality and inspection

Overview of the Fisher Body Program

Over approximately ten years, the Fisher Body Manufacturing Ergonomics Program has gone through an evolutionary growth, which can be outlined in the six steps shown in table 1.

Figure 2 presents this evolution in schematic form, starting at the center with data analysis and moving outward to the larger spheres. Additional information on PLACE and SAFAC can be referenced in the 1983 *Proceedings of the Human Factors Society* (*Practical Ergonomics: The Challenge To Change* by K. Blache).

TABLE 1
Fisher Body Manufacturing Ergonomics Program

	Function Performed	Sample of Function
1.	Data Analysis (medical visits, absenteeism, turnover, productivity, rework, etc.)	SAFAC (Safety Analysis from Accident Computerization) — Medical Visit Analysis Program
2.	Analysis of workplace, environment and individual (health, safety and ergonomic considerations versus known standards)	PLACE (Personal Limitations Analyzed by Computerized Ergonomics) — Computerized and Manual Programs for workplace analysis
3.	Recommendations of practical engineering method changes	Documentation and distribution of savings and ideas in Manufacturing Engineering
4.	Training of engineers and hourly employees	Central Engineering training, plant training, specialized training such as Quality Institute classes on inspection and ergonomics.
5.	Development of a reporting and evaluation system	Divisional Human Factors Committee, ANSER (Analytical System for Ergonomic Review) Ergonomic Index covering SAFAC, absenteeism, workers compensation, sickness and accident, etc.
6.	Use of ergonomic knowledge in future planning/Use a preventive approach	Investigating use of ergonomic rating in time standards data, robotics versus human task allocation, etc.

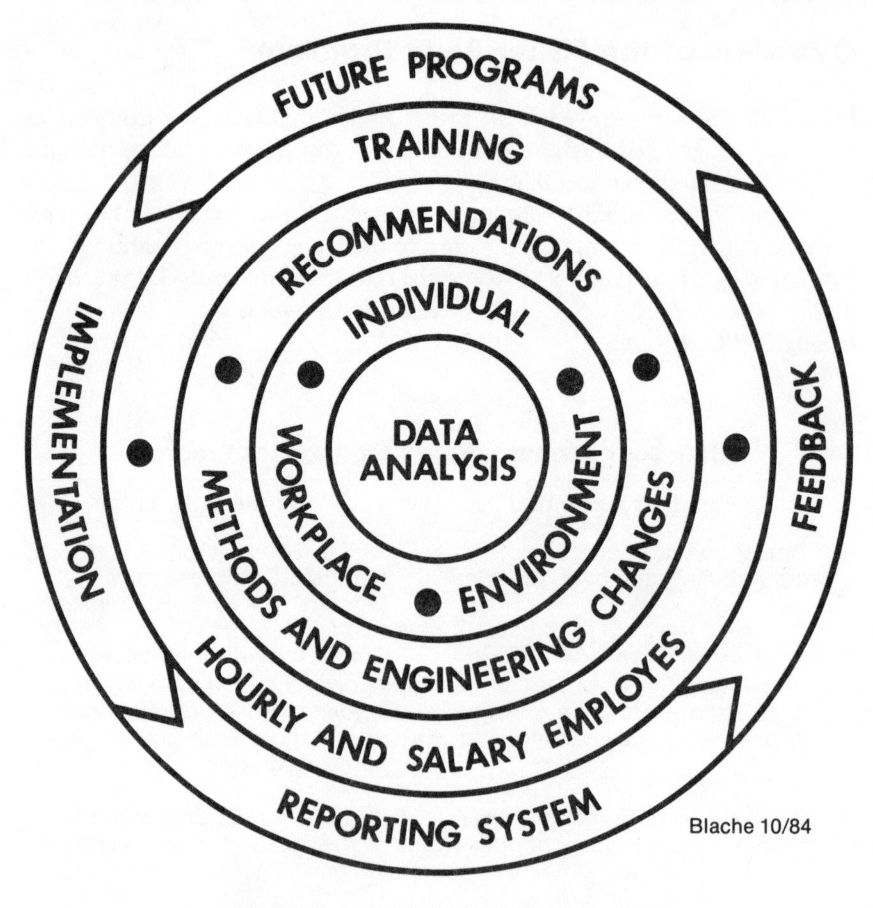

Fig. 2 Schematic of an Ergonomic Program

***Klaus M. Blache** is engineering group manager at General Motors' Chevrolet-Pontiac-Canada Group, Warren, Michigan.*

11

Developing and Implementing a Corporate-wide Ergonomics Effort at Chesebrough-Ponds, Inc.

Paul D. Vernes

Establishing an effective ergonomics program in a large corporation requires a great deal of planning, development work, and management commitment. On the other hand, it will yield reductions in workplace-related injuries and improvements in worker productivity and quality and will provide the workforce with demonstrated proof that management is concerned for their health and well-being.

Chesebrough-Pond's Inc. is a $1.8 billion international manufacturer and marketer of consumer products, including cosmetics and toiletries, foods, children's clothing, shoes, sporting goods, and hospital products. One factor in starting an ergonomics program in our company was management's desire to keep under control worker's compensation costs throughout the corporation by developing workplace designs, methods, and job requirements that do not exceed the capabilities and limitations of our employees.

Once this concept was established and accepted, efforts were directed toward developing and implementing an ergonomics program designed to accomplish this goal.

Program Development

The first thing you need to do is develop an overall plan of your program. After reviewing where you are and where you want to be three or four years down the road, program goals, objectives, and timetables must be developed and approved by management. There are two main concerns that must be addressed in an ergonomics program: (1) training to develop expertise in ergonomics principles and practices, and (2) implementation. If you do not have properly trained people to apply ergonomics, you will do more harm than good, and if you cannot implement your recommendations, you will be ineffective, no matter how well-trained you are. Management commitment, not just lip service, must be obtained for both these areas or you may as well forget the program.

Proper training must be done because ergonomics is a far more involved and comprehensive subject than people realize, and it is going to take time and money to train personnel. A commitment to implementation is mandatory because, until the program proves itself through plant successes, plant people will be asked to take it on faith.

So you need management support right off the bat. Once you have that, you need to develop the objectives and scope of your training programs. We found that two distinct approaches were required. One was an in-depth, comprehensive program for people who would be applying ergonomics. The other was a less intense, orientation-type program for people who needed to know what ergonomics is and why it is applied, but who do not do design work. People in the first category would be engineers and designers and in the second category would be plant management and supervision, direct labor, and craftspeople.

In-Depth Training

Developing a training program to bring your technical people up to par on the latest in ergonomics principles and practices is work for an expert in the field. Do not try to do this yourself without help from someone who has done it before. In our case, we enlisted the services of Colin G. Drury, Ph.D., professor of Industrial Engineering at the State University of New York, Buffalo. As we have some thirty-five plants throughout the United States, we needed a packaged program that could be taken to many different locations, when time could be conveniently scheduled, and put on for various sized groups. Dr. Drury is a "working" ergonomist who has had much experience with this type of program, and was able to work within these parameters very nicely. The result was five forty-five-minute video tapes comprising a very condensed course in ergonomics theory that could be applied equally well across the wide range of industries we have. A list of subjects covered in the tapes is as follows:

- Human Factors Model
- The Human Senses
  - Vision
  - Hearing
  - Kinesthesis
- Information Processing
  - Attention
  - Perceptual Organization
  - Decision-Making
- Muscular-Skeletal System
  - Physiology
  - Thermal Overload
- Task Analysis
- Seating Design
- Workplace Design
- Manual Material Handling
- Physical Limitations

The tapes comprise the nucleus for training in ergonomics theory, but you cannot just put people in front of four hours of tapes and expect them to pay attention. One of the lessons ergonomics teaches is that the human attention span is thirty minutes at most. So you have to build a program around the tapes that keeps your audience awake and interested. To do this, we stop the tapes every half hour or so and show slides of work stations in the facility we are training at so the audience makes the connection between the theory in the tapes and the real world of their plant. Audience participation is a must here, and the trainer will need the skills necessary to keep lively interaction going between all members of the group. In addition, a Chesebrough-Pond's ergonomics manual is distributed that includes a text paralleling the tapes, VDT reference material, and a section on how to conduct an ergonomics audit.

Figures 1 and 2 are examples of the material contained in the audit section of the manual. The audit is a nine-section questionnaire that the engineer takes out onto the production floor and uses to evaluate a work station. Findings are then fed into an Apple computer, on an interactive basis, and the computer performs the necessary calculations to determine if the workplace, methods, etc., need redesign. Areas that can be evaluated are:

- Visual aspects of a job
- Auditory aspects
- Instruments/controls/displays
- Buttons/pedals

Posture while working seated

	Y	N	NA
Can the person assume an optimum working posture according to the criteria:			
r) Head inclined forward at an angle of 17–29° (angle between axes of head and trunk)	____	____	____
s) Spine slightly arched and forward leaning when seen from the side	____	____	____
t) Upper arms vertical	____	____	____
u) Check: twisting of the head or trunk is not evident while working	____	____	____
v) Thighs approximately horizontal	____	____	____
w) Frequent changes of visual object accommodated within an angle of 15–30° relative to the normal viewing direction	____	____	____

Manual Material Handling: Physical Stress Analysis and Energy Expenditure

	Y	N	NA
1. Is a manual material handling task being evaluated? (If no is the answer then skip to next section)	X	____	____
a) Circle (M) for male, F for female			
b) Is there sufficient space to carry out the activity	X	____	____
c) Is twisting evident during the activity	____	X	____
d) Are objects handled bulky	____	X	____
e) Body weight of the material handler in lbs. 175			
f) Does the job involve palletizing, lifting and lowering, or multilevel MMH tasks	____	X	____
g) If any of the above tasks is involved then complete data sets 1 and 2, otherwise complete data set 1 only			

Data Set 1 (For lift or lower to highest tier)

H(1) = Horizontal hand location at origin = 18 inches.

H(2) = Horizontal hand location at destination = 18 inches.

V(3) = Vertical hand location at origin = 6 inches.

V(4) = Vertical hand location at destination = 36 inches.

D(5) = Distance object is moved vertically = 30 inches.

Data Set 2

H(6) = Horizontal hand location at origin = ____ inches.

H(7) = Horizontal hand location at destination = ____ inches.

Figure 1

V(8) = Vertical hand location at origin = ____ inches.
V(9) = Vertical hand location at destination = ____ inches.
D(10) = Distance object is moved vertically = ____ inches.

h) Is the job:

	Y	N
1. lifting	X	
2. lowering		X
3. carrying		X
4. lifting and lowering		X
5. lifting and carrying		X
6. lowering and carrying		X
7. lifting, lowering and carrying		X

i) If objects are being lifted then task frequency is _6_ lifts/minute.

j) Total time engaged in lifting is _8_ hours.

k) Average weight of object lifted is _40_ lbs.

l) Which one of the following best described the posture during lifting

	Y	N
1. stoop lift	X	
2. squat lift		
3. one hand lift (from ground level to bench height)		
4. arm lift (from bench height to a higher level)		

m) If object is being lowered then task frequency is ____ lowers/minute.

n) Total time engaged in lowering is ____ lbs.

o) Average weight of objects lowered is ____ lbs.

p) Which one of the following best describes the posture during lowering:

	Y	N
1. stoop lower		
2. squat lower		
3. arm lower		

q) Grade of walking surface (percent gradient) is ____

r) Total time spent carrying is ____ minutes.

s) Average weight of the load carried is ____ lbs.

	Y	N
t) If carrying, are object/objects held at arm length or sides		

Figure 1 (cont'd)

- Seating
- Manual material handling
- Energy expenditure
- Thermal stress
- Inspection

Figure 1 shows the input on the material handling section of the questionnaire for a theoretical job in which an operator is lifting 40 pounds from the floor directly up to bench height. Figure 2 shows the resulting computer printout, and the engineer knows from this that he has some work to do on this workplace.

Ideally, the training course is done over a period of weeks so that the trainees can be assigned homework between sessions. This includes assignments in their plant to identify and discuss, in front of the class, ergonomic problems of a nature contained in the previous tape and reading assignments in the manual. We have also standardized on a text, "Fitting the Task to the Man," by Grandjean, and each trainee is given a copy. They are urged to become fully familiar with the book so it can be used for reference later.

```
                    C.P.I. ERGONOMICS AUDIT PROGRAM

2/28/85                                                          PAGE  1

DEPARTMENT: TEST               LINE 4              AREA:
PRODUCT BRANDNAME/CODE                     POSITION CODE (FROM SKETCH):
NATURE OF TASK: LIFTING

              MANUAL MATERIAL HANDLING: ENERGY EXPENDITURE

THE ENERGY EXPENDITURE FOR ALL LIFTING IS 1614.3 KCAL.

THE TOTAL ENERGY EXPENDITURE IS 1614.3 KCAL.

                       PHYSICAL STRESS ANALYSIS

LIFT TO HIGHEST LEVEL:

THE AVERAGE WEIGHT BEING HANDLED BY THE WORKER IS 40 LBS.

THE ACTION LIMIT (AL) FOR THIS TASK IS 9 LBS.
THE MAXIMUM PERMISSIBLE LIMIT (MPL) FOR THIS ACTIVITY IS 27 LBS.

THE CRITICAL FACTORS IN THIS ACTIVITY ARE:
    FREQUENCY FACTOR = .5       HORIZONTAL LOCATION FACTOR = .333
    DISTANCE FACTOR = .798        VERTICAL LOCATION FACTOR = .751

*** DANGER! ***   STRESS ON THE WORKER EXCEEDS THE MAXIMUM PERMISSIBLE LIMIT.
                  THE TASK REQUIRES IMMEDIATE ATTENTION!!
```

Figure 2

In addition to theory, practical training must be given in task analysis as performed to identify poor ergonomics in a work station. Our program includes a day for this, and an actual work station from one of our plants is set up in the classroom. All trainees are instructed in the proper method of videotaping the work station. Then, using a workshop format, the analysis is done by everyone and corrections are developed and applied. The improved work station is then videotaped, analyzed, and compared to the original. This method provides hands-on training so people are better prepared when they go into the plant.

All the ergonomics expertise in the world is useless if you cannot get the people in the plant to cooperate and implement improvements. Much of the success of an ergonomics program is dependent upon how well you can deal with people such as supervisors and direct labor. If the operator does not want to cooperate, you will not be successful in implementing your recommendations.

To provide our trainees with the people skills necessary to cope successfully with situations of this nature, we include a short program on supervisory-skills training. This program is presented by our corporate director of training. It prepares people for the situations they will encounter on the production floor and covers subjects such as how to get people to cooperate and assist in problemsolving, how to overcome resistance to change, and how to handle return-to-work adjustments.

Selection of people to be trained to do ergonomics work will depend on your organization, but ideally such work will be assigned to the industrial engineers. They are the people normally responsible for workplace design, methods, and rates, and ergonomics affects all these areas. Provision must be made also for ergonomics to be applied in the design and selection of machinery and equipment that is operated by employees. If this is done by a different engineering group, they should be fully trained also, or at least brought to the stage where they will consult the ergonomists on a cooperative basis. Your personnel, safety, and medical people will also be intimately involved with the program, and should have a good grasp of ergonomics theory and the causes of ergonomically related problems.

Orientation Training

Managers, supervisors, and direct labor people do not have to be able to apply ergonomics in-depth, but they do need to understand what it is, why it is needed, and what their roles are in your ergonomics program. We have developed a forty-five-minute "orientation" for these people based on a seventeen-minute audio/visual presentation entitled "Man the Fallible Machine," developed for this purpose by the University of Guelph (Guelph,

Ontario). We add an explanation of why Chesebrough-Pond's is interested in ergonomics on a corporate basis, what the objectives are for the program at the facility in question, and what role we expect the people attending the meeting to play. Timing of this orientation is critical: It must be done immediately prior to going out into the plant and doing ergonomics. If you wait too long, you will lose the impact.

Intensified Training

There may be occasions when a short program such as the three-day one mentioned above may be insufficient to develop the level of expertise required. This would be the case if ergonomics problems were so severe at a location that a full-time ergonomist was deemed necessary. If so, more intense training can be effected by bringing in the outside consultant for a one-to-one teacher/student relationship. We have utilized this technique where we required an effective, full-time program to be in place quickly.

The theory portion of this type of training program is basically the same, but much more time is spent in developing application skills such as task analysis, prototype development, and implementation.

Implementation

Once the training program has been completed, a determination must be made as to where to start implementation. We base this on worker's compensation costs and injury rates. The plants with the highest cost and incidence rates are reviewed first. The plant medical department is visited and medical records analyzed to determine which jobs have the highest injury rates. The list is then discussed with plant management and prioritized, and task analysis, development of improvements, prototype development, and finally implementation are accomplished.

It is important to select a job with a high potential for success as your first attempt. Nothing sells better than success, and nothing will kill your program faster than having your first work station redesign fail.

The appendix is a summary of a project performed by John Wick, ergonomist, to redesign a sewing work station. This project included videotaping, task analysis, prototype development, and production trials. This appendix is included so the reader can see an example of the results of an actual project in industrial ergonomics. The three photographs illustrate the work station before and after redesign, and the prototype foot treadle.

Computer-Assisted Ergonomics

Certain types of ergonomics analyses require laborious formulas and calculations, which are difficult to handle on a calculator, and certainly take a substantial amount of time depending on how good you are with the machine. One such calculation is a situation in which you have operators working in a hot environment and you are concerned about their internal body temperature and heartbeat rate. Another is when you analyze manual materials handling and need to calculate the stress on the L5/S1 disc using body angles and weight, and weight of load. We have developed computer programs to solve equations for both these situations, not only to save time but also to permit the "what if" game. By changing inputs to the computer, one can determine very quickly what changes are necessary to bring an out-of-spec condition into line.

Figure 3 illustrates an example of the program to calculate stress on the L5/S1 disc, developed for use on the IBM PC. The stick figure shown is not part of the printout, but is drawn by the engineer from a photograph of the work station and is used to identify the body angles. The angles, operator height and weight, and weight of the item being lifted are then entered into the computer and the output shown above the stick figure is generated. From this, the engineer knows the extent of his problem. He then applies engineering expertise to solve it.

In addition, we have developed programs for accumulating and analyzing medical data, such as plant injury incidence rates, and a very comprehensive program to match worker capabilities to job requirements in our back-to-work program. The objective of this last effort is to get people who are out on worker's compensation back to work as soon as possible. To do this, you must assign them to a job that will not aggravate their injury. Where this program is in use, we have evaluated all tasks from an ergonomics point of view, and also the injured worker's capabilities. By matching these up on a computer we can determine what jobs we can assign to an injured worker coming back in.

Measuring the Effectiveness of Your Program

Sooner or later, you will be asked how effective your program is. Measuring this will not be easy, and consideration of how to do it should start at the beginning of your program. We have found the following ways that can be used:

Productivity — Performance against standard before and after for day work, and earnings if you are on piecework.

Medical Histories — Injury incidence rates can be compared before and after program startup, although improvements here usually take a long time to show up.

Damaging Motions per Day — Before and after task analyses will tell you to what level you have reduced the number of harmful body motions per day, or how much you have reduced poor body angles.

DATA INPUTS:

TODAY'S DATE:	02-28-1985 22:23:10
YOUR NAME:	PV
OPERATION DESCRIPTION:	LIFT TEST
OPERATOR'S NAME:	PV
OOPERATOR'S WEIGHT IN LBS:	166
OPERATOR'S HEIGHT IN IN.:	68
OBJECT'S WEIGHT IN LBS.	50
TRUNK ANGLE IN DEG:	45
UPPER ARM ANGLE IN DEG:	16
LOWER ARM ANGLE IN DEG:	110

THE DISK COMPRESSIVE FORCE ON THE L5/S1 IS 489.95 KGS.
WHICH IS CONSIDERED DANGEROUS FOR MOST PEOPLE.

APPROXIMATE MAXIMUM OBJECT WEIGHT FOR SAFE LIFT = 13.2 LBS.

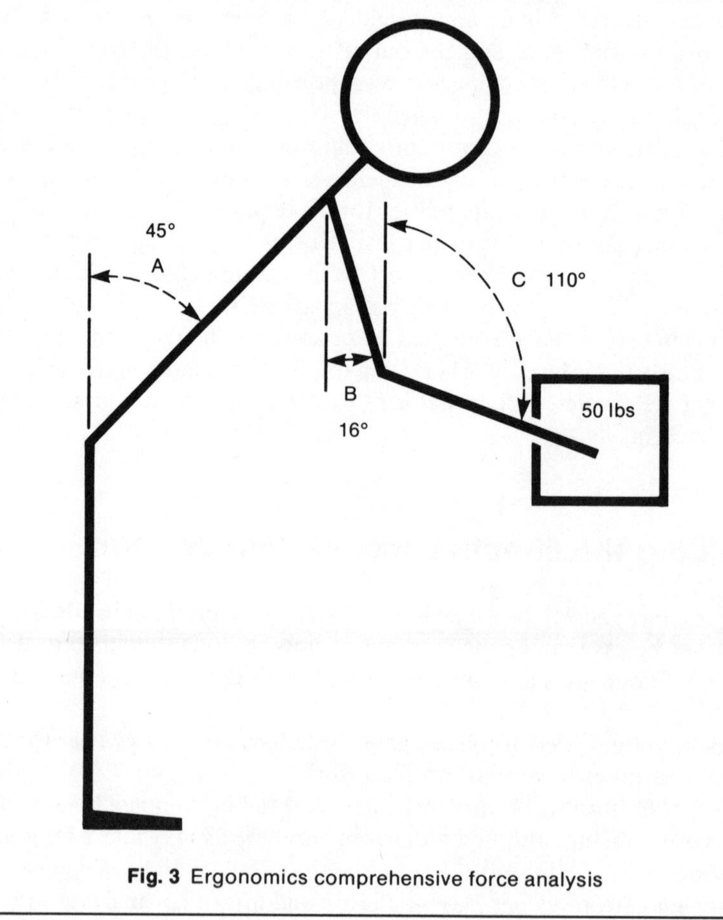

Fig. 3 Ergonomics comprehensive force analysis

Bodypart Discomfort Surveys — Surveys can be used to compare the levels of discomfort perceived by an operator before and after you redesign their workplace. This is particularly useful in evaluating changes in seating.

Attendance and Turnover Rates — Poor ergonomics in the workplace can manifest itself in the form of poor attendance and high turnover. If this is the case in your shop it will show up here, and these records should be monitored and evaluated with this in mind.

Program Maintenance

Getting an ergonomics program started is one thing; keeping it going is another. Goals and objectives, and means to reach those objectives, have to be developed and monitored for each plant. In addition, you must have a program to know where you are at all times compared to your objectives, so you know where to provide assistance. A monthly status report of ergonomics activity should be received from each separate program under your direction.

Upgrading of skills requires constant attention. Employee turnover, the need for reinforcing old skills, and the need for developing programs in new areas require new programs to be developed and old ones to be constantly upgraded. To meet these needs, we have developed an advanced ergonomics training course that is offered to all people who have attended the basic three-day program. It is presented by Dr. Drury and Chesebrough-Pond's personnel in a joint program and concentrates on the causes and effects of cumulative trauma disorders. For the future, we are considering similar programs in office ergonomics and quality control/inspection.

Program Effectiveness

We have had about 100 engineers from twenty-six locations complete the three-day course, and management and supervisory personnel at each of those locations have been through the orientation. In addition, approximately 1,000 direct-labor people have been oriented as part of implementation programs in various plants.

Particularly in plants where worker's compensation costs are high, the response by local management has been good and we have been able to install effective programs. We have seen improvements in productivity and reductions in injury-incidence rates. The workforce has responded very well, since when you actually do something to help somebody, the new travels very fast through a plant. In these areas, we have developed many true believers in both management and labor.

Future

The thrust of an ergonomics program should be to get ergonomics included in all workplaces when they are first built. Retrofitting is difficult and expensive and is by its nature a response to an injury that has already occurred. We want to prevent the injury from happening in the first place. To this end, we are maintaining our programs to correct existing problem areas and emphasizing getting it done right the first time. We see office ergonomics as offering the greatest opportunities in the years to come, and we will be developing programs to provide expertise in this area.

Ergonomics is a viable and powerful tool for the IE to have in his bag of tricks. An effective program requires much planning and effort, but will reap benefits for your company for years to come.

Appendix
An Ergonomically Designed Sewing Workstation

Ergonomics has been applied to the design of sewing work stations in the Bass Division. The traditional layout of industrial stitching machines causes the user to assume improper posture without being able to vary his/her position.

By using the method of task analysis developed for the Bass Division, several postural problems were discovered to be common to most shoe-stitching jobs. Operators tend to lean forward, away from any lumbar support of the chair, and to bend their head forward more than 30°. The thighs of most operators slant downward. These positions are very stressful because not only are they biomechanically incorrect, but also static. Medical problems resulting from such stress range from low-back-pain discomfort to bursitis, thoracic outlet syndrome, and migraine headaches.

Changes to the basic design of the work station which would allow the operator to easily make adjustments to suit the individual's anthropometric characteristics are necessary. This new design has evolved over a ten-month period and has been subjected to extensive laboratory and production trials.

The forward posture of the trunk and neck is caused by one or a combination of the following:

- Seat too high relative to the point of operation.
- Point of operation at wrong visual angle or visual distance.

- Treadle too close to operator, forcing him/her to sit too far from the point of operation.
- Downward angle of the thighs, caused by the seat being too high relative to the treadle.

In order for the new work station to be suitable for 90 percent of the users, certain components must be adjustable. However, the amount of adjustability of a work station should be kept to a minimum (the more adjustments to be made, the less likely they will be made). The adjustable (by the user) components of the new design are but three: the chair, the footrest, and the armrests.

The tabletop was fixed at 30-in. high. The height of the point of operation was located a minimum of 4 and a maximum of 7 in. above the tabletop and 4 in. from the table edge. The sewing machine was slanted 11° toward the operator. All of the above specifications allow the full range of users to be at the correct visual distance and angle relative to the point of operation while assuming an upright posture.

This design causes the upper arms to be extended forward more than the recommended 15° during the actual sewing task. For short-cycle sewing jobs, this would not be harmful. However, for jobs in which the sewing task is of long duration, this static stress would be undesirable. The solution is to use benchmount armrests.

Having established a fixed bench height, an adjustable chair and an adjustable footrest become necessary.

An adjustable footrest necessitates a movable foot control for the sewing machine. Manufacturers of the controllers for the newer models of sewing machines provide an optional remote control which is electric and linked to the machine by an electric wire. For older machines, it is necessary to upgrade the machine by replacing the old motor with a new motor and controller with a remote control.

A lightweight, compact treadle was designed to be used with the remote control. This new foot control is placed on the adjustable footrest. The footrest and/or foot controls can be moved about by the operator for maximum comfort.

This new design for a sewing workstation solves many of the postural problems associated with sewing jobs.

Paul D. Vernes *is manager of operations analysis at Chesebrough-Pond's, Inc., Clinton, Connecticut.*

12

Components of an Industrial Ergonomics Program: The Johnson & Johnson Experience

Arthur R. Longmate
Conni Welker

Johnson & Johnson is a decentralized family of companies composed of twenty-four domestic and over 100 international operating companies, each of which function on an autonomous basis, under minimal corporate control. The twenty-four domestic companies operate a total of seventy-five manufacturing facilities and employ approximately 35,000 persons.

Johnson & Johnson maintains the highest commitment to the quality of its products and the health and well-being of its employees. Two of the larger domestic companies, Johnson & Johnson Products Inc. (patient care, health care and oral hygiene products) and Ethicon Inc. (sutures and wound closure products) have demonstrated this commitment through the establishment of occupational ergonomics programs. The programs were established primarily to enable management to be proactive in the prevention and control of work-related medical incidents. Since sound ergonomic job design is a basic building block for an effective program, the corporate industrial engineering staffs were expanded to include personnel with formal ergonomics training and experience. This combination of ergonomic job engineering with effective medical case management form the basis of Johnson & Johnson's industrial ergonomics program.

Ergonomics is the study of the interaction between people and their workplace. Since application of ergonomic principles can lead to a variety of outcomes, a more practical definition is *the design of the workplace and management of workers to enhance productivity, health, and safety rather than to hinder them*. While this definition should form an underlying basis for the design of all industrial procedures, too often the opposite is true. This is not the result of a failure of ergonomic principles, but simply a failure of providing a means of incorporating these principles into the industrial design process.

The result of failure to consider factors such as the variability in worker sizes and abilities is seen in the form of unrealized productivity goals, higher than expected injury incidence rates and the possibility of increasing labor relations problems. The initial goal of an industrial ergonomics program is to create a working environment in which all persons involved with workers and job design (for example, the engineers, physicians, managers and workers) are aware of their critical role and responsibility in the solution and prevention of ergonomic-related problems.

Need for Practical Ergonomic Guidelines

In larger companies, such as Johnson & Johnson, an ergonomics program is most effective when everyone is aware and involved. The program is also most effective when injuries are prevented through ergonomic job design rather than intervention after an injury has occurred.

When numerous job design projects are in progress at any point in time, one person with extensive ergonomics experience cannot be expected to function effectively as a "lone ranger." It is also unreasonable to expect that an entire staff of engineers will ever become qualified, experienced ergonomists. With the right tools, however, engineers and managers with no formal ergonomics training can answer many routine ergonomics-related questions without expert assistance. It is important to set up a working environment in which people are encouraged to think for themselves and yet to provide a review process where the final design criteria can be verified and non-routine questions can be addressed.

Proficiency in ergonomics is gained through two avenues: training and experience. Staff training sessions are valuable for orientation and definition of problems. Beyond this point, the availability of easy-to-use references is the key to application of ergonomic principles. Many textbooks and scientific methods are available which address ergonomic issues. Some equipment design engineers may take the initiative to identify potential ergonomic information sources, but realistically, the majority probably won't. Since ergonomics is a science which involves many disciplines (physiology, biomechanics, anthropometry, psychology, etc.), available information sources often tend to be comprehensive and somewhat discouraging for a person looking for a few simple answers. The simpler the procedure to *identify* ergonomic problems, the higher the probability of successful detection of these problems.

Development of a *first-cut*, ergonomic design checklist is immensely useful in reviewing proposed equipment designs. Sources such as the American Industrial Hygiene Association's *Ergonomics Guideline* series attempt to provide many answers in a reasonably short format. This format can be abbreviated further into a checklist format such as found in table 1, which addresses design factors relating to potential development of upper-extremity disorders.

The checklist concept is not a final analysis tool, but only a flag-raiser that will prompt more questions and analyses if stressful work practices are identified. Whenever possible, the checklist should provide answers to the questions asked, rather than simply asking questions.

Each engineer must be responsible for performing baseline ergonomic assessments and requesting expert assistance as needed. Training of engineers and managers is usually effective in creating an awareness of ergonomics problems, but a checklist is a constant, practical reminder.

TABLE 1
Ergonomic Checklist for Prevention of Upper Extremity Disorders

1. Avoid sharp edges on any equipment or fixtures which come in contact with the body.
2. Keep repetitive reaches as close to the body as possible and always within 18 in. of the front of the operator.
3. Tilt the work surface and fixtures toward the worker, particularly above the elbow height of the individual.
4. Avoid pinch grip and use power grip whenever possible (pinch grip is five times more stressful than power grip).
5. Minimize hand force requirements and always keep within ten pounds, if possible.
6. Provide work station height adjustability whenever possible
7. Avoid repetitive pounding with the palm of the hand.
8. Avoid flexing or extending the wrist (toward or away from the palm) more than 15° while performing hand activities (for short *or* tall people).

9. Avoid bending the wrist more than 5° toward the thumb or 15° toward the little finger while performing hand activities (for short *or* tall people).
10. Avoid elevating the elbow above chest height.
11. Avoid reaching below seat or waist level.
12. Avoid reaching behind the centerline of the body.
13. Avoid repetitively rotating the hand and forearm more than 90°.
14. Design repetitively pushed control buttons to be a nominal 3-in. diameter and avoid button guards with sharp edges.
15. Provide adequate spacing between repetitively accessed buttons (nominal 2-in. clearance) in multiple control situations.
16. Provide padded body support surfaces when awkward body postures must be maintained for extended periods.
17. Avoid exposure to cold ambient temperatures or to local cold air sources such as exhaust from a powered tool.
18. If gloves must be worn, provide adequate sizes to fit all workers' hands.
19. Avoid equipment and/or tools which transmit vibration to the hands.
20. Design handles, tools or parts of machinery which must be grasped using the following ergonomic criteria:
    - A. The nominal diameter of single handles should be approximately 1.5 in.
    - B. If the hand must span two handles, the span should be between 2 and 3 in.
    - C. Construct the handle of some material other than metal, since metal has a tendency to be cold.
    - D. Use a soft, compliant, textured handle material rather than one hard and smooth.
    - E. Orient the handle to prevent excessive wrist bending and torque.
    - F. For vertically oriented handles, provide a lower support surface to prevent the handle from sliding out of the hand.
    - G. Design tools and surfaces which contact the hand to be thick or long enough so that forces are not concentrated in the center of the palm.

Prevention Versus Intervention

Often, ergonomic objectives are classified into two categories: (1) To intervene into existing problems; and (2) to prevent new problems from developing.

Intervention procedures are often most closely aligned with the medical function from the standpoint of recognition, treatment, and management of work-related disorders. In addition, epidemiological studies of medical-visit information are used to identify departments with the most severe problems. After specific problem jobs have been identified, engineering modifications of the workplace should be initiated, in addition to medical treatment and management of affected workers. This two-faceted approach aids medically restricted workers to return to work and is an important step in preventing new incidents from occurring.

Prevention, on the other hand, most often resides in the engineering domain. If jobs are ergonomically designed in the first place, then many work-related illnesses never would have occurred. Physicians rarely become involved in the design process except when injuries or illnesses have occurred.

This potential segregation of professional involvement leads to a third important objective of ergonomics: Increasing the interaction between all functions to provide a more resourceful review process for job design and medical management.

Information must be accessible before it can serve a useful purpose. Medical records are not normally available to engineers, nor are machine design plans normally within reach of physicians. A task-force approach has been effective in opening and maintaining these critical channels of communication.

The Ergonomic Task Force

One of the keys to successfully maintaining this vital communication link is to bring representatives of each discipline together to discuss ergonomic issues on a dynamic periodic basis. Multidisciplinary groups which are organized to discuss ergonomic issues are usually referred to as ergonomic task forces (ETF); however, any similar designation for the group is acceptable.

The disciplines generally represented on the ETF are medical, safety, manufacturing, management, engineering (industrial and equipment) and wage representatives. *At least* one person with ergonomics experience should be on the ETF, either someone who has completed comprehensive ergonomics training or an ergonomics specialist. Actual attendees at individual meetings will change, depending on the particular jobs or problems being discussed.

The ETF can serve many functions as follows:

1. Review medical incidents, employee complaints and productivity or safety problems.
2. Analyze problem jobs to identify potential ergonomic problems.
3. Determine feasible job modifications, obtain funding and develop implementation plan and schedule.
4. Assess effectiveness of implemented job modifications.
5. Review new equipment designs for adherence to ergonomic design criteria.
6. Conduct employee orientation sessions to sensitize people to "think" ergonomics.

The work of the ETF is plain and simple hard work. The final products that the ETF must sell are *changes from the status quo*. Obtaining upper management approval for an ergonomics program and obtaining initial recommendations for the problem solutions are usually not difficult. From this point on, however, final stages such as determining practical, cost-effective solutions; implementing and following up; and winning acceptance of job changes by the workers may be far more tedious and frustrating.

This method of dealing with ergonomic issues is very new to some organizations and requires extensive groundwork to inform management and workers as to the goals and objectives of the program. Employees and/or managers who have been performing a job using a set procedure may need considerable convincing to accept changes congenially, no matter how ergonomically sound is the new design.

Through the ETF concept, the classification of intervention into the medical domain and prevention into the engineering domain becomes obscure. There is clearly a preventive component involved with each intervention into existing problems if an effective communication system exists. Conversely, as physicians become familiar with new ergonomic concepts in work methods and machine design, they can become more accurate in the diagnosis and treatment of current and future medical cases. Physicians won't be expected to design machinery and engineers won't be expected to diagnose medical problems, but only to interact in common problem areas.

Management of Cumulative Trauma Disorders (CTDs) of the Upper Extremity — A Practical Application

An extremely important aspect of preventing or successfully intervening into occupationally related disorders is understanding the disorders themselves. CTDs of the upper extremities have received considerable attention in recent years after studies revealed that certain manual work methods were factors in substantially elevated injury incidence rates among workers.

While the problem is indeed a serious one, it is very critical to understand the type of problem that is being reacted to. The following sections compare relatively simple acute disorders to more chronic and serious CTDs. Understanding the subtle differences allows allocation of resources only where necessary and can prevent unnecessary medical procedures for affected employees.

Acute Upper Extremity Disorders

Classic cumulative trauma disorders, which are the result of performing repetitive, stressful work elements over extended periods of time (months of exposure or longer), are chronic in nature and are sometimes referred to as "overuse" syndromes. Other types of disorders, generally acute and referred to by names such as "learners tendinitis" or "Monday morning syndrome'' are the result of performing physical exertions for which the body is not sufficiently conditioned to sustain the initial activity. The body has been trained to perform one set of specific, required job motions and was unable to make the change to the new motions without a sufficient conditioning period. A similar reaction is experienced outside the occupational environment when engaging vigorously in a sport for which a person is not conditioned. These situations can arise from sudden changes in work methods or work rate or by simply returning to the same job after an extended layoff (two or more days off work), and are referred to as ''overexertion'' injuries. Some methods for prevention of these *acute* disorders are as follows:

1. Begin work at a slower pace after a layoff and ''work up to speed.''
2. Treat employees being *transferred* to a new job as if they were *new* employees, since they are really new to this particular set of job requirements. Experienced, motivated employees, being transferred to a new job, feel motivated to start out working at the same rate as experienced employees in the new area. Since their bodies are not conditioned for the different physical exertions required by the new job, acute muscle or tendon irritations may result. Athletes experience similar problems when attempting exertions for which they have not adequately prepared themselves.
3. When job modifications or line-speed changes are implemented, care should be taken to do so on a gradual basis. A sudden change, without a conditioning period, is almost certain to result in occurrence of ''learner's tendinitis'' in some workers.
4. Implementation of a *carefully administered* program of stretching exercises which help to maintain body flexibility and range of motion should also be effective in reducing the occurrence of acute disorders.

Job modifications may not necessarily be warranted in the case of acute disorders unless, of course, stressful work practices are identified. A short period of light duty, followed by a gradual working up to speed and perhaps conservative physiotherapy, should provide relief in most cases. Management reminders and employee training on the above points have also helped to reduce acute incidents.

It is important to be able to distinguish between acute and chronic disorders since the action taken in each instance can be considerably different. A detailed work history, which should be a part of the medical examination process, will provide insight regarding the basis of the problem.

Chronic Upper Extremity Disorders

When the detailed work history indicates that the disorder is chronic in nature, a somewhat different action plan is indicated:

1. Conduct comprehensive job analysis to determine physically stressful work elements.
2. Through the ETF process, determine feasible workplace and methods modifications and implement them.
3. Consider job rotation if this is acceptable to all parties, including the union if one exists.
4. Conduct orientation programs to inform and sell workers and management on reasons for job changes.
5. Consider a remedial stretching and strengthening exercise program. An exercise program was implemented at Ethicon in 1982 and consists of three five-minute periods of exercise per shift (fifteen minutes total). If employees choose not to exercise during these periods, they are required simply to rest, since job pay is based on incentive or piecework.
6. Administer physiotherapy (such as paraffin wax baths, ultrasound and whirlpool therapy) and physical therapy as indicated.
7. Use a holistic approach to deal with all factors: physical, psychological, and psychosocial. Any significant injury to the hand may have tremendous psychological impact on the individual. Use of an employee-assistance program in counseling and developing support groups for injured workers has been effective.

Occupational Health Information Systems (OHISs)

As stated previously, availability of both medical-incident and job-design data is critical to ergonomic program effectiveness. A data-management system must be provided that requires and provides a consistent data-recording structure and easy access. Most organizations interested in management of ergonomic problems are larger companies that have access to powerful computer capability. OHISs, which usually contain a medical data management module, are becoming more and more common due to legal requirements under right-to-know laws. Some available OHISs are more easily adaptable to include ergonomic information than others and this should be considered important criteria to be evaluated during system selection.

Computer-compatible questionnaires and other data entry vehicles are necessary for collecting both medical-visit and job-design data and inputting this information into the OHIS.

If medical information is currently maintained on a computerized system, the addition of ergonomic job information should not be difficult. Job-design questionnaires, which are designed to document the physical work requirements of each job, are currently being developed. The resulting ability to query physical work requirements on jobs where injuries have occurred will provide invaluable insight into their work-relatedness. A winning combination is offered through an effective data-management system supplying current information to a multidisciplinary ergonomic task force.

Fig. 1 Traditional sewing machine workstation

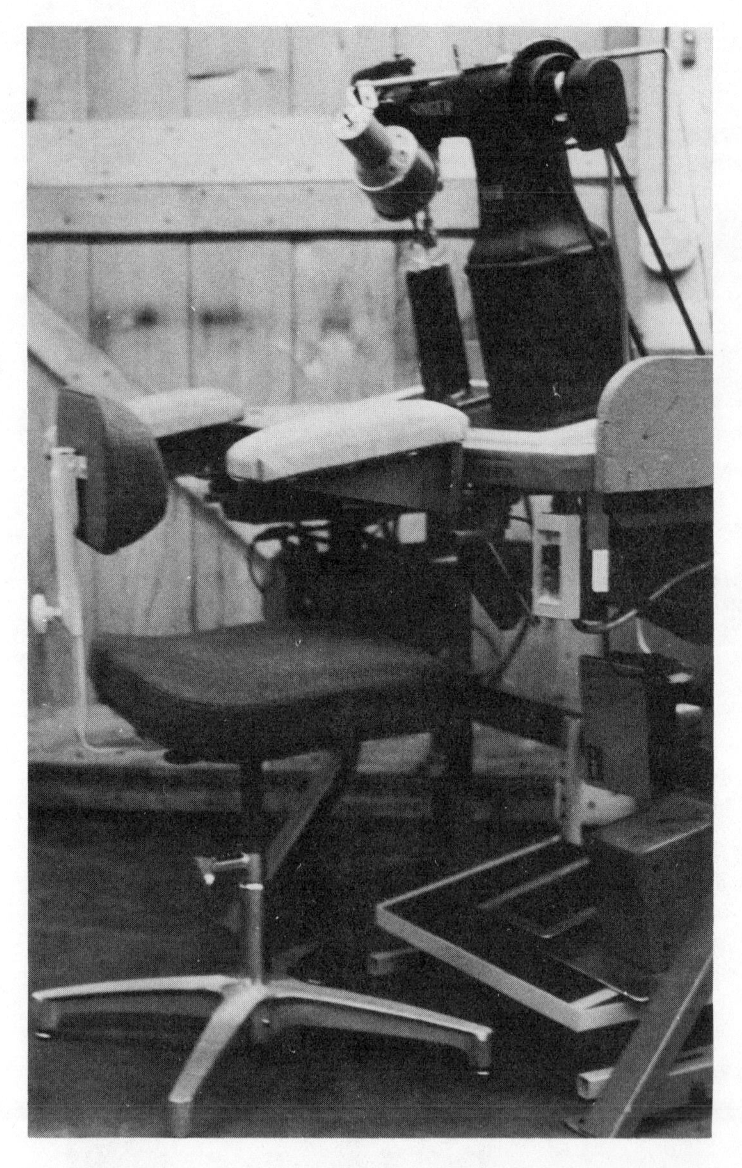

Fig. 2 New design of sewing machine workstation with adjustable footrest

Fig. 3 Prototype "treadle"

Arthur R. Longmate *is staff industrial engineer, Johnson & Johnson Products, Inc., New Brunswick, New Jersey.*

Conni Welker *is ergonomics engineer, Ethicon, Inc., Summerville, New Jersey.*

13

Industrial Ergonomics at Tennessee Eastman Company

David C. Alexander, P.E.

The ergonomics program at Tennessee Eastman Company was formally announced in March 1975. Tennessee Eastman Company is the largest company of the Eastman Chemicals Division — the chemical manufacturing unit of Eastman Kodak Company. The Eastman Chemicals Division employs approximately 18,000 people on a world-wide basis and has plants in five states and Great Britain.

The startup phase of the ergonomics program was fairly typical. Correction of existing problems and prevention of future problems were both needed. The ergonomics problems facing management were (1) the manual handling of material and the resulting injuries, and (2) the introduction of females to many traditional industrial jobs. Ergonomic skills were expected to help resolve both of these problems. At the same time, an orientation to ergonomics was needed for approximately 1,000 supervisors and managers within the company. Over 500 engineers and designers needed a more intensive exposure to ergonomics and how it could help them with their design work. Equipment was needed to measure worker stress and performance at the workplace and on physically demanding jobs. There were many other issues such as determining the areas of emphasis, planning priorities for studies, and developing outside contacts. These areas are discussed briefly below.

Industrial Ergonomics Areas of Emphasis

There are three common areas for the use of ergonomics as it relates to industry. One is the area of in-plant studies, which involves improvements for operations and maintenance jobs. The second is the design of equipment and facilities so that they are usable by people. The third is in the design of products. The first two were emphasized. Design of products was not emphasized since the Eastman Chemicals Division does not produce any end-use consumer products.

In-plant studies primarily dealt with analysis and prevention of accidents, improvements in work methods, improvements of specific tasks such as inspection or maintenance, and the improvement of areas involving heat stress or manual material handling. The design of equipment and facilities primarily involved workplace and work-space design, equipment layouts, design of control rooms, and tool design.

Contacts

An ergonomics program is able to bring a special focus on the person and the job. There are, however, many people who have an existing interest in this area. Establishing and maintaining contact with professionals from medical, safety, industrial hygiene, personnel, and materials handling will enhance the focus on the person at work and will continue their emphasis on improvements in this area.

Work Priorities

Initial problems facing the ergonomics group were injury rates and the introduction of females into traditional jobs. At the same time, the need to prevent additional problems was also gaining momentum. To balance these needs, a priority system was established which emphasized safety and health first, cost control second, and areas of comfort third. The priority system is shown in table 1.

Training

Another problem facing us was teaching others how to design new facilities and equipment to prevent chronic ergonomics problems. A manual of design guidelines was developed which included over 100 pages of recommended equipment, facilities, and job designs. The contents of the manual are shown in table 2. The purpose of the manual was to anticipate and answer many typical questions that the design engineer might have during the design process.

TABLE 1
Priority System for Industrial Ergonomics Work

1. Employee health and safety — Correction of existing problems or prevention of potential problems.
2. Equal employment — Design or redesign of jobs so that the entire work population can perform the job.
3. Productivity/cost — Projects emphasizing cost control or productivity and quality enhancements.
4. Surveys/inspections — Tours of current work areas to anticipate and correct possible ergonomics problems.
5. Development projects — In-house work to develop additional skills in ergonomics or to compile and develop information specific to the company.
6. Training — Training of others in the field of ergonomics.
7. Employee comfort — Projects that would only enhance employee comfort (where no safety and health problems existed or where no cost reduction was anticipated).

TABLE 2
Contents of Ergonomics Design Guidelines Manual

Chapter	Topic	Number of Pages*
1	Reaches and Clearances	7
2	Design of Individual Workplaces	9
3	Tool Design	6
4	Displays and Controls	28
5	Designing for Maintainability	10
6	Labeling and Coding	4
7	Inspection	1
8	Manual Material Handling	4
9	Physical Work and Fatigue	2
10	Environmental Conditions	3
11	Checklists	2
12	References	1

*Based on information available on this topic and on anticipated applications within Eastman Chemicals Division.

In conjunction with this, a widespread training program was developed and used. Design engineers were exposed to ergonomics and how it could benefit them. They were given a design manual and led through several case studies which helped introduce them to ergonomics and how the design manual could be used to answer questions that might arise. An outline of that course is provided in table 3. There were several variations of ergonomics training offered. The objectives of the different courses are shown in table 4.

TABLE 3
Outline of Ergonomics Design Seminar Training Course

Topic	Time, Min.
Introduction	20
"Designing for People" slide tape program	30
Overview-design guideline book	30
Case studies	
Lifting	35
Inspection	25
Workplace design	40
Maintainability	30
Tool design	20
Summary	10

Equipment

The equipment used was not extensive. The most-used pieces of equipment were a tape measure and a push-pull gauge. We were always concerned with physical measurements and with forces.

For physiological monitoring, we had a portable cardiocorder for monitoring heart rate, and a Max Planck respirator and oxygen-analyzing equipment to measure the use of oxygen on the job. While the physiological equipment was not heavily used, it was essential whenever there was a need for that detailed kind of information.

One other useful instrument was a wet bulb globe temperature recorder which was used to measure temperatures in the work areas. This helped greatly in the assessment of heat stress. Two models are shown. One is portable, and it has a rapid response time. The other contains twenty-four-hour recording charts and is excellent for providing a heat profile for an area. It was designed from guidelines provided in *The Industrial Environment — Its Evaluation and Control* (Chapter 31 — "Thermal Standards and Measurement Techniques," Bruce A. Hertig, figure 31-10).

The final piece of equipment that we regularly used was a Kodak high-speed 16-mm camera to film work operations. Although portable video equip-

TABLE 4
Objectives of Ergonomics Training Programs

Audience:	Designers	Management	First line supervisor
Time:	Four hours	One hour	Thirty minutes
Purpose:	Problem solution	Problem management	Problem detection
Objectives			
1. Define ergonomics*	X	X	X
2. Benefits of designs that consider people	X	X	X
3. Increased recognition of ergonomics problems	X	X	X
4. Cover specific project areas	X	X	
5. Provide ergonomics design guidelines	X		
6. Solve ergonomics case studies	X		

*A 20-minute slide-tape program was used to define ergonomics and its application, by covering a number of specific problems and their solutions.

ment is now available for this purpose, the 16-mm camera provides higher resolution than video equipment and the high-speed camera is able to capture details that a video camera cannot. In one instance, the film revealed why one operator was particularly good at a textile operation. He was left-handed and the operation required a special twist which suited the biomechanical strength of the left hand.

Photos of the equipment are shown in figures 1–5.

At the same time a number of books were purchased, and subscriptions to more common ergonomic journals were obtained. These helped to develop a broad based library resource in the field of ergonomics. Some of these resources are listed in the Bibliography.

Ergonomics — Maintaining the Effort

While the startup was a critical time, after four or five years the program developed a different character. No longer was there the rush associated with answering pressing chronic problems on the shop floor. Most of the problems had been resolved. Now we moved into a longer term approach where ergonomics was used in the prevention of specific problems. During this

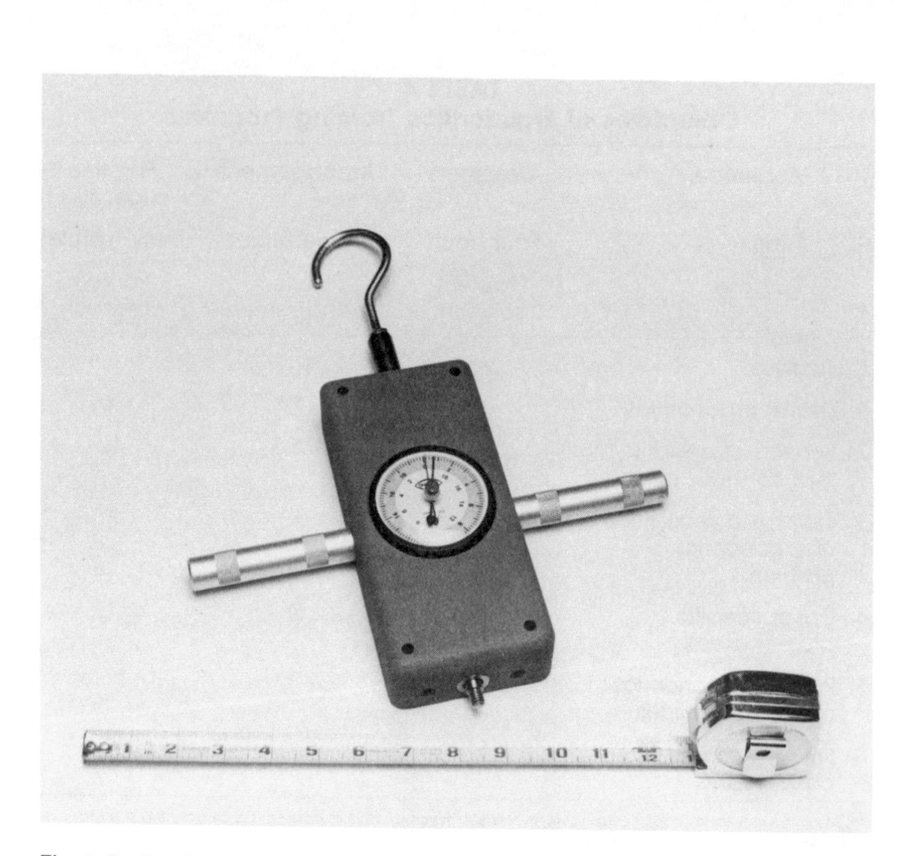

Fig. 1 Push-pull gauge and tape measure

period, for example, work was done on the prevention of lifting injuries — not specific injuries on one job, but overall prevention of lifting injuries on a widespread basis. Automation to perform difficult jobs was introduced. A lift school, based on a concept similar to defensive driving, was developed to let the lifter anticipate problems with lifting tasks.

Another major project involved the use of ergonomics to evaluate operating control systems for major chemical processes. In addition, surveys and inspections of operating areas to anticipate and prevent injuries took more and more time. Consulting with design engineers on all types of designs has become much more common and having design questions asked early enough in the design project to make meaningful changes is becoming commonplace.

Also during this period, contact with other ergonomists outside Tennessee Eastman Company increased. Those contacts gave us a deeper insight into the area of ergonomics. Eastman personnel participated in several of the Brouha Work Physiology Symposiums. A member of our ergonomics group served as director of the Ergonomics Division for the Institute of Industrial Engineers and personnel were able to present several papers for

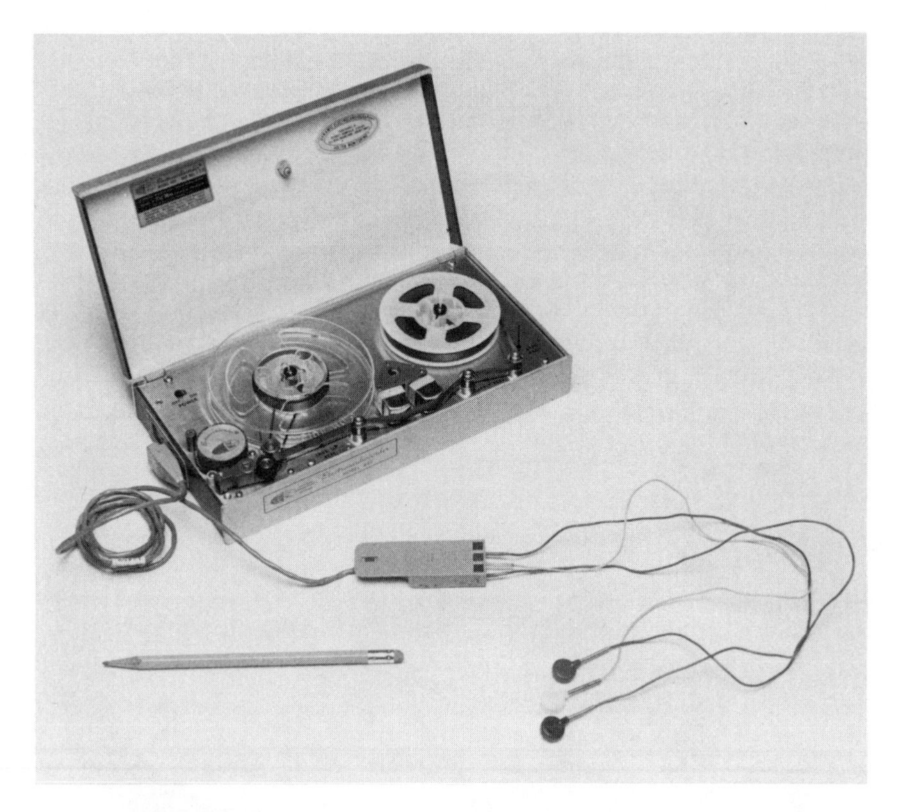

Fig. 2 Cardiocorder with leads

the Human Factors Society. Eastman was eventually requested to participate on a task group on ergonomics for the Chemical Manufacturers' Association. All of these contacts helped provide broader views of ergonomics and how ergonomics could enhance our operations.

There was a clear change of character in the ergonomics program at this time. In hindsight, it was a necessary step in the maturing of a strong industrial ergonomics program.

Ergonomics — The Next Generation

After ten years of experience, we are beginning to see yet another horizon. The initial focus of our ergonomics effort was on the correction and alleviation of pressing ergonomic problems. The next stage was one of prevention, that is, teaching others how to design to prevent specific problems. While the need to correct problems is the catalyst that initially starts many ergonomics programs, both correction and prevention are usually dealt with by most new industrial ergonomic groups. This was true for us.

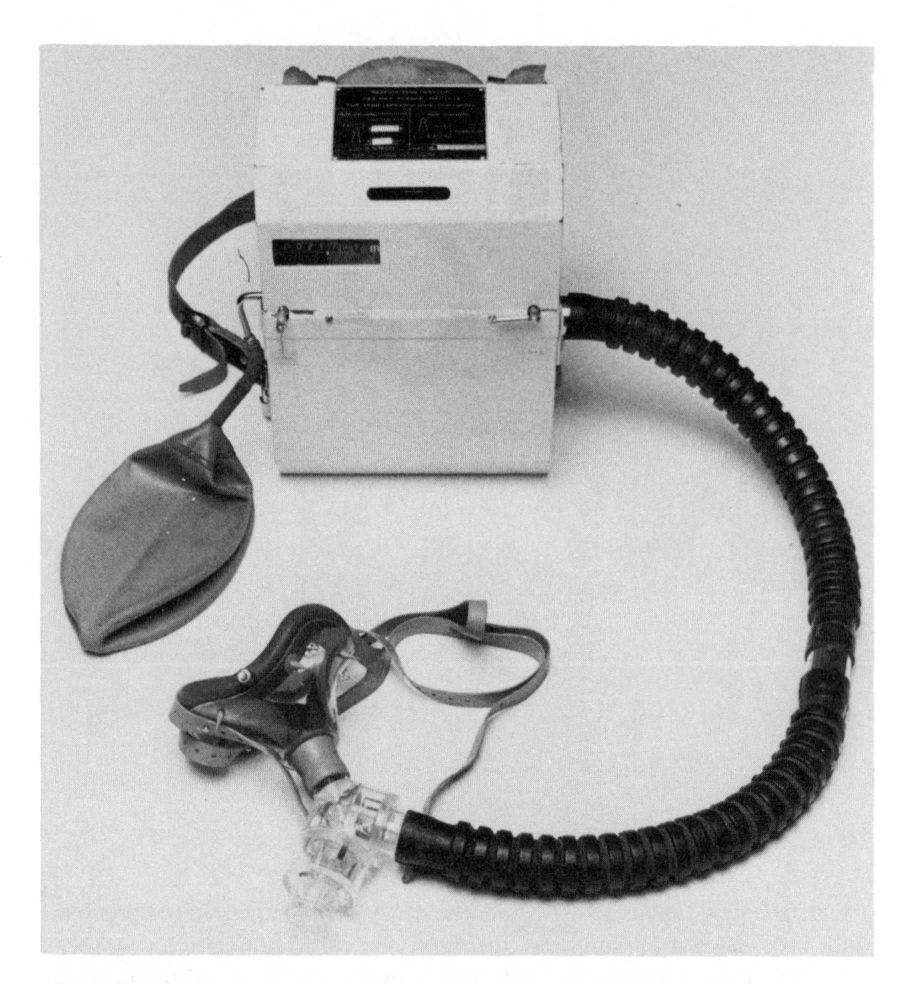

Fig. 3 Max Planck respirometer

The new horizon that is presenting itself, however, is in the area of administration and policy.

Policy decisions have widespread and long-range impact on an operating company. Policy-making is a complex matter and normally involves input from many different points of view. Policy questions are never simple. Now ergonomics is beginning to play a more important part in those policy decisions. Long term, this will further enhance the strong impact that ergonomics is having on people.

An excellent example is in the use of video display terminals (VDTs). Early in the introduction of VDTs, the ergonomists were able to point out the need for flexible jobs and adjustable equipment. There were detailed design recommendations, but simply specifying that computer work stations be adjustable was the most important item for design and purchase decisions. Virtually all of our VDTs have separate keyboards and adjustable screens.

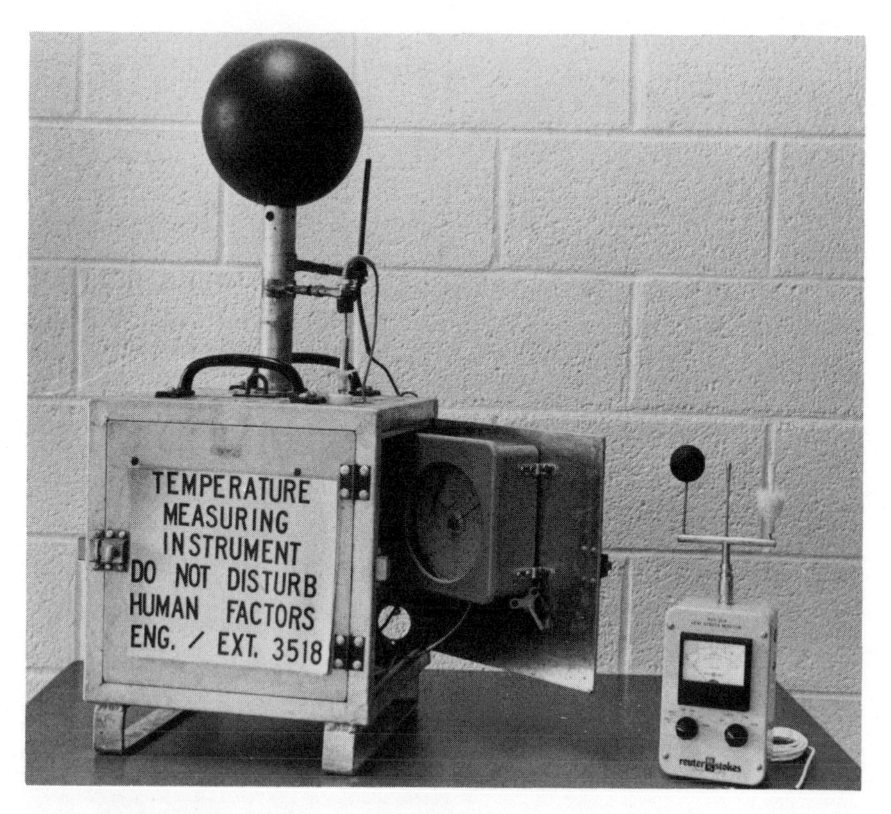

Fig. 4 Wet-bulb globe temperature recorder

At the same time, jobs were designed for flexibility. Operators are allowed to move about and usually to retrieve their own material from the printer. This provides enough movement to avoid the chronic back and neck problems that personnel in some companies have experienced.

A second example where ergonomics is now making a major impact is the use of shift schedules. Although Eastman has used a traditional rotating shift schedule for over fifty years, some new research dealing with sleep-wake patterns became available to the ergonomists. This information was used to redesign a more physiologically desirable shift schedule. The schedule is now being tried on a pilot basis in several plants. While shift schedules are complicated administrative issues — they involve questions related to work, pay, and quality of time off — ergonomics was able to influence this area based on strong research data.

Recently, ergonomics has helped introduce both robotics and bar-coding systems. When key problem areas failed to respond to traditional ergonomic solutions, advanced automation was proposed as a means of resolving these problems. Since the problems involved product identification errors, and injuries due to manual handling of bagged and drummed products, this technology was appropriate. Ergonomics initially justified these projects, but

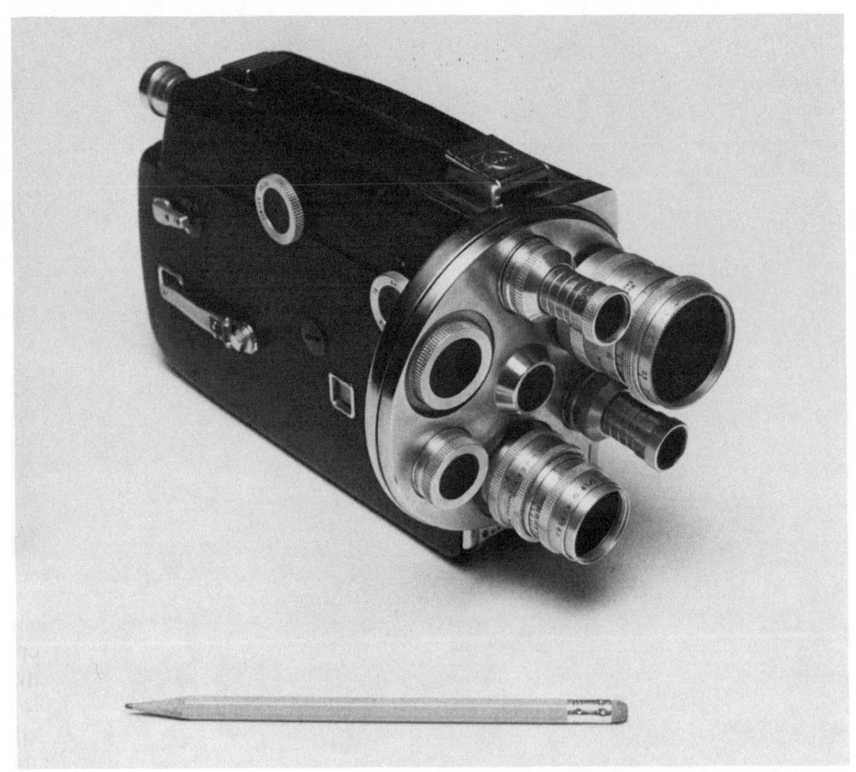

Photos courtesy of The Tennessee Eastman Company.

Fig. 5 Kodak Cine 16 mm high speed camera

the equipment was eventually justified from an economic basis. Designers are more able to see the use of automation as a complement to the human worker. When people experience problems doing a job, automation is now a viable solution.

Over the long term, ergonomics will become practiced by more and more people within the Eastman Chemicals Division. They won't call themselves ergonomists, and they won't have thirty ergonomics books on their bookshelves like I have, but their feelings and understanding of the human worker will make a far larger difference in designing for people than I could ever make by myself. The spread of ergonomics away from a small group and toward a natural way of doing business is one of the most important things that an ergonomics group can do as it strives to make a workplace more suitable for the human.

Bibliography

BOOKS

General

Chaffin, Don B., and Leo Greenburg. 1977. *Workers and their tools*. Ann Arbor: University of Michigan.

McCormick, E.J. 1964. *Human factors engineering*. New York: McGraw-Hill Book Co.

Van Cott, H.P., and Robert G. Kinkade. 1972. *Human engineering guide to equipment design*. Washington, D.C.: U.S. Government Printing Office.

Military Standard 1472 C. Human engineering design criteria for Military systems, equipment, and facilities. Washington, D.C.: U.S. Government Printing Office.

Konz, Stephen. 1983. Work Design: Industrial Ergonomics. New York: Wiley.

Anthropometry

Panero, Julius, and Martin Zelnik. 1979. *Human dimensions and interior space*. New York: Whitney Library of Design.

Environment

National Institute of Occupational Safety and Health. 1974. *The industrial environment—Its evaluation and control*. Washington, D.C.: U.S. Government Printing Ofice.

Industrial Ergonomics

Alexander, David C. 1986. *The practice and management of industrial ergonomics*. Englewood Cliffs, N.J.: Prentice-Hall.

Eastman Kodak Co. 1983. *Ergonomic design for people at work*. Lifetime Learning, vol. 1. Eastman Kodak Co.

——. 1985. *Ergonomic design for people at work*. Lifetime Learning, vol. 2, Eastman Kodak Co.

Inspection

Harris, D.H., and F.B. Chaney. 1969. *Human factors in quality assurance*. New York: Wiley & Sons.

Handicapped

Mueller, James. 1980. *Designing for functional limitations*. The Job Development Laboratory, The George Washington University Rehabilitation Research and Training Center, Washington, D.C.

Lifting

National Institute for Occupational Safety and Health. 1981. *Work practices guide for manual lifting*. Cincinnati, Ohio: NIOSH.

Physiology

Brouha, L. 1967. *Physiology in industry*. 2nd ed. New York: Pergamon Press.

Process Control

Edwards, Elwyn, and Frank P. Lees, eds. 1974. *The human operator in process control*. London: Taylor & Francis, Ltd.

JOURNALS

Applied Ergonomics. New York: IPC Business Press.

Ergonomics. London: Taylor & Francis, Ltd.

Human Factors. Baltimore: Johns Hopkins Press.

Industrial Engineering. Norcross, Ga.: Institute of Industrial Engineers.

Americal Industrial Hygiene Association Journal. Akron, Ohio: American Industrial Hygiene Association.

14

Ergonomically Sound — Everyone Benefits

Richard N. Coughenour

The Bibb Company is the largest textile and sewing manufacturer in the state of Georgia, employing over 5,000 people in thirteen plants. It is a major producer of sheets, pillowcases, bedspreads, comforters, drapes, apparel fabrics, carpet yarns, industrial yarns and fabrics.

By the early 1980s a majority of industries in the United States had heard, belatedly, about something called ergonomics/human factors. This new discipline received casual attention by many, but by and large seemed to be thought of as a nicety that had few immediate practical benefits.

As more and more publicity began to emerge regarding hazards to workers caused by poorly designed work stations, machinery that did not interface properly with employees, inadequately engineered work methods and pending OSHA regulations and lawsuits, industry became concerned and companies began to investigate means of implementing formalized ergonomic programs. Yet, the improvements to productivity and quality brought about by the sound application of ergonomics seemed to have been overlooked.

Learning about Ergonomics

During the original investigative process it was quickly realized that in-house knowledge in this field was sadly lacking. Perhaps a few recent industrial engineering graduates had completed an introductory ergonomics course, and this was a step in the right direction. However, ergonomics covers many different disciplines and to qualify as an ergonomist takes years of study.

In the absence of degreed ergonomists on staff, two basic alternatives are left. One, contract with an outside ergonomics consultant. But heed a word of warning. Ergonomics has received much attention recently and many consulting firms advertise expertise in this area. Research their qualifications and programs successfully implemented *within* your industry. Two, begin researching and reading the many articles on the subject that have appeared in magazines such as *Industrial Engineering*, papers by the U.S. Department of Health and Human Services, *The Journal of Occupational Medicine* and books by such noted authors as E.R. Tichauer, E.J. McCormick, and Don B. Chaffin.

Information from these sources may not always be applied directly to your specific situation; however, the principles and procedures can often be tailored to particular areas in need of improvement. Imagination is a prerequisite.

For those with a limited knowledge of physiology, biomechanics, illumination, and the many other disciplines encompassing ergonomics, this first introduction to a program can be confusing and frustrating.

To the layman, unfamiliar words and terms run rampant through much published material. Particulotactic, metacarpophalangeal joint, compression ischemia, tenosynovitis, symmetric asymmetric exertions and articulation index are examples of a few.

Out of this frustration may have grown the simplistic idea that the application of ergonomic principles entails no more than the use of common sense. *Newsweek* magazine (Begley, Carey, and Bruno 1983, 68) made the following statement about ergonomics: "Its terminology might sound faddish, but its strength is common sense." If this is true, we might add, *educated* common sense. To begin making changes helter-skelter, with no knowledge of human anatomy, review of available research, etc., may result in more harm than benefits to the employee.

The success of an ergonomic program hinges on three requirements:

- A philosophy that improvement is needed
- A program for improvement
- A procedure to implement improvement.

Tichauer (1978, 3) expresses the basic philosophy of ergonomics as that of considering man to be subjected to two sets of laws:

- Laws of Newtonian mechanics
- Biological laws of life

Problems arise when the environment is not compatible with the human body, resulting in possible stress, fatigue, injury, or illness. These conditions usually are not brought about suddenly, but accumulate over a period of time. Thus, they may be referred to as cumulative trauma disorders.

Although research has not been able to pin down every specific cause or condition that will bring about these ailments, the triggering mechanisms may be categorized into "Tichauer's Five Ecologic Stress Vectors."

1. Climatotactic — Contact with climate
2. Biotactic — Contact with organisms
3. Chemotactic — Contact with chemicals
4. Particulotactic — Contact with hostile particles.
5. Mechanotactic — Contact with mechanical devices.

To a large degree, the area or areas of most immediate concern will depend upon the industry or job. However, each stress vector will affect us all to some extent, regardless of where we work or how we spend our leisure time.

Planning the Ergonomics Program at the Bibb Company

In 1982, the Industrial Engineering and Industrial Relations Departments of The Bibb Company requested recommendations as to: Should the company implement a formal ergonomics program? If so, what would be the objectives? And, how would the program operate?

It was recognized that textiles and sewing operations are somewhat labor-intensive and often require employees to perform repetitive motion patterns. Therefore, our types of jobs would be prime targets for improvement. Our initial thrust would be in the biomechanical area of ergonomics, items related to the operating characteristics of the human body as they interact with the machinery and devices we work with.

Data were gathered from all plant medical clinics pertaining to the frequency and severity of musculoskeletal disorders reported over a specific period of time. Out of the total company population, 0.23 percent had diagnosed cases of some type of musculoskeletal disorder. None, however, were specified as being job-related.

Even with this low incidence of diagnosed problems it was felt that the company had an obligation to apply the latest information and techniques available for the continued protection of its employees. Also, a formal program would result in industrial engineering becoming concerned with experimenting with and testing new work station layouts and operator motion patterns.

Answers to the question of objectives varied.

— To comply with present or future OSHA regulations
— To reduce injuries and illnesses which affect workman's compensation and medical cost
— To reduce stress and fatigue, resulting in greater efficiency and improved quality.

Examination will show that these are not objectives, but rather results, results of designing work place layouts, operator methods, material handling aids, tools and training which best interface with the employee to provide the most efficient, least stressful working environment feasible.

After careful consideration, upper management gave its approval and total support for initiating an ergonomics program within all Bibb facilities. This type of support is absolutely essential for success. Without it, an ergonomics program will become just "another program that will fade away quickly."

Next came the organizational structure for implementing and maintaining a viable program. There are basically five areas of responsibilities (responsibilities not all inclusive):

1. Corporate Ergonomic Steering Committee
   a. Establish policy and procedures for the organization and implementation of the program.
   b. Set overall objectives and communicate these within the policy.
   c. Review plant recommendations and exercise final authority prior to implementation.
   d. Determine funding.
2. Corporate Coordinator
   a. To act as a liaison between the plants and the Corporate Steering Committee.
   b. To assist the plants in setting up and maintaining viable implementation teams.
   c. To offer technical assistance to the implementation teams.
   d. To assist in the development and to approve all educational material.
3. Ergonomic Consultant
   Sits as an ad hoc member of the Corporate Steering Committee, acting as a resource and advisor on ergonomic-related items.
4. Plant Coordinator
   a. To act as a liaison between the plant and the corporate coordinator.
   b. To coordinate and monitor all aspects of the plant ergonomics program.
   c. To compile and summarize all required reports.
   d. To communicate plant needs to the plant manager and the corporate coordinator as they relate to the ergonomics program.

5. Plant Implementation Team
   a. To conduct surveys on job design, employee postures and motion patterns.
   b. To recommend, implement and follow up on corrective action taken.
   c. To conduct evaluation studies on employees who report pain or discomfort.

Implementation

The vehicle for the program was now in place, but the expertise for implementation was still lacking. Education and training sessions would be required for all concerned. We began with employee and supervisor briefings consisting of:

- — Defining ergonomics and program objectives
- — Defining musculoskeletal disorders
- — Describing possible contributing factors related to these disorders
- — Describing what the company was doing to improve and maintain safe and healthy working conditions.

Industrial engineers, training personnel and personnel managers attended several days of in-house workshops covering types of musculoskeletal disorders, what contributes to these disorders, preventive and improvement steps, job design, motion patterns, materials handling, training, job and operator evaluations, documentation, etc.

Nurses attended in-house workshops conducted by an industrial physician and a Ph.D. in ergonomics.

Local physicians were invited to review the program for suggested improvements and to tour the manufacturing facilities. Their understanding of the program and the job content and motion patterns of our employees would aid in diagnosing and prescribing treatment for employees referred to them.

Successful Projects

I sincerely believe that education, training and open communication with everyone affected by the ergonomics program has been the key to a successful implementation. The initial results are proving that ergonomically designed jobs will improve efficiency and quality, while providing employees with safe, comfortable, and healthy working environments. Everyone benefits.

Although the number of projects is too numerous to list in entirety, several include:

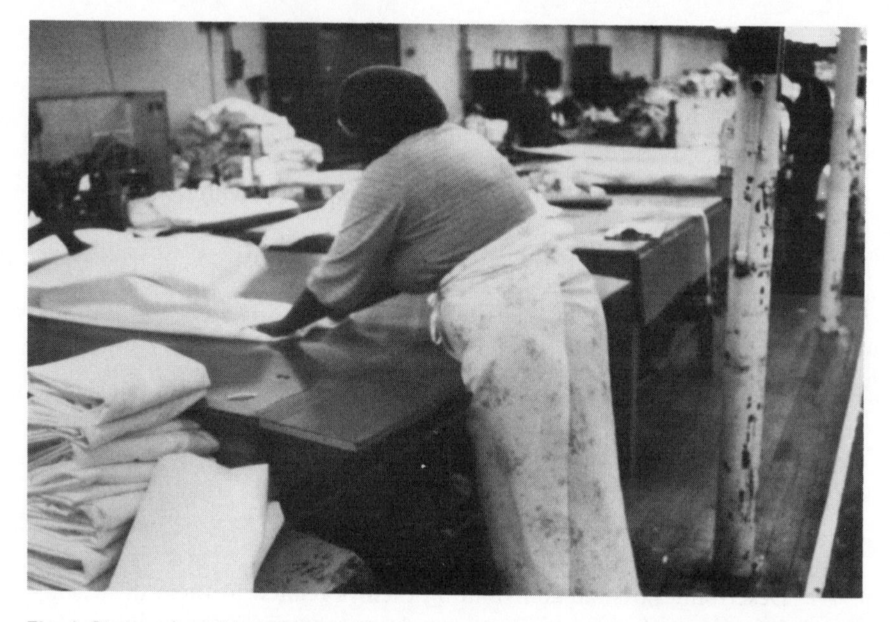

Fig. 1 Sharp edge of inspection table caused pressure and discomfort in abdomen and pelvic area

Fig. 1A Foam padded edges of inspection table. Reduced pressure and eliminated discomfort

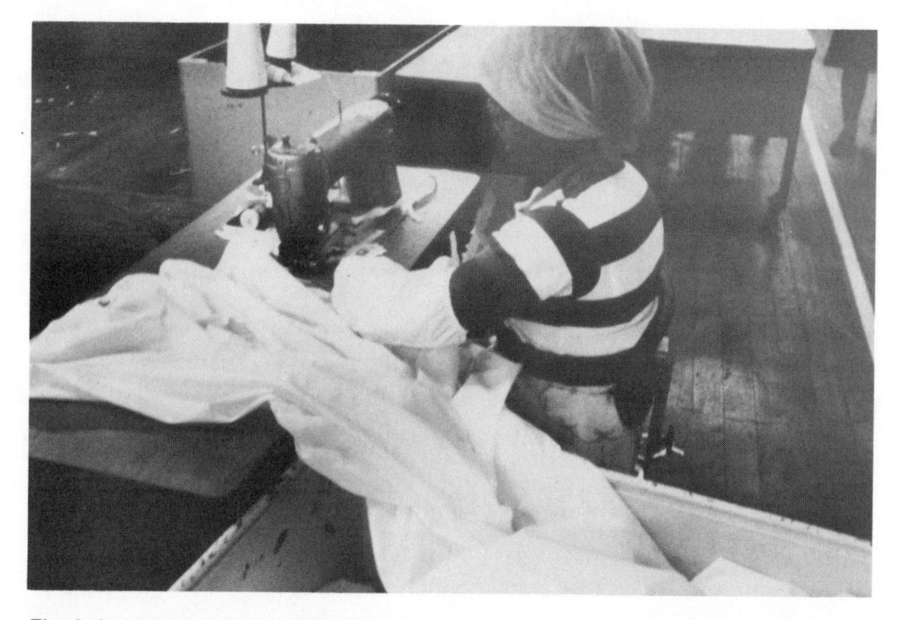

Fig. 2 Arm bands for sewers. Reduces possibility of contracting contact dermatitis

Fig. 3 Cloth upholstered chairs, individually adjusted and positioned at machine for specific individuals

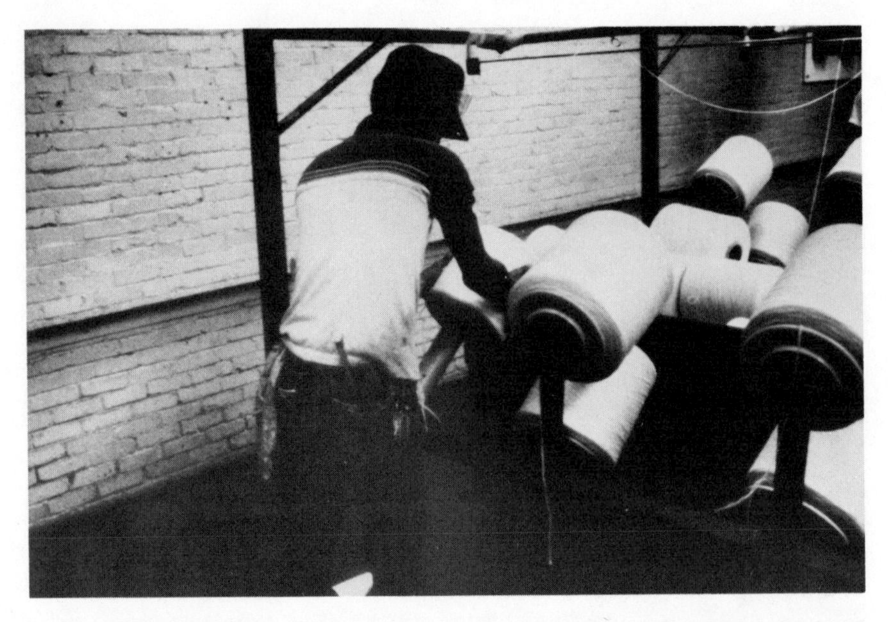

Fig. 4 Carpet yarn creels — Creel pegs stationary, facing away from operator. Required excessive bends and arm extensions while creeling packages from outside of creel

Fig. 4A Improved carpet yarn creels — Pegs horizontal and swivel on ball bearings. Reduces bends and allows for packages to be held close to body while creeling

Fig. 5 Packing yarn packages — Due to height and angle of the packing station bends and arise from bends were prevalent. Also position of the pin truck resulted in excessive body turns and cone handling

Fig. 5A Improved packing station — A pneumatically operated piston raises the station to a minimum height of 16 inches with a 54° tilt toward the operator. All bends and arise from bends to place packages in the case were eliminated. Visual inspection of packages now accomplished while on pin truck. This reduced package holding. These changes increased standard units packed 8 percent.

Several other projects include:

1. Stress mats for all standing jobs
2. Elevated footrest for seated employees
3. Gravity assisted "get" and "aside" where possible
4. Improved lighting to reduce glare and insure proper lighting distribution and color definition
5. Required rest periods
6. Job rotations
7. NIOSH action limit formula applied to all lifting jobs.

The ergonomics work has just begun, but with dedicated, innovative industrial engineers and other support personnel the definition of industrial engineering can and will be better fulfilled: "The engineering approach applied to all factors, including the human factors, involved in the production and distribution of products or services" (Maynard 1963, 1-3).

References

Begley, Sharon, John Carey, and Mary Bruno. 1983. *Newsweek* (August 29):68.

Maynard, H.B. ed. 1963. *Industrial engineering handbook*. New York: McGraw-Hill Book Co.

Tichauer, E.R. 1978. *The biomechanical basis of ergonomics*. New York: John Wiley and Sons, Inc.

Richard N. Coughenour *is manager of operations training with the Bibb Company, Macon, Georgia.*

15

Human Factors Engineering at 3M

Nicholas Simonelli, Ph.D.
Satu Suominen-Troyer, Ph.D.

The human factors discipline is a true chameleon in that a human factors group takes on the discipline of the organization that surrounds it. If a human factors interest evolves in the medical department or in industrial hygiene, for example, human factors engineering is likely to be called *industrial ergonomics* and will consist of avoiding back injuries, carpal tunnel syndrome, and other physiological harm. Human factors group members will probably be industrial engineers, perhaps with an ergonomics specialization. There could also be psychologists who are expert in training and education. They will handle workshops, safety courses, etc.

On the other hand, if the interest in ergonomics evolves in a marketing research environment, human factors engineering will involve the psychology of human perception. How much bigger is bigger? How much heavier before someone notices? Is this color readily distinguishable from that one? What problems do people encounter when trying to read the owner's manual that comes with a product? Group members are likely to be experimental psychologists or sociologists. Their specialty is observation of human performance and they will gather, generate, and analyze data to answer specific human performance questions.

A third area tailor-made for the evolution of interest in human factors is a product-development laboratory. Here, the engineers work for years to finish and commercialize a new product and issues of human performance arise all along the way. For example, questions arise concerning how potential product users will react to control and display arrangements. Questions of body size arise that must be answered to select the correct dimensions of a product to accommodate the targeted user population. Questions of reasoning patterns and modes of thinking arise that must be answered to design computer interfaces on any product containing a microprocessor.

Similarly, in other environments, ergonomics means attention to those areas of human psychological and physiological performance that are relevant to the issues of that environment. The members of the human factors group will have the backgrounds needed to address those issues.

Human Factors History at 3M

There was no human factors group at 3M prior to 1974. Ergonomics issues were dealt with, of course, but on an ad hoc, seat-of-the-pants basis. No one carried an ergonomic calling card.

In the summer of 1974, an employee in the then Duplicating Products Division came across the course description of the summer Human Factors Engineering course at the University of Michigan. This engineer was in the technical service group of the division. The group handled many issues dealing directly with what they called "customer error." Did the user forget to reset a switch after opening the machine to clear out jammed paper? Was black toner powder spilled all over the place while replenishing the supply? Did staples or paper clips fall into the machine and short out a circuit board? Did a customer load a supply in backwards?

It appears that there was relevance in this short course to these technical service problems. These errors were, historically, the customer's fault, but might it not be possible to understand the user better to help guide design? Was it possible that "error" had two sides? There was also the possibility that human factors engineering could address quality-assurance problems.

The reviews of the summer course were favorable and other service personnel attended in the following summers. An ergonomics awareness was evolving and the most dedicated of the converts were becoming a human factors interest group. They began approaching product design teams with the thought of influencing copier design in the early phases. Management support at this point, however, was still a wait-and-see approach. Could they prove that they had an impact on the cost or success of a product? And hire a psychologist. . . ?

A well-known ergonomics consultant was brought in to lecture to a wider design audience. Engineers were told where they could improve on their designs to facilitate operability and serviceability, but many received this information skeptically. Videotaping was suggested as a good investigative tool to analyze the performance of various people in these areas and a few equipment purchases were made. The human factors interest group grew to a few service personnel, and the manager of the group sought other consultants to advise on the direction of growth the group should take.

In late 1977, a human factors/industrial design consultant was brought in to interview key personnel, analyze the design process, and recommend where human factors specialists could have the most impact. A Human Factors Group structure was drawn up depicting a liaison between several of the larger design labs and a new center of ergonomics expertise. The plan did not, however, call for hiring human factors professionals. Management believed that engineers and designers who were educated in human factors would be the most useful contributors. They were not sure what use could be made of research professionals such as experimental psychologists.

Shortly after the Human Factors Group structure was arranged, a new management team was in place and it approved construction of a small videotaping/experimentation laboratory. The human factors group leader was given permission to hire an experimental psychologist and one was employed to investigate the ergonomics of copier operation and maintenance.

The utility of such a lab, personnel, and data quickly became apparent. A second psychologist was hired in 1979 and the group found itself taking on projects from other business machine design labs: microfilm readers and printers, facsimile machines, audio visual products, etc. To be sure, the requests were narrowly defined and often involved "putting out fires," but the value of ergonomic thinking and experimentation was making an impression on the laboratories. Still, 3M was a huge corporation with over forty product divisions, and very few design teams knew of the Human Factors Group. The medical department, which continued to handle industrial human factors, was evolving its own response to the increased public attention to ergonomic issues. They addressed VDT radiation, computer work station comfort, etc.

The Human Factors Group eventually moved out of its product division into a companywide service function and was renamed Human Factors/Ergonomics. Exposure increased through word-of-mouth advertising. By the summer of 1984, the group had grown to five Ph.D. professionals (four psychologists and an industrial engineer), and the original laboratory had doubled in area. Versatile audio and videotaping equipment was installed, allowing sophisticated recordings both in the lab and in the field.

Human Factors in Product Design

The Human Factors/Ergonomics Group is now in a corporate service organization where industrial design and CAD/CAM services are also found. The group has worked for nearly all of the corporation's product division laboratories, as well as many marketing and industrial groups. The group also works with both the industrial designers and industrial hygienists, providing ergonomic data useful in a variety of settings. Projects have even come in from outside companies who have heard of the group's activities.

In product development, typically a product lab will contact a group member with a prototype of a potential product. The services provided after that depend entirely on the type of product and the market perceived for it. One or more of the human factors specialists may examine the product for a day or so and brainstorm for potential problems. How might users abuse this device? What else might it be confused with? What population stereotypes are involved?

If one or more human performance issues are raised that seem fruitless to pursue in the literature, a series of short, empirical studies may be suggested. The studies may be in the form of on-site observations, surveys/interviews, or formal laboratory experimentation. Participants in the evaluations come both from within and outside the company. When a product is not yet ready (for patent or other reasons) to be revealed to the public, it is appropriate to use company employees to test the product. Otherwise, outsiders may also be called in.

A database of volunteers within the company is maintained from which people are selected to participate in the laboratory studies. Basic data such as height, sex, handedness, interests, and job on each volunteer is maintained. Using this, an appropriate sample may be obtained. There is some sampling bias using company personnel, of course, but with 12,000 employees on the large corporate research campus, a sample of people can be easily obtained who have no knowledge of the project at hand. Volunteers come from clerical, secretarial, technical, and administrative backgrounds.

Despite any sampling bias, however, the choice may be between some preliminary, impartial observation and none at all. These studies do not replace traditional market research. They simply help designers take a user perspective (hopefully early) in their work to eliminate problems that they do not see, but that would take considerable time to eliminate later. And, in many cases, this work complements other market research — usually at considerably less cost.

An example of product development in the Human Factors/Ergonomics Laboratory is the Label Protection Tape Pad. This office product is essentially a pad of mailing-label-sized pieces of Scotch tape. A number of them are layered onto a cardboard backing and each has its own paper tab. The user who desires to protect a shipping label from water, scratching, etc., grabs the top tab and peels a label protector from the pad. It is then applied to cover the entire shipping label and adheres it to the package. Several versions of the prototype product were brought into the lab and a variety of people were videotaped using them. Survey data were collected to analyze opinions on the product: rankings, ratings, etc. It was videotape review by the product designers, however, that provided the most exciting benefit. There had been no decision made on the recommended method of removing the paper tab after application. During the study, one woman used a method of removal that was quick and neat and had not come up in the design laboratory. The lab liked it. Eventually, they sought out this woman to include her as one of the inventors of a potential patent application. The value of a new perspective on a product cannot be overestimated.

Another example of laboratory evaluation is the Model 6200 portable overhead projector. The commercialization team desired to have a set of wordless instructions attached to the product depicting setup and lamp changing. After drawing up the instructions, they were evaluated in the lab and suggestions made for improvement. During the testing, it became clear that certain parts within the machine needed to be brightly colored to stand out easily. This made identification easier for the user and allowed the instructions to coordinate more readily with the machine. With wordless instructions in particular, every nuance of the machine and illustrations has an effect on the user.

In-house products are not the only ones evaluated in the Human Factors/ Ergonomics Lab. OEM equipment also comes through for review. The results of the ergonomic analysis is an influencing factor in the decision to accept or reject the OEM design.

Other work in the lab includes much review of control panels and display designs. Color, symbols, decals, lights, etc., are considered for overall usability. Computer software is reviewed for ease of use, market data are analyzed, literature searches are performed, surveys are administered in both the lab and in the field, assistance is given in field test design.

For the most part, requests come in to the group during middle and late design phases. Many requests come in to evaluate the product's decals, owner's manual, operating instructions, etc. This is an unfortunate (and sometimes useless) time to uncover minor design problems or confusions, but when product changes can be made, the testing is beneficial. When changes cannot be made, thorough testing of the documentation will maximize the user's chance for success. Changes not possible for the first design may be useful in later ones.

Increasingly, however, requests for assistance are coming earlier in the life of a new product. Group members are sometimes asked to sit in on conceptual brainstorming sessions to provide an additional perspective. In these cases, there are no product prototypes, nothing to test. Ideas must be generated that will lead to new products. Sometimes, a total unfamiliarity with a product area (but an expertise in searching for ergonomic problems) allows a session participant to suggest novel approaches to dealing with design challenges.

Human Factors in Production

In the area of industrial ergonomics, the Human Factors/Ergonomics Group performs similar services as they do for product design. Emphasis in this area has been growing since early 1984. One group member is an industrial engineer who responds to factory requests for work-design assistance. In many respects, this work resembles the usual product design, but of much larger products — and some "products" that are actually environments. Industrial ergonomics aims at preventing physical injury and discomfort, as well as optimizing operator satisfaction, production quality, and productivity. The activities include providing workplace layouts, tool and equipment design, environmental analyses, and contextual, temporal, and administrative work organization.

Four areas can be identified as the activities supporting in-plant industrial ergonomics. First is providing human factors awareness and training to both plant personnel and their corporate representatives. The Human Factors/ Ergonomics Group, company training center, industrial hygiene, and medical departments all are active trainers. Also, some plants have used outside training and consulting facilities.

The second activity which is concurrent with training includes support of in-plant ergonomics programs. Such programs allow on-going workplace evaluation by different plant representatives. Established production functions which can actuate the programs include industrial and production engineering, medical and safety groups, and operator representative groups. Involvement of industrial and production engineering yields access to work standards, and quality and productivity data which are necessary in identifying areas of ergonomic need outside of direct medical concerns.

The third activity involves accumulating solutions for work design problems which are generic to the industry. For example, process control issues in tape production involve control panel designs, process setup and closedown procedures, material handling, and inspection tasks which have several similarities across tape production plants. In-depth evaluation of improved designs can be performed in the Human Factors/Ergonomics Laboratory, such as control panel operability tests or work posture evaluations.

The fourth activity is identifying anticipated future production technologies and associated human factors concerns. An example is the research carried out for an electronic component work station design. Both postural issues — seating, workpiece height, wrist-elbow supports, and visual environment concerns — and job training and arrangement issues have been addressed in this expanding production area.

Apart from ergonomics in the production facilities, the group reviews industrial product designs. This activity parallels product design activity, except for specific concern for potential application methods and process repetitiveness. For example, a coating application tool distributed for industrial use was analyzed in the Human Factors/Ergonomics Lab. Different application methods and use frequencies were documented from several client plants in the U.S. Simulations of different user methods were set up and hand-wrist-arm positions were recorded for a wide range of operator sizes. A few alternative tool design prototypes were suggested and their use was TV-taped. Also, electromyograms were recorded for the different tool modifications to allow quantitative comparison of the application methods used with the different guns.

While the Human Factors/Ergonomics Group provides design services to improve existing work arrangements, its emphasis is to influence future equipment and work station designs. This is achieved by training and working with both in-plant personnel and corporate manufacturing support/design groups.

The medical department traditionally addresses current work-related medical problems and prescribes therapy, job reassignment, and job redesign. Cooperation between the Human Factors/Ergonomics Group, manufacturing services, the medical department, and plant groups in providing training, job organization, and work design is the underlying means for viable Industrial Human Factors at 3M.

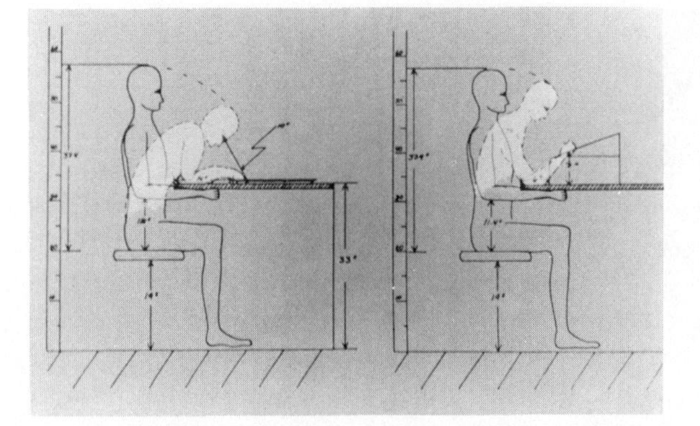

Fig. 1 Before and after diagrams of posture used in performing micro-circuit component insertion. Wrist, elbow, and back problems are greatly alleviated.

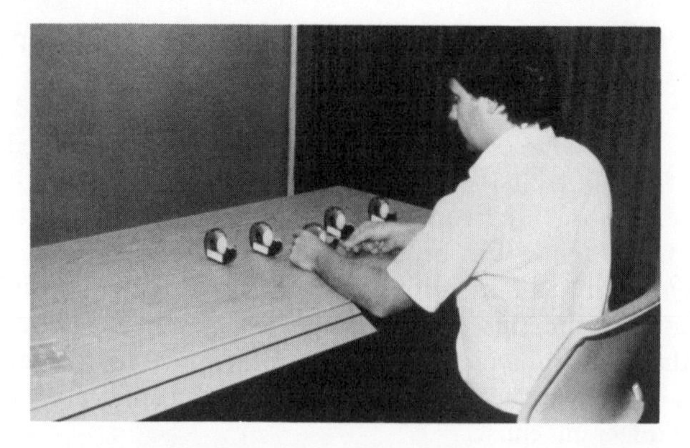

Fig. 2 Product testing in human factors lab: comparing tape dispensing

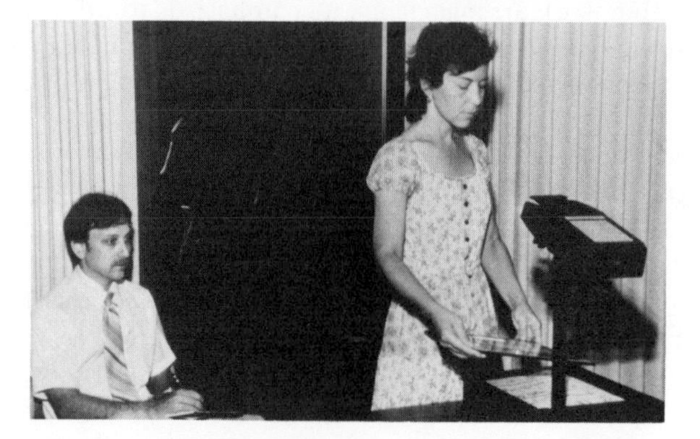

Fig. 3 Product testing in human factors lab: evaluating the Model 6200 wordless instructions

Fig. 4 Product testing in human factors lab: Evaluating the label protection tape pad

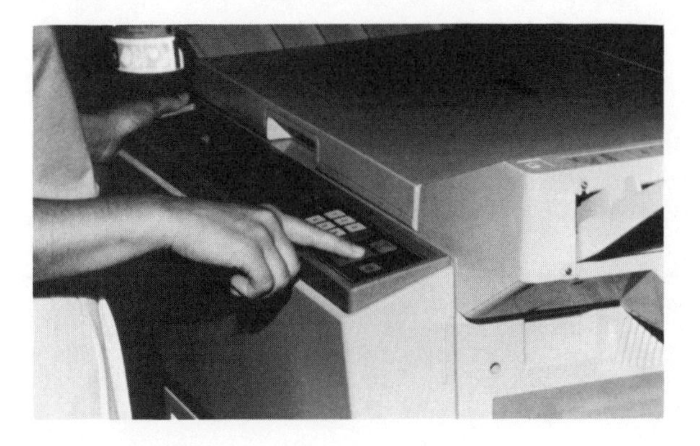

Fig. 5 Product testing in human factors lab: evaluating a control panel for useability

---

Nicholas Simonelli *is specialist, Human Factors Group, 3M, Saint Paul, Minnesota.*

Satu Suominen-Troyer *is senior human factors engineer, 3M, Saint Paul, Minnesota.*

16

Ergonomic Group Organization

David C. Alexander, P.E.

The purpose of this article is to help define an "ideal ergonomics group." There is no one "ideal group" since the duties, responsibilities, group size, and project work are so dependent on the needs of the local organization.

Upon examination of the preceding articles, it seems that there are six key issues associated with an ergonomics group: (1) the type of work performed, (2) the responsibilities assumed by the group, (3) the specific project categories, (4) the functions performed, (5) the size of the group, and (6) the resources used by the group. Each of these areas is discussed in detail below.

Type of Work

Simonelli states that the human factors discipline is a true chameleon since the human factors group takes on the discipline of the organization that surrounds it. He further states that when the human factors interest evolves in the medical department or industrial hygiene, for example, ergonomics will emphasize avoiding back injuries, carpal tunnel syndrome, and other physiological harm. If the interest evolves in a marketing research environment, on the other hand, ergonomics is the psychology of human perception.

He is correct — there are many areas where the ergonomics group can have an influence. It's appropriate for the ergonomists to identify initial areas of need and then seek to expand its role so that all appropriate areas of industrial ergonomics are covered. As noted by Alexander, there are three general areas of use for ergonomics in industry, yet not all are appropriate for every company. Each of the three areas is discussed further.

In-Plant Ergonomics

In-plant studies typically center on improvements to existing plant operations. Some studies include analysis of accidents, methods improvements, reduction of heat stress, and investigation of heavy jobs. This area is a traditional one for ergonomics. In industry, it joins the industrial engineer's role in improving performance. Many industrial ergonomics groups in the United States start with this emphasis. Smith emphasizes this point, as do Vernes, Coughenour, and Longmate.

Design of Equipment and Facilities

The second area of emphasis is the design of equipment and facilities for in-house use, with applications similar to those in the military and aerospace fields. Here, the equipment is designed so that a known population of people can operate it effectively. Traditionally, this area is the responsibility of in-house design engineering.

Applications in this area include the design of equipment, control design, the layout of areas for accessibility, and the layout of equipment for ease of operations. Many of the ergonomics texts provide information that is usable for an emphasis on equipment design. Longmate and others discuss the development of in-house design guidelines.

Product Design

The third area of emphasis is product design. This is the area that Simonelli discusses most heavily. It is an important area, yet the one that industrial engineers seem to be involved with the least. Product design, of course, centers on assisting with the design and usability of a consumer product. The design of labeling and instructions are also part of this area. Extensive work in experimental design and judgment in anticipating accidents and misoperations by the ultimate user are important here.

The home area for the ergonomics group to a great extent determines its character. The associates, the work requests, and the budget and equipment support one has will vary from one to another, whether it is plant operations, design engineering, or a product emphasis. The ergonomics group should be aware of all three areas of emphasis, so attempts to sell ergonomics can be made in those areas where ergonomics is not currently being utilized.

Responsibilities

The responsibilities assumed by ergonomics groups are to improve worker safety and health, to enhance performance, and/or to improve the quality of work life.

Worker Safety and Health

A strong consensus emerges from these articles that a key role of the ergonomics professional is to increase employee safety and health. Virtually all the groups operating in an industrial environment take this as one of their main responsibilities. Even those in product design recognize in-plant safety and the avoidance of accidents and injuries as a key consideration in their work.

Worker safety and health are so important that most groups see this as the starting point for their efforts. Certainly if not the starting point, a high injury rate was one catalyst that helped the group to begin. The worker safety and health area focuses on injuries, lost time, disabilities, and return-to-work issues. These are discussed in detail in the previous articles.

Performance Issues

Improving performance is frequently a responsibility of an ergonomics group in industry. Performance issues include reducing operating cost, enhancing productivity, and improving quality. Smith, in particular, notes the importance of using the performance issues to justify an ergonomics program, since these are always issues that concern management. Unfortunately, however, they are difficult to anticipate and to quantify before the ergonomics group has gained much experience. Therefore, performance improvement is not as strong an issue as it might be for justifying the ergonomics program. An outside consultant may help anticipate improvements, but internally they are difficult to estimate without experience.

Quality of Work Life

Quality of work life is mentioned by Smith as a social responsibility that may be used to aid in justifying the ergonomics area. Few of the groups actually mention this directly, although they do imply that removal of sources of injury and the creation of better work stations and work environments tends to enhance the quality of work life. It doesn't seem to be embraced as a clear responsibility by most groups, perhaps because it is seen as being too intangible to justify the ergonomics efforts. Smith indicates that it could be a positive area for an ergonomics group to focus on, and may be appreciated by management.

Project Categories

An ergonomics group will perform most of its projects in its home area. Nonetheless, any group should be able to handle a project in another area. There are four general project categories for most groups. The most traditional category deals with the improvement or redesign of existing work areas. Another category is that of new design, the third is the area of training, and the fourth deals with information accumulation and data bases.

Improvement/Redesign

This category is mentioned most often as the actual starting point for many ergonomics groups. Improving existing operations can reduce the injury rate or improve other aspects of performance like costs or quality. This is one of the more common project categories, especially for in-plant projects. Examples include the biomechanical analysis of material handling operations, the examination of workplaces to reduce injuries, error reduction, methods improvements, or heat stress projects. Blache discusses human factors committees and Longmate presents the use of ergonomics task forces directed toward the examination and improvement of existing operations.

New Design

This category is directed toward prevention rather than correction of existing ergonomics problems. The ergonomist is responsible for providing design information from the ergonomics field to the designers and engineer. The ergonomist may also work with the designer to conceptualize critical human interactions in the new design. Finally, the ergonomist may critique the design for possible design flaws.

An important role for the ergonomist is to ensure that the traditional designers include ergonomics throughout the design process. Ergonomics will then be built in rather than being added on. Most groups report the use of or need for ergonomics design guidelines for the designers and engineers. Other authors have reported difficulties in gaining full use of this material, yet that was not mentioned as a problem.

Training Efforts

Vernes and Coughenour report extensive training efforts. In ergonomics training for others, there are two levels of detail: general awareness and skill-based knowledge. General awareness is used for those in management and operations who need to be aware of ergonomics and need to identify problems, yet are not intimately involved in the design process. Skill-based knowledge of ergonomics is used for the designer or engineer. This training ranges from a minimum of four hours to three-five days.

In addition to the overall coverage of ergonomics, specific emphasis on topics such as manual material handling or inspection or office ergonomics or product design was used for specialized groups. This training is tailored to specific needs required by that organization.

Information/Databases

Blache and Longmate discuss databases established to collect ergonomics information. The databases have several uses. One is to identify injury trends by highlighting areas where accidents and/or injuries are more prevalent. Second, the information is useful for documenting improvements from applications of ergonomics. Reductions in injuries can be used to justify further efforts in the ergonomics area. Third, the databases, when they have specific information about job difficulty, can be used for the placement of returning workers with temporary or permanent disabilities. The matching of the worker's capabilities with job requirements will provide information to assess job suitability for the returning worker.

Functions of the Ergonomics Group

The functions of an ergonomics group will change over time, as reported by Alexander. Most groups will emphasize specific project categories at different times. The functions of an ergonomics group from initiation through maturity form the basis for this section.

All groups begin with selling the ergonomics function and gaining approval from management. Then pilot projects are done and, if successful, efforts are made to spread the word to others. Next, an emphasis on identification of existing problems and on the prevention of new problems takes over. Finally, sustaining the ergonomics effort over the long term becomes important.

Selling the Ergonomics Function

It can be difficult to gain initial approval for the ergonomics function. Smith presents several alternatives that he has found to be successful. Vernes and Coughenour both discuss initial efforts in their organizations. Most organizations in industry today will require some type of selling of the ergonomic function. Simonelli aptly points out ergonomics has been practiced in many organizations, but on a less formal basis.

Presentations for selling ergonomics require a definition of ergonomics and its benefits. Examples of prior work or expected projects are also informative.

Initial Projects

Typically, initial projects are very specific and stem from existing, clearly identified, well-understood operational problems. Several authors point out the need to estimate the benefits of these projects, and they caution against overestimating those benefits. These initial projects have high visibility and serve to verify claims made while selling the ergonomics function. Most initial projects emphasize the reduction of injuries, with enhanced performance being a second choice.

Spreading Ergonomics to Others

Regardless of the initial area of emphasis of the ergonomics group (in-plant ergonomics, design of facility and equipment, or product design), there usually is a need to provide an awareness of ergonomics to others in the organization. Often there is a curiosity about this new tool, what it can do, and how it is being used. Also, many people have heard of ergonomics but have no idea of how to apply it. Typically, the demand for awareness comes after the pilot projects as the group is seeking to spread itself more widely on other projects.

Identification and Prevention of Problems

The natural evolution of the ergonomics group is from correcting problems to preventing problems. The ergonomist who recognizes the limitation of trying to identify all of the problems alone will soon get others involved in identifying and correcting problems. The correction of problems is inherently more costly and difficult than preventing problems.

The emphasis of the ergonomics group will naturally switch to the design of proper facilities, equipment, and products so that injuries simply don't occur in the first place. The appropriate activities at this stage are the development of design guidelines, skill training for designers, and assignments to design teams. This effort will continue for a long while.

Sustaining the Efforts

Longmate states: "Each engineer must be reponsible for performing baseline ergonomic assessments and to request special assistance as needed." Vernes discusses the measurement of results. The best way to sustain the outcomes desired by an ergonomics program is to have more and more people feel a responsibility to design for people. This attitude seems to be a fundamental point in the ergonomics program as mentioned by Alexander.

The need to make a cultural shift in the thinking of the organization so that all design personnel automatically consider the human in the design process is important. Once this is achieved, the efforts seem to be sustained for a long period of time, and the need for the ergonomist to identify and/or resolve all problems diminishes.

Size of the Ergonomics Group

Virtually all of the ergonomics groups have started small and then grown as demand for them within the organization has increased. Few groups start with more than one professional, and most begin with someone spending only part of their time on ergonomics.

The growth of the ergonomics group can take two distinct directions. One is through internal growth, where additional personnel are added to the existing ergonomics group. The second direction, growth external to the ergonomics group, requires extensive training of designers and engineers to apply ergonomic principles. Within the industrial framework, external growth seems to be the more common of the two. Long term, it may be the most profitable and the most effective.

With growth, the multidiscipline aspects of ergonomics become stronger. If the growth is internal, often people with other academic backgrounds are added to the groups. For example, Simonelli mentions the addition of an industrial engineer to a psychological-based ergonomics group. Blache notes the use of multidisciplinary people on the ergonomics committees. Likewise, Longmate mentions the variety of people on ergonomics task forces.

Resources

The resources required by most groups are consultants, training resources, equipment, and arrangements for the further development of the ergonomist.

Consultants

Several groups mentioned the use of external consultants in their ergonomics program. Consultants seem to be particularly valuable during the startup phase, when they are able to share expertise gained in similar situations. Likewise, consultants were valuable resources for specific problems like carpal tunnel syndrome, or biomechanical analysis. The consultants often came from universities and did consulting work in conjunction with their normal academic duties.

Training Resources

Again, all groups mentioned the need to train others. Resources in this area include classrooms, the use of textbooks, orientation slide/tape programs, and design guideline manuals developed for that purpose. Some of these resources are available externally, some were developed by consultants specifically for the particular organization, and some were developed internally by the ergonomics group itself.

Equipment

The ergonomics group will need measuring equipment like push-pull gauges to measure weights and forces. Tape measures are needed for work heights, work spaces, and distances. Measuring temperatures and humidities for heat stress analysis and measuring heart rate and oxygen consumption in the study of physically demanding jobs may be required as well.

The second type of equipment is recording equipment. While cameras are still used, video seems to be used more and more. This recording equipment can record specific operations for detailed analysis. It's also useful to record several subjects performing the same task.

The third type of equipment is computer equipment used for databases. This includes both hardware and software used in the tabulation of injuries and accidents, job requirements, and perhaps even capabilities and limitations of the employees in a specific plant.

Development of the Ergonomist

This was mentioned only briefly in several articles, yet it remains a key area for the ergonomist. Technical development may occur through initial academic training, through tutorial sessions with experienced ergonomists, or through short courses available from universities. Many of the authors have been involved in professional development activities like technical presentations, conferences, seminars, and short courses in the area of ergonomics. All of these remain critical to the further development of the individual ergonomist and to the continued development of the ergonomics field in general.

Summary

The early articles and this summary article provide an excellent overview of the application of ergonomics. Six critical areas of concern were defined and discussed.

The ergonomist working in industry has many difficult decisions to make: how big should the group become, where are the applications, what is the best way to enhance employee safety and health, and many others. These articles don't answer those questions for each specific situation. They do, however, through examples, show how some people have answered these same questions.

ERGONOMICS APPLICATIONS IN INDUSTRY

17

Introduction to Ergonomics Applications in Industry

David C. Alexander, P.E.

Industry is responding to changes thrust upon it. More and more people are beginning to use computers at their workplaces. Rising medical costs are forcing employers to look at ways of reducing injuries and medical expenses. Rehabilitation of injured workers is becoming more common. In addition to these major changes, industry is keenly aware of the need to enhance productivity and improve quality in the face of rising international competition. Industry must emphasize "full use of the human resource" in the same way that it strives to gain full use of other resources like equipment, facilities, materials, and the capital that it uses.

Ergonomics can help industry meet these key issues head on. This section of the book is designed to present applications of ergonomics that will help industry meet these needs.

Preview

The material in *Ergonomics Applications in Industry* is applied information, since the authors present material that can be used to solve problems through both managerial and design decisions. Many of the questions and solutions discussed in this section are classic ergonomic concerns. They range from gaining a wider use of the work population to issues such as manual material handling and seating. These authors have shown carefully and in detail how to use the principles of ergonomics to attack and resolve some of these thorny problems.

Many experts believe that the productivity of office computer systems can be enhanced by 20 percent to 30 percent with the proper use of ergonomics in the work station design. The effective design of computer work stations will be an issue for some years to come as industry increases the use of computers. Kroemer in his discussion of "Office Ergonomics: Workstation Dimensions" presents an uncommonly clear example of the use of anthropometric information to design work stations. He presents several design alternatives in the process. An interested party can easily follow this example for other anthropometric problems.

Medical costs are one of industry's fastest growing costs. Industry is attacking the problem from several directions, such as reducing the cost of medical services and the prevention of injuries. Chaffin, in his articles on manual material handling, thoroughly discusses lifting and its suitability for the human. Finally, there is a method to answer adequately the age-old question "How much should people lift?" In addition to answering that question, the techniques outlined by Chaffin also provide a way to diagnose improper and excessive lifts so that improvement efforts can be carefully targeted.

Rhyne, in his article, discusses the use of disabled personnel at the worksite. This is another key issue in the medical-costs area, since the costs of long-term disabilities are continuing to rise. One sure way to control those costs is to use disabled employees at the worksite rather than forcing them into medical retirement with monthly stipends. Rhyne not only covers the legal and economic concerns of the employment of the disabled but also discusses several job accommodations.

One issue promoted by ergonomists for a number of years is now being embraced by industry — the full use of the human resource. Several of these articles emphasize drawing from bigger work populations. Rhyne, for example, discusses the use of disabled people on the job. Both Johnson and Nemeth, in their sections on workplace and tool design, discuss designing for a much wider work population. These articles provide careful analyses of anthropometric information and its translation for use at the workplace and in the design of tools that people use. Ayoub, in his article on selection, presents a way of assessing whether individuals can fully perform a task or job.

While the goal remains to design jobs for the full range of the population, that goal has not yet been obtained. However, a wider use of the work population in industry can be obtained if managers are able to screen workers from jobs where they are more likely to sustain an injury. These techniques point out those difficult jobs that need to be redesigned and replaced.

Summary

The articles in this section address some of the major problems that both ergonomists and industry are facing in the future. While some of these articles, on the surface, may not seem applications-oriented, they, in fact, present excellent processes that allow the practicing ergonomist to make better use of the data so readily available.

Being from industry, I am painfully aware that many of my colleagues say that ergonomics is not applications-oriented. This section is intended to demonstrate the potential for translation from data and information to a practical answer of an industrial problem. The applications in this section are broad ranging. Some answer relatively simple questions, and others deal with complex issues where there are many trade-offs.

The use of ergonomics in industry will continue to expand. In the future, these examples may seem commonplace, yet today they do begin to provide those answers that industry needs.

18

Office Ergonomics: Work Station Dimensions

K. H. E. Kroemer, Dr. Ing.

Word processing, computerized bookkeeping and inventory control, and other procedures relying on computers are changing the office dramatically. Major changes in human tasks, skills, and responsibilities are foreseeable; also, more males will be in the new office, similar to the conditions around the turn of the century. However, the olden-day conditions will not be restored, but computer-aided transacting, controlling, documenting, and designing will involve clerks, teachers, accountants, brokers, managers, technicians, lawyers, bankers...by 1990, every second worker in the U.S. will use electronic terminal equipment daily (Helander 1985).

The computer revolution in the office has brought with it an appreciation of ergonomic issues as they affect health, attitudes, and work performance. Interfacing the person with the computer requires, on the technical side, the adaptation of the product and of the procedures to the capabilities, limitations, and preferences of the human operator. If the psychology and physiology of the worker are disregarded, major problems in the person-equipment-work system will occur.

During the early and often hasty introduction of computers in the office, many such problems have been reported and evaluated (Cohen [1984], Salvendy [1984], National Research Council [1983]). Intertwined with sociological and psychological functions, the "human engineering" of software, of hardware such as keyboards, lightpens, mice, and of the display or printout, has come into focus. Working conditions in general, and particularly illumination (avoidance of glare from the screen), have also drawn major attention.

Is office work with a computer more stressful than without? The question is difficult to answer, since tasks and working conditions are not the same with the computer as they were in the traditional office. However, if one compares doing the same work with hard copy and with a computer terminal, it appears that the strain on the subject is about the same, perhaps even a little less, with the computer (Gould and Grischkowsky [1984], Staff [1984], Kruk and Muter [1984], National Research Council [1983]). Such a statement, however, can be made only if the equipment and working conditions are ergonomically correct.

The emphasis is, then, on ergonomics. It has come into focus with manufacturers, researchers, and, of course, users. "Ergonomic" chairs and seats of widely varying designs and prices are being advertised, as are "ergonomic" computer stands, tables, and furniture systems. Admittedly, use of the buzzword and associated claims may appear somewhat suspect; however, interest in the human as the "driving and deciding force" in office work is desirable.

The following text will discuss specifically dimensions of furniture for computer work stations. While this is only one of many ergonomic aspects related to computerized office work, it is a rather important one. The body posture at work is determined primarily by the design features of the furniture. One major component is the seat, which supports the body and determines to a large extent the body posture (Lueder 1983). However, the posture is also affected by the table (on which writing or keying is done), by the supports for display and source document (which must be looked at), and by the support for the feet (which may be the floor or a footrest). The furniture components all interact in determining the body posture of the operator (Kroemer 1983).

Rationale

It is fallacious to design for the ghost "average person," since the resulting furniture is too small for 50 percent of the users and too large for the rest. Hence, one has to select ranges of body dimensions to be fitted by the design. Often, this range is from the fifth to the ninety-fifth percentile. In this case, only persons below the fifth percentile (very small) and persons above the ninety-fifth percentile (very big) would remain unaccommodated, while the central 90 percent of all users would have a work station that fits them. Unfortunately, furniture that can be adjusted to fit nine of ten users is rather expensive. Hence, one may consider a narrower fit range, such as the sixteenth to eight-fourth percentile. In this case, two-thirds of all users would be accommodated, while, for one-sixth, the work station would be too small, and, for the other one-sixth, too large. Conversely, one might consider fitting the work station arrangements to nearly everybody, such as ranging from the first to the ninety-ninth percentile. Clearly, one must balance the desire to fit many users with the associated effort and cost.

Data and Decisions

Statistical procedures are at hand to calculate needed adjustment ranges so that associated cost can be determined. They require:

- An anthropometric database describing the user population
- Decisions on which body dimensions to fit, and how
- Systematic procedures of fitting work station dimensions to user dimensions.

The following text describes this approach and its results. The underlying anthropometric data describe the U.S. civilian population, male and female, as reported first in 1981 by Kroemer. Table 1 lists these dimensions. These anthropometric data are assumed to be normally distributed and therefore can be described statistically by mean (average) and standard deviation. To calculate percentile values, multiples of the standard deviation are added to or subtracted from the mean — for example, the multiplier is 2.33 for the first and ninety-ninth percentile and 1.00 for the sixteenth and a half and eighty-third and a half percentiles. Table 2 lists these multiplication factors.

Human body dimensions that determine primary workstation dimensions are listed in table 3. For example, the depth of the seat surface is determined by buttock-popliteal length, while its width must accommodate hip breadth. Seat height should correspond to lower leg length, which is approximated by popliteal height (plus heel height). This assumes, obviously, a traditional chair with backrest, possibly armrests, and a seat pan that is essentially horizontal. Other designs, such as saddle types or severely forward- or rearward-inclined seat surfaces, could be based on different considerations and possibly on different anthropometric dimensions.

Work surfaces in the office — that is, the height of the table for writing or supporting keyboards — need to be high enough to allow clearance for the thighs of the sitting person and to permit a suitable posture of the arms,

TABLE 1
U.S. Civilian Body Dimensions, Female/Male, in cm, for Ages 20 to 60 Years*

	Percentiles			
	Fifth	Fiftieth	Ninety-fifth	Standard Deviation
Heights				
Stature (height)	149.5/161.8	160.5/173.6	171.3/184.4	6.6/6.9
Eye height	138.3/151.1	148.9/162.4	159.3/172.7	6.4/6.6**
Shoulder (acromion height	121.1/132.3	131.1/142.8	141.9/152.4	6.1/6.1
Elbow height	93.6/100.0	101.2/109.9	108.8/119.0	4.6/5.8
Knuckle height	64.3/69.8	70.2/75.4	75.9/80.4	3.5/3.2
Height, sitting	78.6/84.2	85.0/90.6	90.7/96.7	3.5/3.7
Eye height, sitting	67.5/72.6	73.3/78.6	78.5/84.4	3.3/3.6**
Shoulder height, sitting	49.2/52.7	55.7/59.4	61.7/65.8	3.8/4.0
Elbow rest height, sitting	18.1/19.0	23.3/24.3	28.1/29.4	2.9/3.0
Knee height, sitting	45.2/49.3	49.8/54.3	54.5/59.3	2.7/2.9
Thigh clearance	35.5/39.2	39.8/44.2	44.3/48.8	2.6/2.8
height, sitting	10.6/11.4	13.7/14.4	17.5/17.7	1.8/1.7
Depths				
Chest depth	21.4/21.4	24.2/24.2	29.7/27.6	2.5/1.9**
Elbow-fingertip distance	38.5/44.1	42.1/47.9	56.0/51.4	2.2/2.2
Buttock-knee distance, sitting	51.8/54.0	56.9/59.4	62.5/64.2	3.1/3.0
Forward reach, functional	64.0/76.3	71.0/82.5	79.0/88.3	4.5/5.0
Breadths				
Elbow-to-elbow, breadth	31.5/35.0	38.4/41.7	49.1/50.6	5.4/4.6
Hip breadth, sitting	31.2/30.8	36.4/35.4	43.7/40.6	3.7/2.8
Head Dimensions				
Head breadth	13.6/14.4	14.54/15.42	15.5/16.4	.57/.59
Head circumference	52.3/53.8	54.9/56.8	57.7/59.3	1.63/1.68
Interpupillary distance	5.1/5.5	5.83/6.20	6.5/6.8	.44/.39

*Courtesy of Dr. J. T. McConville, Anthropology Research Project, Yellow Springs, OH 45387, and Dr. K. W. Kennedy, USAF-AMRL-HEG, OH 45433.

**Estimated by the author.

of the head, and of the trunk. This example shows that there are many interactions among body dimensions that affect the same piece of equipment. These interactions may depend on preferred and/or healthy body postures,

TABLE 2
Calculation of Percentiles

Percentile p associated with x		Central Percent Included	k
$x = \bar{x} - kS$	$x = \bar{x} + kS$		
0.5	99.5	99	2.576
1	99	98	2.326
2	98	96	2.06
2.5	97.5	95	1.96
3	97	94	1.88
5	95	90	1.65
10	90	80	1.28
15	85	70	1.04
16.5	83.5	67	1.00
20	80	60	0.84
25	75	50	0.67
37.5	62.5	25	0.32
50	50	0	0

on work tasks (such as typing, word processing, computer-aided design), and on work equipment such as pencils, "mice," lightpens, and keyboards or writing paper, source documents, and electronic displays. Given these many interactions, one has to decide which ones are the main determining factors, and which ones are secondary, tertiary, etc.

Premises

The following considerations for fitting work station dimensions to user dimensions are based on these premises:

1. Seat height is determined by popliteal height (plus heel height). The primary reference plane is the floor.
2. The open legspace of the work station must clear the thighs of a sitting person.
3. The height of the visual target (writing paper, source document, display) is determined by eye height, by the preferred forward-viewing angle (above or below horizontal), and by the preferred viewing distance.

TABLE 3
Primary Relations Between Anthropometric and Equipment Dimensions

Anthropometric Dimensions	Equipment Dimensions
Popliteal Height	Height of seat surface, height of footrest
Thigh Clearance Height above seat	Height of table
Eye height above seat (depends on posture)	Height of visual display
Line of Sight (preferred angle and distance)	
Popliteal Height **Buttock-Popliteal Length** Hip breadth Body weight	Seat surface
Shoulder Height, sitting **Back curvature** Height of the lumbar vertebrae Muscle tension Buttock-popliteal length Mobility of trunk/shoulder blades	Seat backrest
Elbow Rest Height above seat	Armrests
Thigh Clearance Height **Buttock-Knee Length** **Knee Height** Hip breadth Leg length Foot length	Leg room
Angles of Wrist, Elbow, and Shoulder Elbow-hand length Hand and finger dimensions Upper-arm length Shoulder height, sitting Trunk, shoulder, arm, wrist and finger posture; muscle tension	Keyboard

Accordingly, the primary anthropometric data for work station design are: lower leg length (popliteal height), thigh thickness above the seat, and eye height above the seat. Statistics for these body dimensions are contained in table 1, which also presents data on other anthropometric variables. These are important for other work station design features (elbow rest height for armrests, forward reach for work surface depth, etc.).

Procedures and Formulas

As just discussed, primary workspace dimensions and their anthropometric determiners are:

- Seat height S is popliteal height plus heel height
- Table height T is seat height plus thigh thickness plus tabletop thickness
- Footrest height F is seat height S minus popliteal height minus heel height
- Eye height E is seat height S plus eye height (sitting) minus slump. When leaning back against a suitable high backrest at $\pi = 105°$, eye height needs to be corrected for this angle.
- Display height is determined by the eye height E, viewing angle α against the horizontal, and viewing distance V. The visual target (the center of the display) is at a height d over the support surface, which in turn is at a height D above the floor.

Figure 1 shows these dimensions schematically.

The following equations can be used to calculate the variables listed above:

$$\text{Seat height } S = \text{Popliteal Height} + \text{Heel Height} \tag{1}$$

Heel height is assumed to be 2 cm

$$\text{Table height } T = S + \text{Thigh Thickness} + \text{Tabletop Thickness} \tag{2}$$

Tabletop thickness is assumed to be 2 cm

$$\text{Footrest Height } F = S - \text{Popliteal Height} - \text{Heel Height} \tag{3}$$

$$\text{Eye Height } E = \text{Eye Height} \times \sin \pi - \text{slump} \tag{4}$$

$\pi = 90°$ for upright sitting

$\pi = 105°$ for reclined sitting

Slump is assumed to be 2 cm

$$\text{Display Support Height } D = S + E - d - V \times \sin \alpha \tag{5}$$

d is the height of the center of the display above D

V is the viewing distance, assumed to be 40 cm

α is the preferred viewing angle, above (+) or below (-) horizontal, in the lateral view.

In recent experiments (Kroemer 1984), the viewing angle has been found to be:

For upright sitting, $\pi = 90°$: $\alpha = -28.6°$, $SD = 11.62°$
For slightly reclined sitting, $\pi = 105°$: $\alpha = -19.58°$, $SD = 11.66°$

This is in agreement with findings of other researchers (Grandjean, Huenting, and Pidermann 1983; Lehmann and Stier 1961) and clarifies rather diffuse recommendations scattered throughout the human engineering literature.

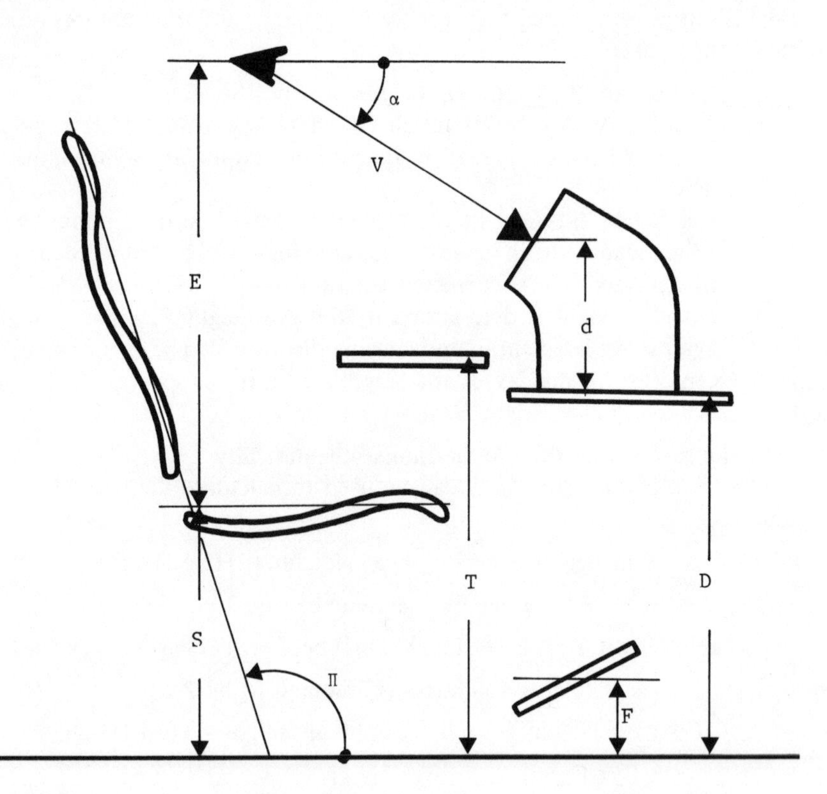

Fig. 1 Notation for computation of the heights of computer furniture

Results

With formulas (1) through (5), the heights for seat, table, footrest (if needed) and the display can be calculated. The results of these calculations are shown in table 4.

TABLE 4
Equipment Heights, in cm

		First Strategy S seat adjustable T table adjustable D display adjustable			Second Strategy T table fixed S seat adjustable D display adjustable			Third Strategy S seat fixed T table adjustable D display adjustable		
Percentile range fitted		1 to 99	5 to 95	16 to 84	1 to 99	5 to 95	16 to 84	1 to 99	5 to 95	16 to 84
S Seat	Max	52.7	50.8	49.0	61.5	57.9	53.2	52.7	50.8	49.0
	Min	35.7	37.5	39.2	52.7	50.8	49.0			
	Adj. Range	17.0	13.3	9.8	8.8	7.1	4.2	0	0	0
T Table	Max	73.1	70.5	67.1	73.0	70.5	67.1	73.0	70.5	67.1
	Min	47.2	50.1	53.1				64.2	63.4	62.9
	Adj. Range	25.9	20.4	14.0	0	0	0	8.8	7.1	4.2
F Footrest	Max				25.8	20.4	14.0	17.0	13.3	9.8
	Min	0	0	0	0	0	0	0	0	0
	Adj. Range				25.8	20.4	14.0	17.0	13.3	9.8
S+E Eye	Max	137.7	133.2	129.2	146.5	140.3	133.4	137.7	133.2	129.2
	Min	97.1	103.0	104.8	114.1	114.0	114.6	114.1	114.0	114.6
D+d Display	Max	139.9	130.1	120.9	148.9	137.2	125.2	139.9	130.1	120.9
	Min	66.3	73.4	81.4	83.2	86.7	91.2	83.2	86.7	91.2
	Adj. Range	73.6	56.7	39.5	65.7	50.5	34.0	56.7	43.4	29.7

Population Ranges

Table 4 lists the minimum and maximum values, and the included adjustment range, for three population ranges:

- First to ninety-ninth percentile, thus including 98 percent of the user population

- Fifth to ninety-fifth percentile, including 90 percent of the user population*
- Sixteenth and a half and eighty-third and a half percentiles, including 67 percent of the user population

The user population consists of both males and females. All small dimensions (first, fifth, and sixteenth and a half percentile) are derived from female anthropometric data while the large percentiles are derived from male dimensions.

Design Strategies

Table 4 also shows the results of three design strategies:

— In the first approach, seat, table, and display support are all independently adjustable. The starting plane for the designer (reference plane) is the floor.

— The second design strategy assumes a fixed table height, to which seat and display must be adjusted. Hence, the designer starts at the table level.

— The third design strategy assumes a fixed seat height, to which table and display heights must be adjusted. The design starts at seat height level.

The first design strategy, relying on complete height adjustability with respect to the floor, requires no footrests. The second design strategy relies on fixed table height which needs to be at such a high level that even people with long lower legs can fit thick thighs underneath. Hence, the fixed table height is the maximum value determined in the first strategy. The third design strategy is based on a fixed seat which must accommodate persons with long lower legs. Hence, the fixed seat height is the maximum seat height calculated in the first strategy.

Given the maximal and minimal seat heights, the values for eye height above the floor ($S + E$, listed in table 4) determine the height ranges for the center of the display, $D + d$. The resulting maximal and minimal values (and the included adjustment ranges) reflect the largest and smallest values found when considering either an upright ($\pi = 90°$) or a reclined ($\pi = 105°$) sitting posture, and the maximal and minimal values for the visual target depending on the preferred viewing angles α. In each case, the highest eye height above the seat was associated with the highest viewing angle, and the lowest eye height with the lowest viewing angle.

*Data taken from table 1, not calculated as the others.

Discussion

The results of the computations compiled in table 4 and excerpted in table 5 allow the evaluation of the absolute dimension values and of the adjustment ranges, resulting from the three design strategies, in light of the fitted population portions.

As expected, fitting diverse population ranges requires adjustments between low and high values, that is, varying adjustment ranges. Using for

TABLE 5
Adjustment ranges, in cm

	First Strategy S seat adjustable T table adjustable D display adjustable			Second Strategy T table fixed S seat adjustable D display adjustable			Third Strategy S seat fixed T table adjustable D display adjustable		
Percentile range fitted	1 to 99	5 to 95	16 to 84	1 to 99	5 to 95	16 to 84	1 to 99	5 to 95	16 to 84
S Seat	17			9			0		
		13			7			0	
			10			4			0
T Table	30			0			9		
		20			0			7	
			14			0			4
F Footrest	0			26			17		
		0			20			13	
			0			14			10
D+d Display	74			66			57		
		57			50			43	
			40			34			30

convenience the fitted range fifth to ninety-fifth percentile as reference, a reduction of the fitted to two-thirds (from nine-tenths) (that is, fit from the sixteenth to the eighty-fourth percentile) does not reduce the adjustment ranges proportionally to the reduction in the number of fitted persons. On the other hand, an increase of fit by 4 percent on each side (that is, from first to ninety-ninth percentile) requires much increase in the adjustment ranges, despite the fact that only a rather few people are additionally accommodated. Essentially, this supports the customary approach of designing equipment so that it fits from the fifth to the ninety-fifth percentile of the user population.

The three design strategies lead to rather diverse results. Following the first strategy of adjusting all equipment heights requires the largest adjustment ranges in seat height, table height, and display height of all design strategies. However, footrests are never needed in this case.

In the second design strategy, table height is kept constant (at the highest level required by tall persons with thick thighs). This strategy requires intermediate adjustment ranges for seat, footrest, and display.

The third design strategy relies on fixed seat height (at the highest value required by persons with long legs). The adjustment ranges for table, footrest, and display are the least of all design strategies.

It is of considerable interest to note that whichever population portion is fitted or whatever design strategy is used the resulting height values for computer furniture are well within the ranges currently used by industry. The first strategy, in which all equipment is adjustable, does not require any footrests, which may be deemed a highly desirable simplification in the office. It also requires only moderately high seats even for the tallest persons (as does the third strategy).

The second design strategy begins with a fixed table height, which has some appeal for those who like to have uniformly high tables in the office. However, this requires that all seats be rather tall, and high footrests are needed for many users.

The third design strategy would mean a return to seats that are not adjustable in height, and which must be kept relatively tall (although not taller than the highest adjustment ranges resulting from the first design strategy). Tables need to be adjusted up and down, and footrests are needed for many users.

The results for the display height are, of course, the most variable of all since they depend on several variables: seat height, eye height, posture of trunk and head, and preferred viewing angle. The actual height of the support stand for the display is below the preferred visual target by an unknown value (called *d* in this text), which depends on the type of display used and the housing in which it is contained. Given these facts and unknowns, most height adjustment for the display support is needed in the first design strategy, and least in the third.

Conclusions for Work Station Dimensions

Considering practicality, adherence to previous procedures, and minimization of cost, the following arguments are brought forth.

Use of a fixed table height is the least appealing, since even at present various table heights are in use. Furthermore, it is not desirable to require footrests for most users, and in fact very high footrests for many. This eliminates the second design strategy. The third strategy, relying on a seat of fixed height, is quite appealing since it requires the least adjustability. However, many persons would need footrests. Nevertheless, this appears to be a interesting alternative to the currently preferred first strategy, where adjustments are incorporated in seat, table, and (as in the other strategies) display stand. In this case, footrests are never needed, but the adjustment ranges are relatively large.

In terms of fit ranges for population percentiles, accommodating the central 90 percent (that is, fitting the fifth to the ninety-fifth percentiles) appears most reasonable and is in accordance with current government and industry practices.

On the basis of these considerations, figure 2 presents recommended dimensions for furniture to be used in the office with computers.

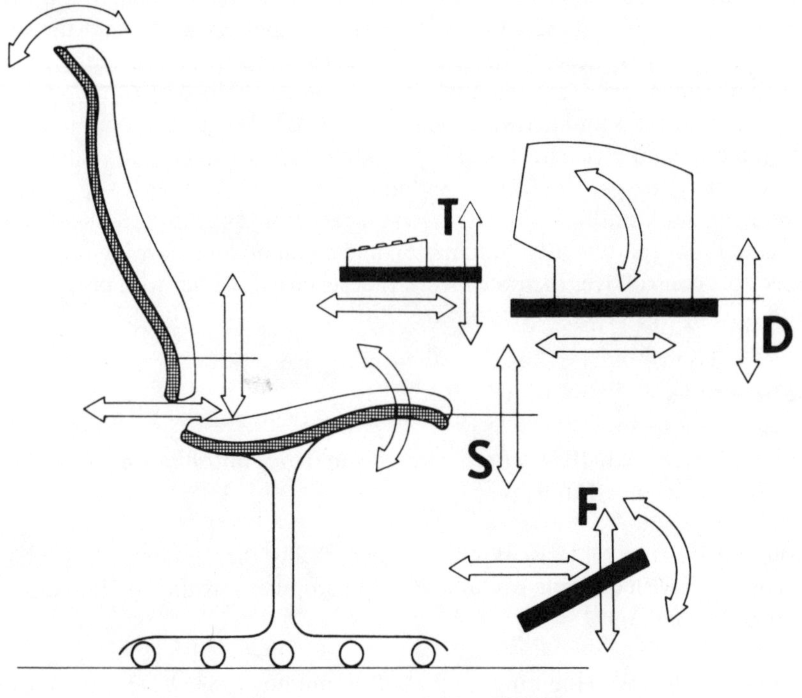

Fig. 2 Recommended adjustments for computer furniture

Seat height S should be adjustable between approximately 38 and 51 cm (15 to 20 in.). Table height T should be adjustable between about 50 and 71 cm (20 to 28 in.). With these adjustments, nobody needs footrests. The height of the center of the display should be about 73 to 130 cm (29 to 51 in.), from which one must deduct the display height above the table d to arrive at the height of the display support D. This assumes an "ergonomic" seat with a full backrest and with support for neck and head, as sketched in figure 2.

Obviously, these adjustments need to be made independently from each other. There are, of course, other adjustments that are necessary or at least desirable. These are also shown in figure 2. For example, the seat pan should be tiltable below and above horizontal. The seat back should be tiltable and move back and forth, as well as capable of being raised or lowered with respect to the seat pan. The table should be movable fore and aft with respect to the seat, which of course can be achieved by simply having a seat on coasters. The display on its support should be tiltable so that the display surface can be kept about perpendicular to the line of sight. (Also, screen tilting can help to avoid reflections.) Furthermore, the display should be movable back and forth to suit the preferred viewing distances of the individual users. No "hard" numeric recommendations for these adjustments are available. However, various sources have recommended ranges (Kroemer 1983 and Kroemer and Price 1982). Other dimensions, such as width and depth of working surfaces, need to be selected according to the given requirements and limitations at the specific jobs. They can be determined by common sense.

Many factors interact with each other to make work at a computer work station easy and efficient (the aim of ergonomics) or unhealthy, uncomfortable, uneasy (hence, inefficient and unsatisfactory). Proper foresight in introducing work stations with computers, in assuring appropriate environmental conditions (particularly illumination and climate), and allowing the human operators control over their own work is necessary, together with proper selection and use of computer furniture.

References

Cohen, B.G.F., ed. 1984. *Human aspects in office automation*. New York: Elsevier Science Publishing Co.

Gould, J.D., and N. Grischkowsky. 1984. Doing the same work with hard copy and with cathode-ray tube (CRT) computer terminals. *Human Factors* 26(3):323-37.

Grandjean, E., W. Huenting, and M. Pidermann. 1983. VDT workstation design: Preferred settings and their effect. *Human Factors* 25(2):161-75.

Helander, M.G. 1985. Human factors of emerging office automation systems. *Human Factors* (in press).

Kroemer, K.H.E. 1981. Engineering anthropometry: Designing the workplace to fit the human. *Proceedings, Annual Conference American Institute of Industrial Engineers* (May 17-20):119-26. Norcross, Ga.: AIIE.

——. 1983. Design parameters for video display terminal workstations. *Journal of Safety Research* 14:131-6.

——. 1983. Ergonomics of VDT workplaces. *Ergonomic Guide*. Akron, Ohio: American Industrial Hygiene Association.

——. Preferred direction of sight. *Report 1284*, Ergonomics Laboratory, IEOR Department. Blacksburg, Va.: Virginia Polytechnic Institute and State University.

Kroemer, K.H.E., and D.L. Price, 1982. Ergonomics in the office. *Industrial Engineering* 14:24-32.

Kruk, R.S., and P. Muter. 1984. Reading of continuous text on video screens. *Human Factors* 26(3):339-45.

Lehmann, G., and F. Stier. 1961. Normal declination of the line of sight while standing and sitting. In *Hanbuch der Gesamten Arbeitsmedizin*. E.W. Baader, ed. Berlin: Urban and Schwarzenberg.

Lueder, R.K. 1983. Seat comfort: A review of the construct in the office environment. *Human Factors* 25(6):701-11.

National Research Council. 1983. *Video displays, work, and vision*. Washington, D.C.: National Academy Press.

Salvendy, G., ed. 1984. *Human-computer interaction*. New York: Elsevier Science Publishing Co.

Starr, S.J. 1984. Effects of video display terminals in a business office. *Human Factors* 26(3):347-56.

K.H.E. Kroemer *is professor and director of the Ergonomics Laboratory, Department of Industrial Engineering and Operations Research, Virginia Polytechnic Institute and State University, Blacksburg.*

19

Workplace Design Application to Assembly Operations

Steven L. Johnson, Ph.D.

There are many sources of information that pertain to the design of workplaces (see Chapter 5). The various workplaces addressed in these sources vary from aircraft cockpits to kitchens in the home. The most easily accessible sources of information have traditionally been published by the military/aerospace community; however, there is an improving literature base pertaining to civilian applications (automobile occupants, industrial operations, etc.). A list of references that provide more detailed information is provided at the end of Chapter 5.

The general topic of workplace design often includes such concerns as control and display placement, workplace lighting, and environmental factors. Some of these areas are covered in detail elsewhere in this book. The purpose of this chapter is to provide the industrial engineer with examples of the important principles that can be used to design the physical layout of assembly workplaces.

Comfort Affects Efficiency

It is interesting to note that the military services have a long history of being concerned with the comfort of the human operators in their systems. In many contexts, it has been established that there is a natural relationship between the physical accommodation of the human and the resulting performance of that person. In contrast, in many industrial organizations it has been (and, in some organizations, is still) assumed that the comfort of the worker is not necessarily related to the productivity of the organization and the quality of its output. For example, one of the more frequent management comments along this line is: "Our company pays its operators well. There will be no sitting down on chairs in my plant."

This statement illustrates a lack of understanding of the ergonomic aspects of effective workplace design. If you look around the plant that this person manages, you will notice that the operators often "develop" chairs (for example, piled boxes, crates, or parts). The operator understands that standing requires more energy than sitting, and that the additional energy is not contributing in any way to the effectiveness of performing the job. In fact, the manager also understands this to the extent that neither he nor his office personnel stand at their desks to perform their tasks.

The issue is not whether to have comfort *or* efficiency; rather, it is how to maximize the efficiency by increasing the comfort. It should be noted that the goal of ergonomics is *not* to minimize effort; rather, it is to maximize the output with a level of effort that is not harmful to the operator. Requiring the operator to stand is an example of increasing effort with no increase in output.

On the other hand, it is similarly uncomfortable to be restricted to a sitting posture for long periods of time. The results of studies on the design and use of visual display terminals (VDTs) have illustrated this point. It is interesting to note that a methods engineering analysis often specifies a job requirement to stand and transport a part a short distance as an "ineffective worker movement." In fact, that movement can be very effective in relieving fatigue caused by a static posture.

An ergonomic analysis of a job includes an evaluation of the human, as well as of the physical (time and distance) aspects of the job. The remainder of this chapter is devoted to examples illustrating how the human's physical characteristics can be effectively incorporated into the design of a safe, productive workplace.

Utilizing the Physical Differences Between People

It is obvious to the casual observer that not all humans are identical. For example, some people are very tall, some are very short, and a large number of people are of medium height. The study and documentation of the physical dimensions of the human body is referred to as *anthropometry* (also, physical anthropology) and is introduced in Chapter 5. In general, the frequency distribution of anthropometric dimensions (for example, height on the horizontal axis and the number of people with that height on the vertical axis) resembles the familiar bell-shaped curve illustrated in figure 1a. A method of presenting the data that is often more easily used is the cumulative relative frequency distribution that illustrates the percentage of people (verticle axis) that fall at or below a value (for example, height on the horizontal axis). This cumulative distribution is illustrated in figure 1b.

Prior to utilizing these data to establish workplace dimensions, it is important for the engineer to determine if the set of data being used represents static (structural) dimensions or dynamic (functional) dimensions. For example, tables of static dimensions would indicate a reach distance much shorter than would be indicated by the dynamic dimensions in that the latter includes the fact that an operator can bend forward in the process of reaching. Similarly, an individual standing erect with knees locked will have an elbow height higher than a person standing in a somewhat more "natural" posture at a workbench.

The use of anthropometric data is like the use of any other handbook data; the engineer's intuitive common sense must be applied as well. Applying common sense without supporting data can lead to sub-optimization; applying data without common sense can be dangerous.

The use and misuse of the differences among people can be illustrated by considering a situation that existed in an automobile engine assembly plant. In this case, the assembly line was structured so that the engines were suspended from an overhead conveyor. As the engine moved down the line, various components were added to the top of the engine and later, down the line, to the bottom of the engine. There were two individuals working on this line, one being 6 feet 2 inches in height and the other being 5 feet 1 inch in height. The individual differences in height were initially being misused in this situation in that the short operator was assigned to attach the parts to the top of the engine and the tall operator assembled parts to the bottom of the engine. The shorter operator experienced sore shoulders, elbows, and wrists due to the awkward posture required during hand assembly and the use of powered tools. Similarly, the taller operator's misassignment resulted in complaints of lower back fatigue due to the required bent posture. The opposite assignments used, rather than misused, the inherent physical characteristics of the operators. Is this ergonomics or common sense? Obviously, it is both.

The above example illustrates that there are two basic methods of improving workplace effectiveness: (1) change the equipment, and (2) change the person. In the previous example, installing a conveyor that could raise or lower the engine depending upon the height of the person would obviously be more costly than placing the operators on the appropriate job. However,

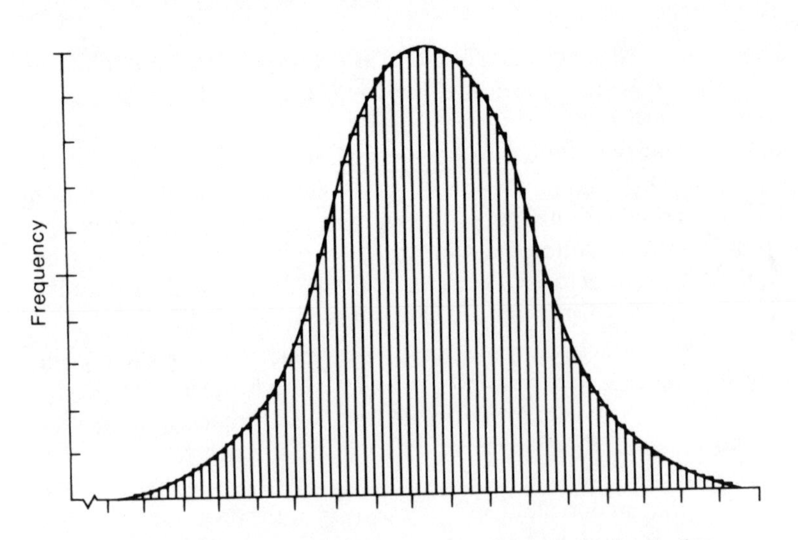

Fig. 1a "Normal" shape of anthropometric dimensions distribution.

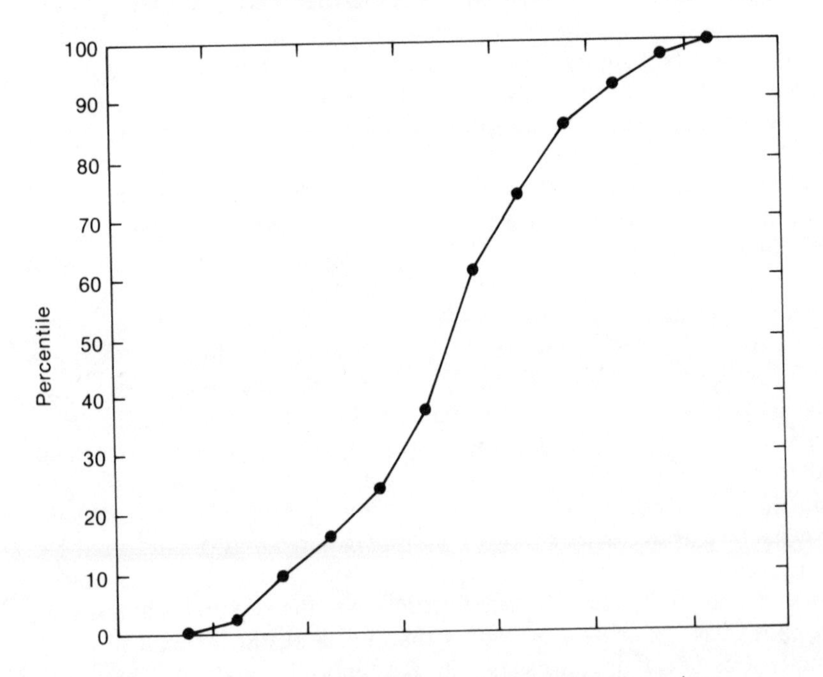

Fig. 1b Cumulative distribution of anthropometric dimensions.

the primary goal of the engineer should be to accommodate the maximum number of workers while minimizing the cost of the installation. The remainder of the discussion will address examples of how the workplace can be designed to accommodate the "majority" of the workforce, recognizing that some people will be inconvenienced. In general, the "optimum" workplace in assembly operations involves designing for the majority of operators, with conscientious placement of the individuals that would be inconvenienced.

Examples of the Use of Design Criteria

The previous discussion presented examples of how the operator can be fitted to the job. The other desirable goal is to design the job (workplace) for the operator. There are three basic alternative design criteria that can be implemented when establishing the physical layout of any workplace. These criteria are: (1) design for the extreme, (2) design for the average, and (3) provide for adjustability. Each is appropriate, given particular situations. The uses of each will be illustrated through examples.

Design Reaches for Smaller, and Clearances for Larger, Operators

When the engineer is determining the placement of the fixtures and parts bins for an assembly operation, one of the primary concerns is whether the operator is able to reach the parts. The question then becomes: Which operator? This is illustrated by the example of an assembly operation where the workplace had been established many years ago. However, over time there was a change in the makeup of the workforce on the assembly line from being exclusively male to being predominantly female. The reach distances that had been acceptable (albeit, marginally) became unacceptable.

As the reach distance is increased, the proportion of the workforce that is capable of performing the reach decreases (illustrated in figure 1b). For example, the tallest 5 percent of the males can reach approximately 26 in., whereas, the shortest 5 percent of the females can reach approximately 22 in. These data provide an example of a possible misapplication of anthropometric data. Although it is reasonable to require a reach of more than 22 in. if the action is required infrequently, for repetitive operations, a much shorter reach (for example, 15 in.) is preferable to allow the upper arm to be more relaxed. Also, it does not require the arm to be fully extended at the elbow.

This example illustrates the use of the criterion of designing for the extreme. That is, if the shortest person can reach a part, the person with the longest reach would have no trouble reaching it. It should also be noted that if the workplace is designed at the fifth percentile, five out of 100 individuals will be inconvenienced, if not excluded from performing the task.

Inconvenience the Fewest People the Least Amount

The second design criterion that is applicable to assembly operations it to design for the average. This is probably the most overused method of deciding on workplace dimensions. Daniels and Churchill (in U.S. Air Force Aerospace Medical Laboratory Report WCRD-TN-53-7, 1952) illustrated that if the middle third of the distribution is considered "average," when only four body dimensions were included, there were no individuals, out of the 4,063 people measured, who were "average."

The concept behind designing for the average person is that the resulting design will inconvenience the minimum number of people a minimum amount. An example of the misapplication of this criterion is the design of a toilet stool that is designed to be at the "correct" height to fit the "average" person. Obviously, 50 percent of the population would not be able to touch the floor with their feet. Although the normal (bell-shaped) distribution is symmetric, the consequences of constructing a component (for example, a workbench) too high versus too low are seldom symmetric.

Engineers must ask themselves whether the consequences of being too high are greater or less than the consequences of being too low. For example, a chair that is too high is much less comfortable than a chair that is too low by the same amount. Therefore, combining this criterion of design for the average with a consideration of the effects on the larger and smaller individual can be very effective in designing effective assembly workplaces.

Make the Workplace Adjustable To Fit the Worker

The previous two design criteria assume that the workplace (bench, conveyor, etc.) is fixed and cannot be adjusted. The disadvantage of these approaches is that, no matter where you set your values, you will inconvenience, or even exclude, some portion of the workforce.

An alternative is to make the component being designed adjustable. The obvious advantage of this method is that a larger proportion of the workforce can be accommodated. The disadvantages include the cost of design and manufacturing, time of adjustment, and reliability of the component (that is, maintenance costs).

Given that the engineer decides to make the workplace adjustable, the problem becomes what proportion of the workforce to accommodate (for example, fifth to the ninety-fifth percentile). As with the previous example, the consequences to the people outside of the designed range must be considered. For example, are the individuals simply inconvenienced or are they excluded?

As is evident from figure 1b, there are diminishing returns as one attempts to increase the proportion of individuals included. That is, the cost of including an additional 5 percent from the sixty-fifth to seventieth percentile is much lower than the cost of including the 5 percent of the people that are from the ninety-fourth to the ninety-ninth percentiles. One of the most obvious applications of this approach is the chairs or stools that assembly operators use.

An electronics firm went to significant expense to purchase adjustable chairs for its assembly operators. The expectation was that both the operators' quality of working life and productivity would increase due to the new, "ergonomically designed" chairs. The shorter operators would be able to raise the level of the chair so that they would have a better functional work height (relaxed arms and shoulders). After the chairs had been installed for a period of time, they noticed that the shorter workers were adjusting their chairs lower than the taller operators. It was then that the engineers understood that there is a relationship between work height, seat height, and the floor. That is, the workers were adjusting the chairs to accommodate their leg length. This left the posture of the upper torso awkward for the shorter operators. When the company provided footrests of adjustable height, the chairs were then very functional.

Designing Workplaces for Assembly Operations

Chapter 5 presents many general principles of workplace design. For assembly operations, there are two particular principles that can reduce or eliminate most of the design-induced problems in the workplace: (1) avoid requiring fixed postures, and (2) incorporate both the characteristics of the worker and the task requirements in the design. If the engineer keeps these principles in mind in laying out the workplace, the productivity, the product quality, and the operator's quality of working life will all be improved.

One method of avoiding static postures is to design the task (including the workplace) so that it can be performed in both a sitting and a standing position. As was discussed earlier, sitting requires approximately 30 percent less energy than standing and is particularly appropriate for light assembly tasks that require fine eye-hand coordination. If the workplace is designed to accommodate a seated operator, provisions should be made for footrests, possible lateral movement (for example, glide up the line), and swivel (if no lateral force needs to be exerted). Figure 2 illustrates an assembly layout provided by the Methods Laboratory of AC Spark Plug, General Motors Corporation.

The particular job is held primarily by females. Standing workplaces provide advantages such as increased operation mobility, greater ability to apply force, and increased reach envelopes. It is often the case that conveyor heights are at an appropriate height for sitting or standing, but that the parts bins and/or fixtures are placed so that the knees cannot fit under the conveyor. That is, the placement of the parts and fixtures may be "optimal" from a methods and work measurement standpoint (distance and time) and be very sub-optimal (or even injury producing) from the standpoint of a good "ergonomic" posture.

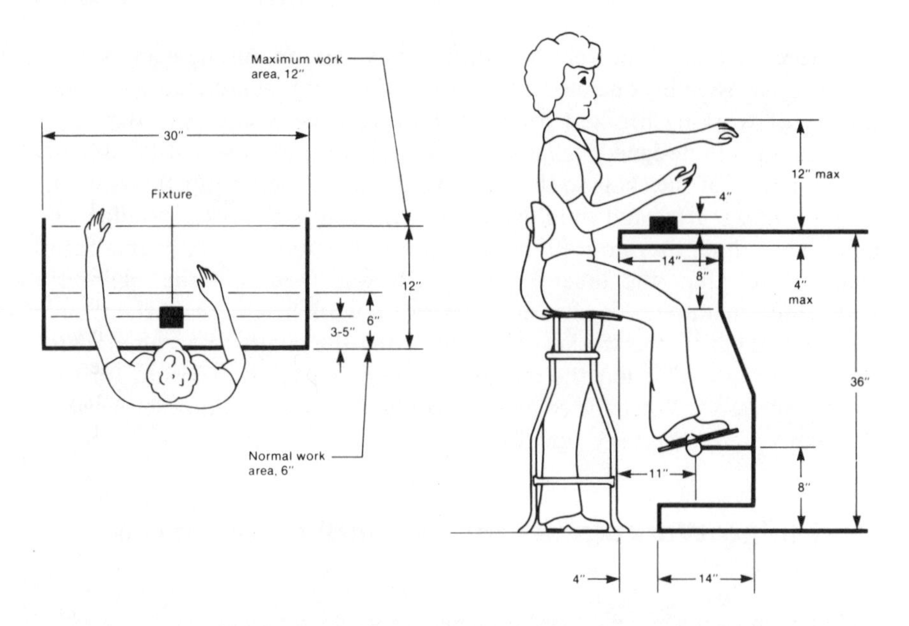

Fig. 2 Example assembly workplace (provided by AC Spark Plug)

The height of the work surface must be established in conjunction with the worker characteristics and the task requirements. Paying attention to the following general considerations will increase the effectiveness of the assembly workplace. For example, the height of interest is not the bench or conveyor height; rather, it is the height of the interface between the operator (generally his hands) and the work.

For example, a conscientious engineer might use the bench heights recommended in an ergonomics handbook and subsequently find that the real height of concern is the bench, plus the fixture, plus the part, plus the tool. The distance from the bench to the hand-tool interface could easily be 12 in. or more. Again, what is needed is data plus common sense.

In general, three categories of assembly tasks each require a different working height. First, a "normal" light assembly task is best performed if the hands are slightly (2 to 4 in.) below the elbow level. Second, if the task has extensive vision requirements, then the work height should be increased (unless the part must be handled during assembly). Third, if the task requires the application of force (for example, grinding), the work height should be lower.

In addition to the task requirements, the operator characteristics must be included in the design process. For example, the elbow heights of the fifth, fiftieth, and the ninty-fifth percentile operators are shown in the following table. The units in the table are inches (centimeters are shown in parentheses).

	Fifth Percentile	Fiftieth Percentile	Nineth-fifth Percentile
Males	39 (99)	42 (107)	45 (114)
Females	36 (91)	39 (99)	42 (107)

Therefore, to design the "normal" assembly work height for the fifth percentile female, 33 in. would seem appropriate. However, to design it for the ninety-fifth percentile male would require a height of 42 in. To decide what value to use, the engineer must consider the workforce characteristics and the relative inconvenience of the work height being too low or too high. Generally, for light assembly work without detailed visual requirements, having the work height too low is better than having it too high. The disadvantage of this decision is that the very tall operator will need to stoop to perform the task.

The following guidelines are recommended for light assembly tasks performed while standing or sitting with footrests:

Male workforce:	38 in.
Female workforce:	35 in.
Mixed workforce:	36 in.

If the task involves visual requirements, the following guidelines are recommended:

Male workforce:	42 in.
Female workforce:	39 in.
Mixed workforce:	41 in.

It should be noted that relatively slight increases in the tilt of the head from a natural position can result in dramatic increases in the fatigue of the shoulder, neck, and back. Therefore, in this case, particular care should be taken in designing workplaces that are not too low. This illustrates the fact that there is a task-workplace relationship. A particular workplace requirement might be eliminated by improving the assembly methods (for example, reducing the precision of the visual requirements).

If the task requires the application of a downward force or the lifting of parts, the following guidelines are recommended:

Male workforce:	34 in.
Female workforce:	31 in.
Mixed workforce:	32 in.

For these examples, the word *guidelines* has been used advisedly in that there is no such thing as a "normal" task/operator combination. In all situations, trade-offs must be made. The guidelines provided, plus the engineer's knowledge of the operational environment, should lead to workplaces that are effective for the majority of the operators on the job. This is the best that the engineer can expect to accomplish. Beyond this, it is the responsibility of production supervision to place the operators according to the requirements of the job and the operators' characteristics.

Summary

There are many other sections of this book that apply to the design of assembly workplaces (hand tools, manual material handling, etc.). The goal of this section is to discuss the primary principles that an engineer can use in establishing work heights. The examples presented illustrate both the use and the misuse of ergonomic data such as anthropometric measures. If the engineer combines the material in this chapter with the data provided in the reference list provided in Chapter 5, the resulting assembly workplace will be efficient and effective.

Steven L. Johnson *is associate professor with the Department of Industrial Engineering, University of Arkansas, Fayetteville.*

20

Manual Materials Handling Limits*

Don B. Chaffin, Ph.D., P.E.

The act of manually lifting, pushing, or pulling an object has been of continual concern to those planning efficient use of a workforce and to those attempting to prevent unnecessary injury and illness in industry. A recent report from the National Institute for Occupational Safety and Health (NIOSH) stated that approximately one-third of the U.S. workforce is presently required to exert significant strength as part of their jobs (NIOSH 1981). This same report also presented the following statistics:

- Overexertion was claimed as the cause of lower back pain by over 60 percent of people suffering from such.
- Overexertion injuries of all types in the U.S. occur to about 500,000 workers per year (which is about one in 200 workers each year).
- If the overexertion injuries involve low-back pain with significant lost time, less than one-third of the patients eventually returned to their previous work.

*Excerpted from a chapter in *Occupational Biomechanics*, D.B. Chaffin and G.B.J. Anderson, J. Wiley and Sons, Inc., New York, 1984.

- Overexertion injuries account for about one-fourth of all reported occupational injuries in the U.S., with some industries reporting that over half of the total reported injuries are due to overexertion.
- Approximately two-thirds of overexertion injury claims involved lifting loads and about 20 percent involved pushing or pulling loads.

Collectively, these observations indicate that manual materials handling activities are now and will continue to be prevalent in many industries and that such acts are associated with either causing or aggravating musculoskeletal disorders for a large number of workers. The economic cost of such injuries to industry also is quite high. Low-back pain related to occupational factors (60 percent of which is related to overexertion) is estimated in the United States to cost $4.6 billion dollars annually in worker's compensation payments (Snook and Jensen 1984).

It also became clear from review of pertinent literature that a comprehensive program of control would be necessary (Troup 1978). Herrin et al. (1974) proposed that several distinct groups of factors needed to be considered simultaneously in the prevention of musculoskeletal disorders related to manual materials handling. These factors, which define a *manual material handling system*, were grouped as follows:

- Worker characteristics
- Material/container characteristics
- Task characteristics
- Work practices

These factors are illustrated in figure 1, which indicates the interactive nature of each factor in defining the degree of hazard in the system.

This same report concluded that of all the different types of manual material handling acts performed in industry, research fndings were most conclusive regarding the act of *manual lifting of loads which are symmetrically balanced in front of the body*. Based on this, a multidisciplinary team of specialists in epidemiology, biomechanics, work physiology, and ergonomics was assembled by NIOSH to develop *Work Practices Guide to Manual Lifting*. This guide was published by NIOSH in 1981. It represents the first comprehensive approach to the control of the adverse effects of manual materials handling in industry. A brief description of the guide is presented in the following subsections.

NIOSH Work Practices Guide to Manual Lifting

Job-Lifting Analysis

The NIOSH guide recommends that any job suspected of causing excessive musculoskeletal injuries be analyzed. Such an analysis will require the gathering of the following data:

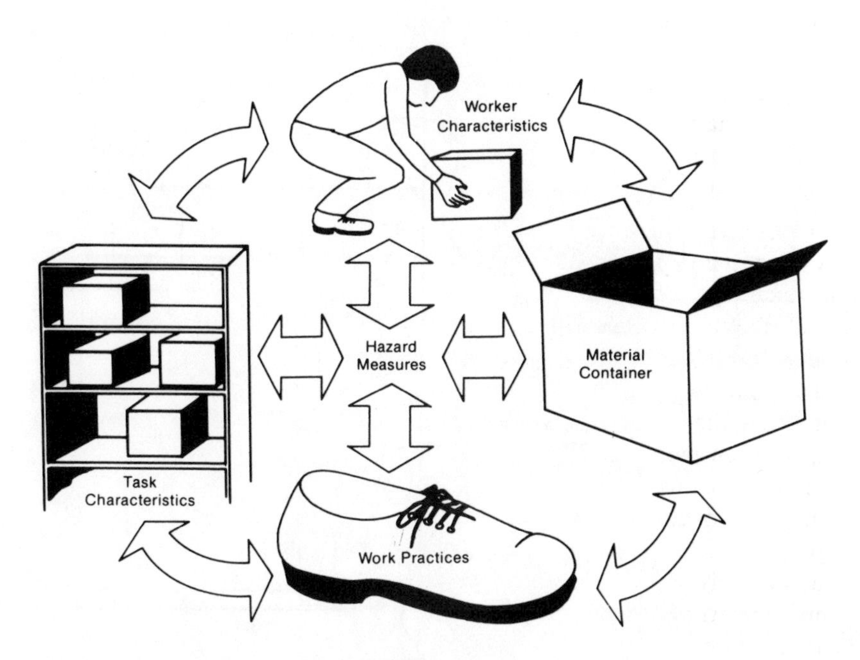

Fig. 1 Illustration of general factors that need to be considered when estimating the hazard in a manual materials handling system

1. *Weight of the object lifted* — This is determined by direct weighing. If this varies from time to time, the average and maximum weights are recorded.
2. *Position of load* with respect to the body — This is measured at *both the starting and ending points* of a lift in terms of horizontal and vertical coordinates. The horizontal location from the body H is measured from the midpoint of a line joining the ankles to the midpoint at which the hands grasp the object while in the lifting position. A rule of thumb is $H = (W/2 + 6)$ inches, where W is the width of the object measured along a horizontal axis (figure 2 depicts this), assuming the object is lifted close to the front of the body. The vertical component is determined by measuring the distance from the floor to the point at which the hands grasp the object. The coordinate system is also illustrated in figure 2. If the four values vary from task to task (for example, stacking cartons on top of each other), the job is separated into individual lifting tasks and each is evaluated separately.
3. *Frequency of lift* — This is recorded in average lifts/minute for high-frequency lifting. A separate frequency should be entered for each distinguishable lifting task if performed at a frequency greater than once every five minutes.
4. *Period (or duration)* — The total time engaged in lifting is noted. This is defined as either being less than one hour or for eight hours.

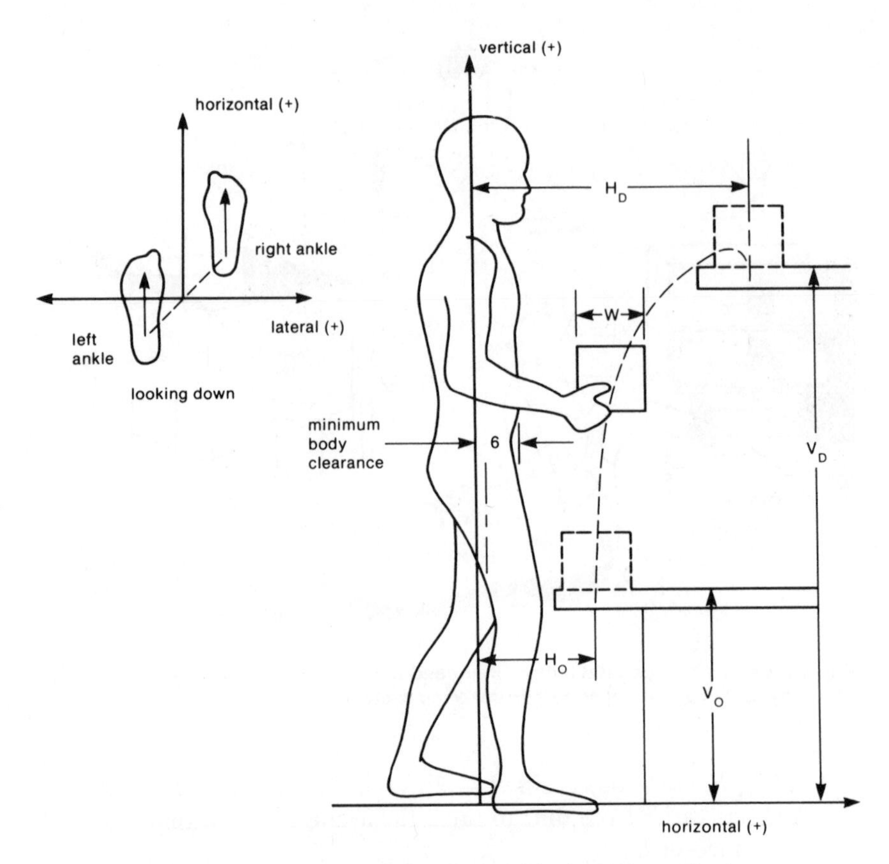

Fig. 2 Graphic representation of vertical and horizontal coordinates (adapted from NIOSH *Work Practices Guide to Manual Lifting,* 1981)

An example analysis is depicted in figure 3 for a person lifting a stock reel into a punch press. The data from this job-lifting analysis are recorded on the data sheet depicted in figure 4. The prediction of the lifting limits for this task follows.

Estimating the Limiting Loads To Be Lifted

Depending on the nature of the lifting activities, load lifting limits may be based on different human performance criteria. Biomechanical and muscle strength demands of the task become the predominant criteria in *infrequent* lifting of large or heavy objects requiring awkward postures. If more moderately sized or lighter-weight objects are lifted *frequently, but for less than a one-hour period,* then limits based on an acceptable psychophysical work load appear to be most appropriate, with the studies of Snook (1978) and Ayoub et al. (1980) being cited most often. If *frequent lifting for an*

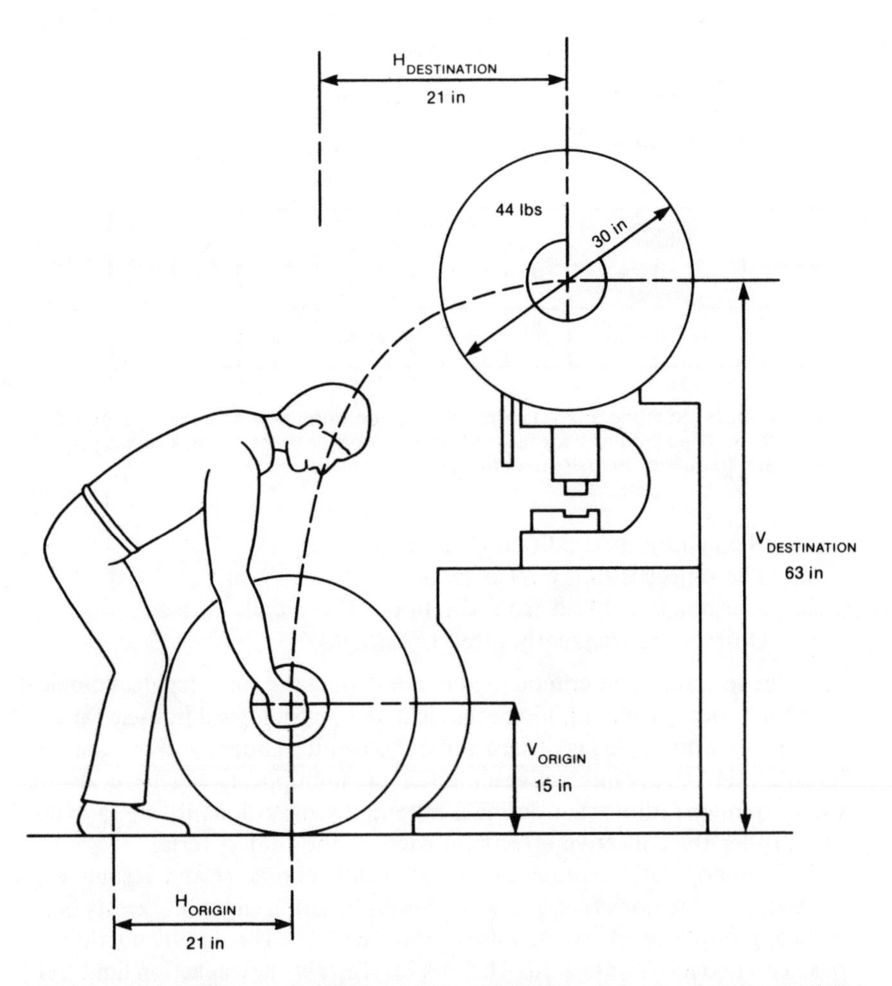

Fig. 3 Example of lifting a stock reel weighing 44 lbs into punch press. It is assumed that the worker steps forward with the load to place it atop the press, i.e., H remains constant, while V changes

entire workday (defined as eight hours) is necessary, then cardiovascular/ metabolic-based muscle fatigue studies provide the limitations. In this case, the work physiology studies cited in Astrand and Rodahl (1970), Bonjer (1971), Kamon and Ayoub (1976), Garg et al. (1978), and Petrofsky and Lind (1978), as well as many others, provide the basis for limiting such sustained, frequent lifting.

From an epidemiological perspective, the NIOSH guide cites studies revealing that musculoskeletal injury rates (number of injuries per man-hours on job) and severity rates (number of hours lost due to injury per man-hours on job) increase significantly when:

Physical Stress Job Analysis Sheet

Department Fabrication Date 2-18-84

Job title Punch Press Analyst's Name EJB

Task Description	Object Weight (pounds)		Hand Location				Task Freq.	AL	MPL	Remarks
			Origin		Destination					
	Ave	Max	H_{in}	V_{in}	H_{in}	V_{in}				
Load Stock	44	44	21	15	21	63	0			

Fig. 4 NIOSH job lifting analysis form filled in for lifting task depicted in Figure 3. Note: The zero entry for task frequency denotes that the stock reel is loaded at a frequency of less than once every five minutes

1. Heavy objects are lifted (L is large)
2. The object is bulky (H is large)
3. The object is lifted from the floor (V is small)
4. Objects are frequently lifted (F is high).

The four different criteria used in developing the guide (epidemiological, psychophysical [strength], biomechanical and physiological [muscle fatigue]) indicate that no single task characteristic acts independently to influence the hazard level. All are interactive and often are multiplicative. This means that the recommendations that define a potentially hazardous lifting task need to consider the collective effects on each of the four criteria.

From population studies of strength, anthropometry and aerobic work capacity, it is obvious that a large variation in lifting capability exists in any normal group of workers. Because of this, the NIOSH recommendations are based on two levels of hazard. The first level establishes an action limit (AL), wherein an increased risk of injury and fatigue for *some* individuals exists if they are not carefully selected and trained for the lifting task found to exceed the limit. The second level of hazard defined in the guide is the maximum permissible limit (MPL), wherein many individuals would be injured if exposed to such conditions. Engineering is recommended to reduce the job lifting requirements if above the MPL.

To allow consideration of the collective effect of the task variables, a prediction equation was defined by the authors of the NIOSH guide. To determine the maximum weight lifting value for a job at the action limit the equation is:

$$AL = 90(6/H)(1 - 0.01|V - 30|)(0.7 + 3/D)(1 - F/F_{MAX})$$

and for the maximum permissible limit:

$$MPL = 3AL$$

where

AL and *MPL* are maximum weight lifting values (in lb) for the given job conditions.

H is the horizontal distance (in.) from the load center of mass at the origin of the vertical lift to the midpoint between the ankles, with a minimum value of 6 in. (body interference) and a maximum value of 32 in. (reach distance for most people).

V is the vertical distance (in.) from the load center of mass at the origin of the vertical lift measured from the floor, with no minimum value and a maximum of 70 in. (upward reach for most people).

D is the vertical travel distance (in.) of the object, assuming a minimum value of 10 in. and a maximum of 80 in. minus the vertical *V* origin height. Note: if the distance moved is small (*D* less than 10 in.), the effect is nominal, so *D* is set equal to 10 in. in this case.

F is the average frequency of lifting (lifts/minute) with a minimum value for occasional lifts of 0.2 (once every five minutes) and a maximum value defined by both the period of lifting (less than one hour or for eight hours) and whether the lifting involves only arm work or significant body stabilization or movement. The maximum values F_{MAX} are given in table 1.

Inspection of the prediction equation reveals that under optimum conditions 90 pounds can be lifted. This would occur for occasional lifts (*F* less than 0.2); when the load is held close to the body ($H = 6$ in.); at carrying height ($V = 30$ in.); and is not lifted far (*D* less than 10 in.). Any deviation from these optimal conditions results in a decrease in predicted lifting capability. In essence, each lifting task parameter in the equation has a multiplicative discounting effect. Thus, the prediction equation can be expressed as:

$$AL = 90(HF)(VF)(DF)(FF)$$

where

HF = Discounting factor due to the *horizontal* location of load at beginning of lift.

VF = Discounting factor due to *vertical* location of load at beginning of lift.

DF = Discounting factor due to the *distance* load is lifted.

FF = Discounting factor due to the *frequency* of lifts.

All of the discounting variables have maximum values of 1.0, which are achieved at the optimum conditions (above). The values of the discounting factors are given in figure 5. Inspection of the graphs reveal that the horizontal location *H* and frequency of lift *F* factors can exhibit the greatest discounting effect. Thus, job evaluations must give these two factors careful consideration. The next most important factor is the vertical location of the load *V* at the initiation of the vertical lift, followed by the distance D that the load is moved.

TABLE 1
Maximum Frequency of Lifts/Minute Allowed F_{MAX} for Different Postures (Hand Vertical Locations) and Lifting Periods (From NIOSH: *Work Practices Guide for Manual Lifting*, 1981)

Duration of Lifting Period	*V* 30 in. (Standing)	*V* 30 in. (Stooped)
One hour (occasional)	18	15
Eight hour (continuous)	15	12

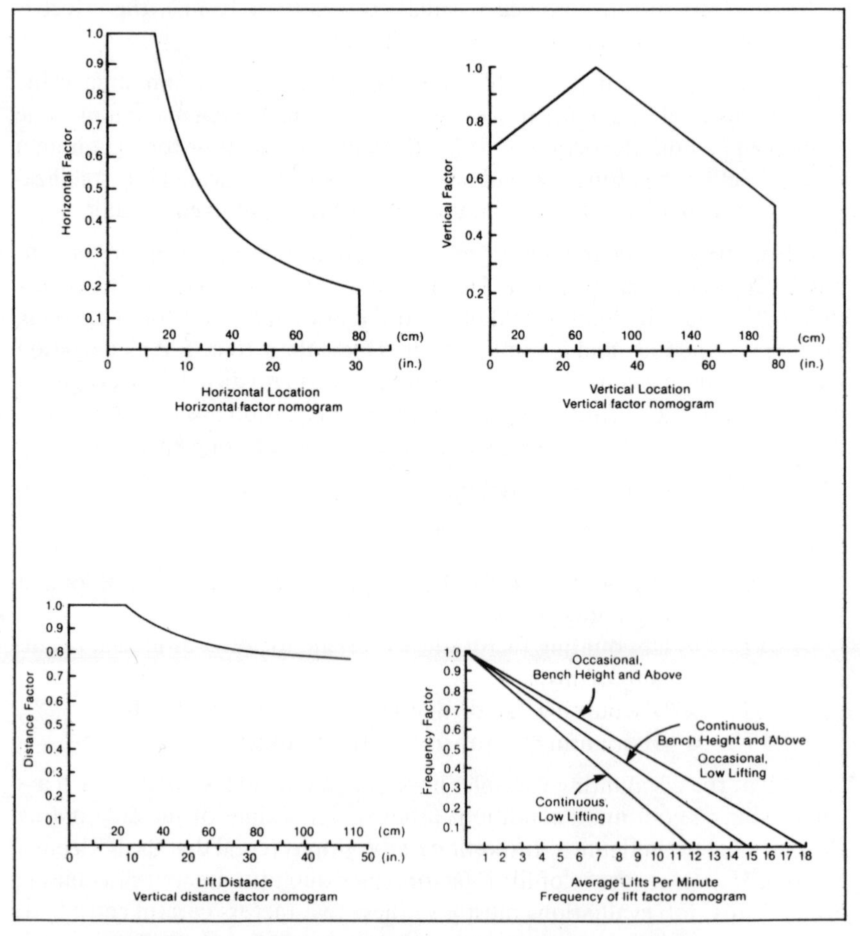

Fig. 5 Graphical depiction of discounting factors in equation (from NIOSH *Work Practices Guide for Manual Lifting,* 1981)

An Example Computation for Lifting Limits

Returning to the situation depicted earlier in figure 3 of lifting a 44-pound stock reel, the *AL* and *MPL* limits to the load can now be determined as follows:

$$HF = 6/H = 6/21 = 0.28$$
$$DF = 0.7 + 3/D = 0.7 + 3/(63 - 15)) = 0.76$$
$$VF = 1 - 0.01|V - 30| = 1 - 0.01|15 - 30| = 0.85$$
$$FF = 1 - F/F_{MAX} = 1 - 0/15 = 1.0$$

and

$$AL = 90(0.28)(0.76)(0.85)(1.0) = 16.3 \text{ lbs}$$
$$MPL = 3(16.3) = 48.9 \text{ lbs}$$

Therefore, the stock reel weighing 44 pounds is found to be above the *AL*, and careful worker selection and training, or a redesign of the task, would be needed. Since the weight of the 44-pound reel is close to *MPL*, in fact, a redesign should be considered in this case. For instance, arranging the punch press so the reel could be lifted from the side of the press perhaps could greatly reduce the most stressful factor *HF*. If the *H* distance was reduced to 8 in. (instead of 21 in.), then the *AL* is raised to about 42 pounds, almost equal to that of the reel weight. Thus, most people in good health would be capable of performing the lift at nominal risk.

It should be clear that the NIOSH lifting guide provides a comprehensive approach to the common act of lifting objects directly in front of the body. Unfortunately, research does not appear to support such a guideline for lateral or one-handed lifting. In these cases, more detailed biomechanical analysis is necessary, and the resulting recommendations will be more speculative (Chaffin and Andersson 1984).

Load Pushing and Pulling Capabilities

Unlike the act of sagittal plane lifting, pushing and pulling capabilities have been studied only within a very limited scope. Furthermore, estimates of the number of injuries that occur during pushing or pulling of loads are not complete, though approximately 20 percent of overexertion injuries have been associated with pushing and pulling acts (NIOSH 1981). This underestimates the seriousness of these problems, however, in that foot slip potential also is very high while performing a pushing or pulling act. If the foot does slip, the probability of a person falling and suffering an impact injury, possibly to the head, is high. It should be remembered that one of the leading causes of non-vehicle-related deaths in industry is slipping and/or falling (U.S. National Safety Council 1978).

It would appear from previous work of Fox (1967) and Kroemer and Robinson (1971) that the effect of the coefficient of friction (μ) on push and pull static strength capability is of primary importance. They collectively showed that healthy young males can only exert a mean force of approximately 44 pounds if μ is about 0.3. With μ greater than 0.6, the mean push or pull strength capability increases to 66 pounds for the same group, according to Kroemer and Robinson (1971). Bracing one foot with the use of the back to apply force (rather than using the hands) further increased the static push force capabilities, according to Kroemer (1969) and Fox (1967). Further studies by Martin and Chaffin (1972), Ayoub and McDaniel (1974), Lee (1982), and Davis and Stubbs (1979) reported that the vertical height of the handle and the direction of the exertion had major effects on the low-back stresses and slip potential. These results are reviewed in the text by Chaffin and Andersson (1984).

In general, any time that carts are being moved it is imperative to provide a dry, high-traction floor. Handles should allow the hand force to be exerted at about waist level, and pushing is recommended over pulling when a high level of exertion is required, thus minimizing low-back stresses and the risk of slipping and falling backwards.

Final Comments

Manual materials handling is very prevalent in industry, particularly in service industries where automation is more difficult to use. Careful evaluation of such tasks is necessary to reduce the excessive risk of injury and medical and lost-time costs associated with such tasks. These evaluations can now be quite objective, with quantitative models available to assist in establishing the limits to such performance.

Once these evaluations are performed the results provide the basis for effective re-engineering of the job. The use of lift tables, hoists, tilt tables, and other materials handling aids then can be rationally considered, as described by Chaffin, et al. (1984).

In addition, much more concern must be given to the proper selection and training of workers who perform such tasks. The NIOSH guide recommends an objective assessment of a worker's physical capacity to perform heavy lifting tasks (those above the *AL*). Such medical assessments *must* relate to the specific physical task of concern on the job, or the procedure may unduly restrict qualified individuals from a desirable job. This latter requirement of the law will mean that better job evaluations and improved medical assessments will need to be performed and evaluated in the future.

Also, it is evident that workers are often not carefully instructed on how and why they need to be particularly careful when performing a manual materials handling task. The NIOSH guide recommends that all workers performing jobs above the *AL* value should have training that includes:

1. The specific risk of injury in the job due to handling of objects in a careless or unskilled fashion.
2. Lifting methods and devices available by which one can reduce unnecessary stress.
3. Knowledge and awareness of their own physical capacities to perform required lifts (that sometimes it is best to ask for assistance).

It is clear that the simple approaches used in the past (for example, posters of how to lift and the installation of a hoist that often is not ergonomically designed for the job) have not decreased the pain and cost of manual materials handling injuries. A comprehensive program is needed which simultaneously considers at least those factors that are known to raise the risk of injury. Industrial engineers, with their knowledge of manufacturing or service processes, job methods, statistics, and database management are primary individuals in developing such a program.

References

Astrand, P.O., and K. Rodahl. 1970. *Textbook of work physiology*. New York: McGraw-Hill Book Co.

Ayoub, M.M., and J.W. McDaniel. 1974. Effect of operator stance on pushing and pulling tasks. *AIIE Transactions* 6:185-95.

Ayoub, M.M., et al. 1980. Development of strength and capacity norms for manual materials handling activities: The state of the art. *Human Factors* 22(3):271-83.

Bonjer, F.H. 1971. Temporal factors and physiological load. In *Measurement of man at work*. W.T. Singleton, J.G. Fox, and D. Whitfield, eds. London: Taylor & Francis, Ltd.

Chaffin, D.B., and G.B.J. Andersson. 1984. *Occupational Biomechanics*. New York: John Wiley & Sons, Inc.

Chaffin, D.B., M.H. Pope, and G.B.J. Andersson. 1984. Workplace design. In *Occupational low back pain*. Pope, Frymoyer, and Andersson, eds. New York: Praeger.

Davis, P.R., and D.A. Stubbs. 1978. Performance capacity limits. *Applied Ergonomics* 9:33-38.

Fox, W.F. 1967. Body weight and coefficient of friction determinants of pushing capability. *Human Engineering Special Studies Series, No. 17.* Marietta, Ga.: Lockheed Co.

Garg, A., D.B. Chaffin, and G.D. Herrin. 1978. Prediction of metabolic rates for manual materials handling. *American Industrial Hygiene Association Journal* 39(8):661-74.

Kamon, E., and M.M. Ayoub. 1976. *Ergonomics guide to assessment of physical work capacity.* Akron, Ohio: American Industrial Hygiene Association.

Kroemer, K.H.E., and D.E. Robinson. 1971. *Horizontal static forces exerted by men standing in common working postures on surfaces of various tractions.* AMARL-TR-70-114. Wright Patterson Air Force Base, Ohio: Aerospace Medical Research Laboratory.

Lee, K. 1982. *Biomechanical modeling of cart pushing and pulling.* Unpublished doctoral dissertation. University of Michigan, Ann Arbor.

Martin, J.B., and D.B. Chaffin. 1972. Biomechanical computerized simulation of human strength in sagittal plane activities. *AIIE Transactions* 4:19-28.

National Institute for Occupational Safety and Health. 1983. *A work practices guide for manual lifting.* Technical report no. 81-122. Cincinnati, Ohio: U.S. Department of Health and Human Services (NIOSH). (Available from the American Industrial Hygiene Association, Akron, Ohio.)

National Safety Council. 1978. *Accident facts.* Chicago: National Safety Council.

Petrofsky, J.S., and A.R. Lind. 1978. Comparison of metabolic and ventilatory responses of men to various lifting tasks and to bicycle ergometry. *Journal of Applied Physiology* 45(1):60-3.

Snook, S.H. 1978. The design of manual handling tasks. *Ergonomics* 21(12):963-86.

Snook, S.H., and R.C. Jensen. 1984. Cost (of occupational low back pain). In *Occupational low back pain.* Pope, Rymoyer, and Andersson, eds. New York: Praeger.

Troup, J.D.B. 1978. Manual materials handling—The medical problem. In *Safety in manual materials handling*. C.G. Drury, ed. Cincinnati, Ohio: U.S. Department of Health and Human Services.

Don B. Chaffin *is professor and director with the Center for Ergonomics, University of Michigan, Ann Arbor.*

21

Accommodating the Disabled in the Workplace

David M. Rhyne, Ph.D., P.E.

Significant progress is being achieved in training and placing disabled persons in competitive employment settings. The public's increased awareness of the pressing need for their employment, where feasible, has come principally through federal legislation such as the Vocational Rehabilitation Act of 1973 and its succeeding amendments. The push to meet this need is long overdue. Historically, most disabled persons who have obtained economic support, other than through welfare programs, have done so with home-based craftwork or at sheltered workshops. It has been estimated that only about 10 percent of the vocationally rehabilitated population that is working is in normal, competitive employment settings.

A common belief held by many in our society is that the disabled are essentially helpless and will turn to welfare programs for their economic sustenance. As limited possibilities for meaningful employment have been offered to the disabled, the ideas held by the nondisabled have become self-fulfilling. Many disabled persons have been convinced that they are deficient and even inferior human beings as a result of their inability to break into the workplace.

Incentives for Job Training and Placement

The tide of such stigma and attitude seems to be reversing. The trend toward accepting the disabled as normal with some accompanying disability is encouraging. Factors contributing to the measure of success being achieved in the competitive workplace include the following:

1. Federal and state legislation which provides the legal requirements and guidelines pertaining to equal employment opportunities for the disabled. Principal legislation to date includes the Vocational Rehabilitation Act of 1973, as amended in 1974 and 1978; the Vietnam Era Veteran's Readjustment Assistance Act of 1972, as amended in 1974; Executive Orders 11914 and 12250; and Proclamation 5131 (November 1983).
2. Motivated in part by the Omnibus Budget Reconciliation Act of 1981, state-level rehabilitation agencies are actively seeking employment training and placement opportunities for their clients. That Act prohibits agencies from receiving full reimbursement funding for clients covered by programs of the Social Security Administration until they have placed those clients in successful employment. A successful employment occurs when a vocationally rehabilitated recipient has been employed for at least nine consecutive months and has earned at least $500 per month. Such criteria for reimbursement will encourage agencies to work more closely with private employers in identifying and developing employment opportunities.
3. Competitive employment of the disabled has been enhanced by the vast number of employers — both large and small — who have hired disabled persons. Not every placement has been successful (nor has every placement for the nondisabled); but, for the most part, employers have been pleased. DuPont, Sears & Roebuck, Tennessee Valley Authority, and General Motors are examples of organizations which have administered affirmative-action programs that result in the successful placement of disabled persons. In summarizing the overall performance of the visually impaired employees in his organization, a high-ranking manager with a major automobile manufacturer emphatically stated to the author: "They just make good employees." The frequency of such appraisals has increased through Projects with Industry (PWI) programs that have been developed among rehabilitation agencies, universities, and employers (public and private). These programs are established and developed to provide an exchange of communication among the parties, with the eventual goal of training and placing disabled persons within the employers' settings.
4. New legislation and an enlightened attitude are insufficient to assure employment without another factor — industrial engineering. A significant contribution has already been made by industrial engineers

in universities and in traditional manufacturing organizations in the form of disability evaluation an job accommodation programs.

The Role of the Industrial Engineer

Of all the professional personnel in industrial and service organizations today, there is none who can contribute more to the effort of providing meaningful equal employment opportunities for the disabled than the industrial engineer. Our discipline has been defined as "the engineering approach applied to all factors, including the human factor, involved in the production and distribution of products or services." By highlighting the human factor in the workplace, the industrial engineer can be of particular assistance to disabled persons in at least three areas:

1. The design and implementation of programs and systems that will provide objective evaluative measures of the capabilities and work skills of the disabled.
2. The development of appropriate and reasonable accommodations of facilities, machines, and job duties to meet the special needs of the disabled.
3. The willingness to support the can-do attitude and open-mindedness essential among management and technical professionals who must evaluate the possibilities of training and placing the disabled in normal, competitive employment settings.

Rehabilitation Engineering

A major force in developing these three areas is a relatively new discipline within ergonomics: rehabilitation engineering. The general mission of the discipline is to integrate the concepts and techniques of the physical sciences and engineering with traditional biomedical programs related to vocational rehabilitation. Eight centers across the United States focus on different aspects of this field. The Rehabilitation Engineering Center in Wichita, Kansas, which is closely linked with the Department of Industrial Engineering at Wichita State University, focuses primarily on the vocational aspects of rehabilitation of the disabled.

Task Analysis

A major contribution of this center has been the development of the Available Motions Inventory, a system that provides a quantitative measure of the physical capabilities of the disabled to perform defined job tasks. The evaluation system consists of thirty subtests, each of which is a manual performance of a simulated industrial control device or assembly task. The test raw scores are utilized to develop a uniform ability scale for each test. The performance scores serve as an indicator of the extent to which job modification will be required if the disabled person is considered for a particular job.

Additional evaluation systems, such as the Manual Abilities Scanning Tests that were developed by the Methods Time Measurement technique, are strong candidates for quantitatively measuring the work capabilities of the disabled. The industrial engineer is well-equipped to utilize these approaches or to develop and implement others. Basically, most systems are measuring time expended or required per actuation of a defined task element.

Job Redesign

The second major area that requires input from industrial engineers is accommodation of the workplace or work station — that is, modifying the station or job to match the capabilities of the disabled. The imagination and creativity used so often in developing items such as tooling, work flow routing, and other activities are certainly appropriate in analyzing and implementing job modifications. The concept of accommodation is fundamental in the training and placement of the disabled. Pati and Adkins (1981) have provided guidelines for job analysts considering accommodations at the workplace:

1. Is the accommodation required for performance of job duties?
2. What effect will the accommodation have on the organization's operations, on the disabled employee's performance, and on the nondisabled co-worker?
3. Will the accommodation give the disabled worker the chance to function on a more equal basis with co-workers?
4. Are other alternatives available which would accomplish the same purpose?

Modifications to accommodate the disabled are usually simple and inexpensive. Reviewing the appropriate work stations and rearranging equipment, installing hand or foot equipment controls or holding devices, removing transportation obstacles, and providing readers are examples of changes that can be made at nominal cost and without disrupting the work of nondisabled employees.

Along with those modifications, the industrial engineer may also need to review a job to determine whether a set of prescribed tasks needs to be altered. What is the job? How is it performed? Analyzing job content determines whether the task should be modified or the worker reassigned. The distinction that the industrial engineer must make as this analysis is performed, as opposed to job analysis for the nondisabled, is that now there is an additional item in the skill summary — the characteristic of impaired sight or hearing, amputation, paralysis, epilepsy, heart condition, allergies, nonparalytic orthopedic factors, respiratory weakness, and so forth. The function of the industrial engineer in all of the job restructuring, accommodation, and modification efforts is to transform motions that can be performed by a disabled person into the desired pattern, pace, and workplace defined by the requirements of the job.

For use in organizations where tooling is a major feature of the production system, the following design principles for the accommodation of the disabled have been developed by Meier and Deivanayagam (1980):

1. Keep tool design simple.
2. Eliminate grasp whenever possible.
3. Use holding fixtures whenever possible.
4. Use power or power assist whenever reasonable.
5. Select tables and machinery for seated operations whenever applicable.
6. Reduce materials handling occurrences to a minimum.

Cases

Two additional factors of job redesign or accommodation efforts are that the required costs are usually minimal and the modifications also benefit nondisabled employees. The costs of the more than 3,000 accommodations made for disabled workers at DuPont were nominal overall. This finding has been repeated in other organizations where management was initially apprehensive about costs. Two examples from DuPont will illustrate this point. This company estimates that the costs associated with hiring, training, and keeping a computer programmer approximates $100,000. That amount includes overhead costs for office space and normal equipment, in addition to salary and benefits. A programmer at DuPont for nearly twenty years became blind about ten years ago as a result of a tumor on his optic nerve. When he returned to work, his supervisor worked with him and management to determine what he needed to again be a productive employee.

Over the years DuPont has purchased, and updated, an Opticon — a device which "reads" the written work and transmits this information to the visually impaired programmer through electrical impulses sensed by the index finger. DuPont has also purchased a device which provides audio output for his computer terminal. Overall, about $10,000 has been spent in providing the employee with these accommodations. It should be obvious to anyone that the continuation of the employment of this disabled person as a productive, loyal computer programmer for one-tenth of what it would cost to hire and train another computer programmer is a high rate of return on investment. The programmer is shown at work on his job in figure 1.

Another example also concerns the employment of a visually impaired employee. A spin pump mechanic began working for DuPont over thirty-six years ago, after graduation from a school for the blind in Philadelphia. In 1975, he moved to his current job of repairing and maintaining pumps which supply polymer to staple nylon machines. The job consists of cleaning,

Figure 1 ***Photo courtesy of E.I. Dupont***

lubricating, and testing tasks so that pumps are ready to return to the manufacturing floor. Speaking of his work performance his supervisor has stated: "He knows what's expected of him and he does it — sometimes better than a sighted person could. He can feel imperfections on the pumps that I can't even see." The only special treatment or job accommodations required for the mechanic were the installation of a cover over the grinder at his work bench and having someone meet him at the gate in the morning and leave fifteen minutes early with him at night. The mechanic is shown at work in his shop in figure 2.

The author has been directly involved with the training and placement of visually impaired persons, principally in the textile industry. As a pilot program between Clemson University in Clemson, South Carolina, and the South Carolina Commission for the Blind, a legally blind person was trained and employed as a spinning doffer in a textile production plant. Wamsutta Mills in Anderson, South Carolina, agreed to participate in this pilot venture by providing its plant training facilities. After an intensive review of

Figure 2 ***Photo courtesy of E.I. Dupont***

its training manual, training procedures, and evaluation measures, it was agreed that training would proceed as if the trainee was fully sighted. No accommodations to or changes in the job tasks were made. The portion of the job requiring the piecing-up of broken yarn ends took the longest period of time to master. This additional time extended the training period necessary to achieve satisfactory production levels from the usual eight weeks for the nondisabled to ten weeks for the visually impaired trainee. He was later fully employed and reached the production requirements of his job. He is shown at work in figure 3.

The job trainee in this study had been previously employed and would have been eligible for monthly disability compensation of approximately $500. According to the trainee's rehabilitation counselor, the South Carolina Commission for the Blind spent approximately $2,400 on wages and optical aids

Figure 3

for its client's job training. Analysis of only the effect of the job training on the flow of governmental funds shows:

1. \$500/month is no longer received for disability compensation.
2. \$113 is paid as federal income taxes each month by the visually impaired trainee who is now employed (10.8 percent of gross wages at \$6 per hour).
3. \$48 is paid as state income taxes each month by the trainee (5.0 percent of gross wages).
4. \$128.64 is paid each month in the form of Social Security taxes (FICA) by the trainee and the employer.
5. The payback period by considering these training costs and payments made by the visually impaired trainee who has become employed is (assuming an annual time cost of money of 9 percent):

$$\$2400 = \$500\,(P/A,\, 3/4\%,\, n) + \$113\,(P/A,\, 3/4\%,\, n) + \$48\,(P/A,\, 3/4\%,\, n) + \$128.64\,(P/A,\, 3/4\%\ n)$$

Figure 4 ***Photo courtesy of E.I. Dupont***

where

$(P/A, 3/4\%, n) = 3.309$ and $n = 3.04$ months.

Analyzing the benefit-cost ratio (BCR) of the study in terms of gross wages earned and the rehabilitation agency training costs over a five-year span of time yields the following results (assuming an annual time cost of money of 9 percent and an annual average wage increase of $650 over the next five years):

$$\$2{,}400\ (\text{BCR}) = \$12{,}480\ (P/A, 9\%, 5) + 650\ (\text{P/G}, 9\%, 5)$$

where

$(P/A, 9\%, 5) = 3.890$ and
$(\text{P/G}, 9\%, 5) = 7.111$ and

$$\text{the BCR} = \frac{\$53{,}169}{\$2{,}400} = 22.15 \text{ or } 22{:}1 \text{ (approximate).}$$

These economic analyses do not consider a multitude of factors. The costs incurred by the training firm, the tax benefits gained by the firm for employing the trainee, and the large number of benefits associated with improved socio-economic status have not been quantified. The analyses which have been presented, though, do indicate the study will provide a satisfactory rate of return on investment expenditures. It is hoped these three examples illustrate the point that job accommodations, as a general rule, for most disabilities are not outrageously expensive. Furthermore, the return on the investment for the accommodation is usually significant.

Nondisabled workers will usually benefit from job accommodations that have been developed for the disabled. The removal of obstacles that impede mobility, the modified methods that reduce handling, or the redesigned work station layout that facilitates execution of assigned tasks may have an even greater positive effect on morale and productivity for the nondisabled worker than for the disabled.

Why be concerned about the accommodation of the disabled in competitive employment settings? Apart from the legal requirement that provides for nonexclusion of the qualified disabled, these persons can become solid, stable employees in an organization. For the approximately 2,700 disabled employees of DuPont, a measure of their performance in categories of safety, job duties, and attendance indicated that they performed at a comparable level with the nondisabled employee population irrespective of the type of impairment. Successful training and placement depend on matching people to jobs — an important process for any prospective employee. For the disabled employee-to-be, the intensity and extent of the matching process is increased even to modifying the job duties, work methods, machine controls, transportation routes and facilities, work station layout — whatever is required to efficiently place the disabled employee. The professional person who is best equipped for this opportunity is the industrial engineer.

The Accommodation Process

The accommodation process is best viewed as an opportunity rather than as a task. The author cites from his own experience that no work performed by an industrial engineer will be more rewarding than having a role in the successful employment of the disabled. The reward for having a role in the accommodation of a disabled worker who could not find employment can be immeasurable. The industrial engineer cannot bear the full thrust of the program, for the program begins when the management of an organization is willing to give the vocational rehabilitation process a trial. By having an accommodation plan, the industrial engineer can provide convincing evidence that competitive jobs can be designed, redesigned, or made compatible for the disabled. This role of supportive encouragement whereby the industrial engineer can influence the attitude of an organization is the third major area of contribution to the employment of the disabled. An accommodation plan should be shaped by considering:

1. Which job duties are affected by the impairment?
2. Should those job duties be reassigned?
3. Can a device be procured or developed in-house to compensate for the disability as it affects job performance?
4. How can the medical department assist in the accommodation process?
5. What input can be provided by the training and placement specialist of the state-level rehabilitation agency?
6. How can nondisabled employees contribute to the job redesign or accommodation program?
7. What expertise can be provided by the training department personnel?
8. How can the accommodation be kept as simple as possible?

Nothing breeds success like success. Successful placement of the disabled will not occur in an organization, though, until it is willing to venture into this area of employment. The most difficult barrier for the disabled to overcome is not a curb or a door that will not accommodate a wheelchair. The biggest barriers to the employment of the disabled are myths about their performance. Perhaps some of the apprehension and myths associated with the disabled are evaporating as the disabled prove their ability in the workplace. The industrial engineer, through objective evaluation programs, effective job accommodations, and support of cooperative personnel at all organizational levels, will be the key to bringing the vocational rehabilitation process to its intended conclusion — the successful training and placement of the disabled in competitive employment.

References

E.I. DuPont DeNemour and Co. 1982. *Equal to the task, 1981 DuPont survey of employment of the handicapped*. Wilmington, Del.: DuPont.

Malzahn, Don. 1979. Ability evaluation and job modification for the severely disabled. *Proceedings, 1979 Spring Annual Conference of the American Institute of Industrial Engineers*. Norcross, Ga.: AIIE.

Meier, F.A., and S. Deivanayagam. 1980. A study of job design to improve the productivity of severely handicapped workers. *Proceedings, 1980 Spring Annual Conference of the American Institute of Industrial Engineers*. Norcross, Ga.: AIIE.

Pati, Gobal C., and John I. Adkins. 1981. *Managing and employing the handicapped: The untapped potential*. Lake Forest, Ill.: Brace-Park.

Rhyne, David M. 1984. IEs can play vital role in bringing the disabled into the economic mainstream. *Industrial Engineering* 16(4):60-6.

Urick, Lyndall F. 1963. Development of industrial engineering. *Industrial engineering handbook*. 2nd ed. New York: McGraw-Hill Book Co.

David M. Rhyne *is assistant professor in the Department of Management, Auburn University, Alabama.*

22

Handtool Design

Susan E. Nemeth

A wide variety of handtools are used in the manufacturing environment for the assembly of products as well as for the operation and repair of equipment. Technological advancements in tool design have vastly improved the operating characteristics of many tools. For example, the simple task of driving a screw can be performed with a conventional hand-operated screwdriver, a yankee (push-type) screwdriver, or an electrical or air-driver power tool. Though all three tools accomplish the same task, their speed and efficiency, as well as their impact on the human operator, vary widely. Design of the interface between the human and the tool directly affects the worker's health and safety. Nerve, muscle, and tendon disorders can result from poorly designed handtools or improper tool use in the performance of repetitive tasks.

While the intended function of a handtool dictates major considerations in its design, ergonomic principles incorporated into the design can reduce injuries, as well as improve performance and quality of workmanship, by minimizing operator stress and fatigue. From literature on handtool design, referenced at the end of this chapter, a list of ten principles for the design and use of handtools has been compiled. Each of these principles will be discussed in the following subsections. A Handtool Questionnaire is also provided to aid the engineer in pinpointing the source of current handtool problems.

Principles of Handtool Design

Maintain Straight Wrists

The ability to grasp a handtool is significantly reduced when the wrist is deviated from the neutral position. Figure 1 illustrates the neutral wrist position as well as the extremes of flexion, extension, ulnar deviation, and radial deviation. The muscles which open and close the fingers are located in the

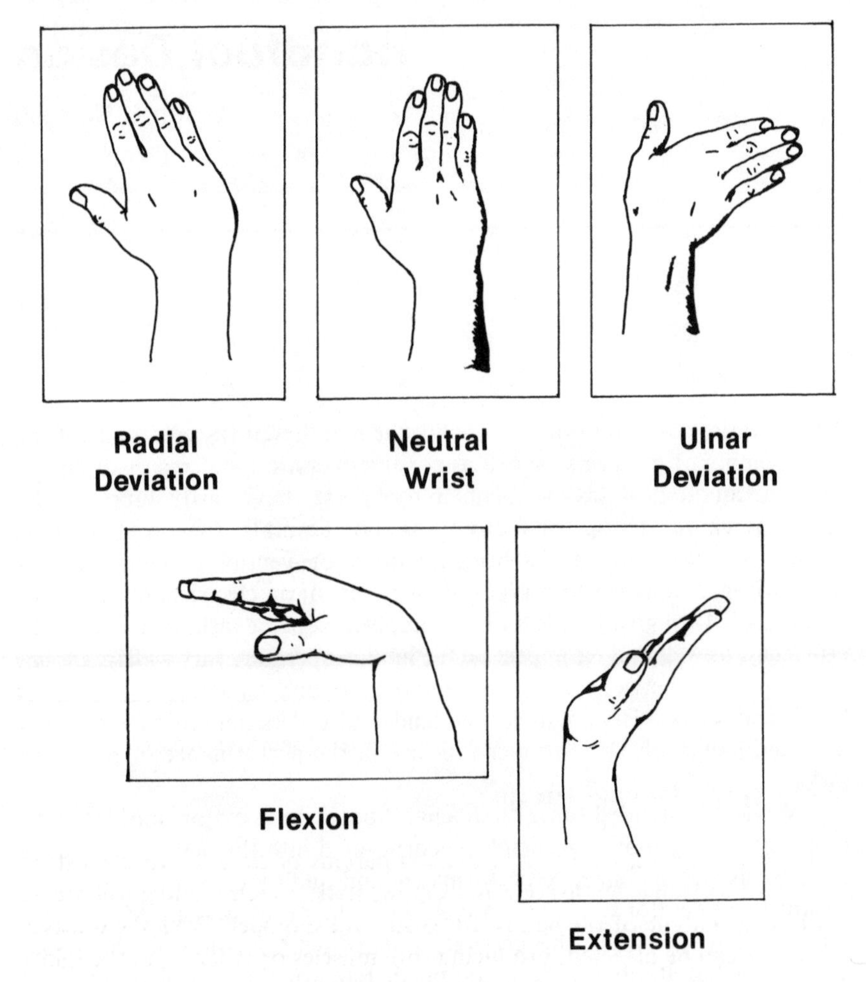

Fig. 1 Wrist positions

forearm, with tendons extending from these muscles to the finger joints to provide movement. These tendons enter the hand through a channel in the wrist called the carpal tunnel. The median nerve, which activates the thumb and the index, middle, and half of the ring finger, also enters the hand through this channel. Excessive wrist deviation, especially while grasping an object, exerts pressure on these tendons and the median nerve at the wrist. When this action is performed on a repetitive basis, the tendons can become inflamed and swollen, pinching off the median nerve. The resultant condition is known as carpal tunnel syndrome and is characterized by numbness, a tingling or burning sensation, and clumsiness in the hand. If the condition is allowed to persist, permanent disability can result.

Handtools should be designed so that the operator can grasp, hold, and manipulate the tool without bending the wrist. The layout of the workplace also plays an important role in the selection of handtools. Figure 2 illustrates the relationship between tool design and the workplace, where the same tool is not appropriate for all applications. Many tools are now available which can compensate for variations in workplace design through the bending of the tool rather than the wrist.

Maintaining power tools at their proper torque setting is also important to avoid the resultant kickback which can jolt the wrist. Power tools should stop when the torque setting is reached.

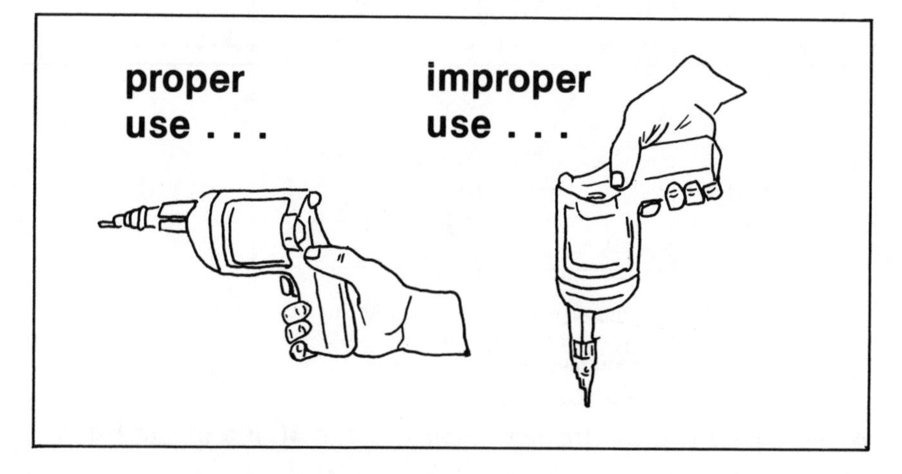

Fig. 2 Layout of the workplace influences handtool selection

Avoid Static Muscle Loading

When heavy tools are held for extended periods of time or work must be performed with an extended or raised elbow, static muscle loading will occur, resulting in fatigue of the hands, forearm, and shoulder. Both the muscles and joints can be affected, producing sore muscles or stiffness in the joints which can impede the operator's ability to work.

The weight of handtools should be kept at a minimum to prevent fatigue. Tools used on a repetitive basis and weighing more than 1 pound should be counterbalanced and adapted for the lightest possible air hoses or cords. To prevent the tool from slipping or rotating during use, the center of gravity of the tool should be as close as possible to the center of the grip.

While operating most handtools, the human body functions more efficiently at the midrange of joint motion. This is accomplished when the work elements can be performed with the shoulder relaxed and the elbow close to the body, with approximately 85-120° between the upper and lower arm, as illustrated in figure 3.

When the nature of the task would make it impractical or too costly to eliminate static muscle loading, frequent rest breaks or job rotation to less fatiguing tasks can provide a solution.

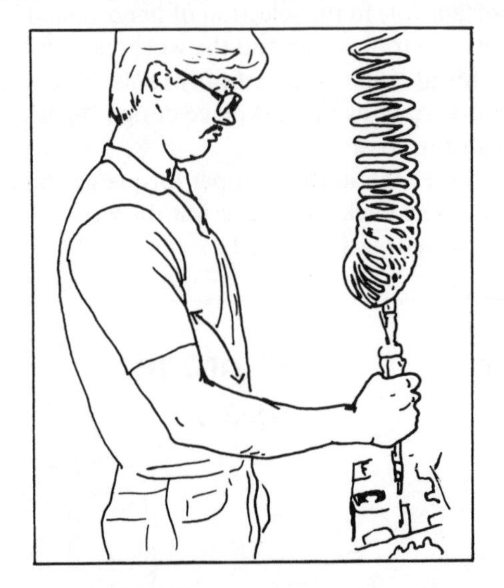

Fig. 3 Optimum working posture with shoulder relaxed, elbow close to body, and 85° - 120° between upper and lower arm

Avoid Stress Concentrations over the Soft Tissue of the Hand

Stress concentrations result from poorly designed tool handles which exert pressure on the palm or fingers, obstructing blood flow or nerve function. A classic example of this is the handtool with finger grooves, where the hand of the user seldom conforms to the grooving pattern, producing stress at the base of the fingers. Stress can also occur when tool handles are not long enough to traverse the hand and press into the hand at the base of the thumb, as illustrated in figure 4.

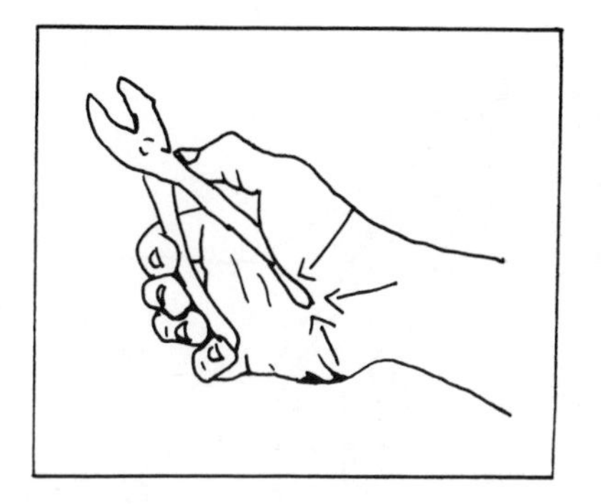

Fig. 4 Stress concentrations at the base of the hand

Reduce Grip Force Requirements

The greater the effort that must be exerted to maintain control of a hand-tool, the higher the potential for injury. Smooth hard plastic or metal handles require undue grip forces, especially when the hand is perspiring. Knurled surfaces or various types of rubber coatings on tool handles can reduce grip-force requirements and prevent tool slippage in the hand. A compressible gripping surface is best, though the handle material should be hard enough to prevent metal chips or other debris from becoming embedded in it. The material should also be nonporous to avoid absorption of oils and other liquids which could irritate the skin. When downward forces must be applied, a flange at the base of the tool handle can also aid in reducing grip requirements.

Maintain Optimal Grip Span

The ability of the hand to exert force when closing a tool such as pliers, scissors, or tongs is a function of the grip span of the tool. To produce the equivalent of a full hand grip, a fingertip grasp requires four to five times more effort. When this is performed on a repetitive basis, it can lead to tendinitis, inflammation and swelling of the tendons in the wrist and forearm.

Optimal grip spans, as illustrated in figure 5, measured from the fingers to the base of the thumb, range from 2.5 to 3.5 in. for maximum force on two handle tools. Grip force is also reduced when handle span of the tool in its open position is smaller than 2.5 in., which again places the hand at a mechanical disadvantage.

The recommended handle diameter for circular-handle tools such as screwdrivers is dependent upon the type of task. When a full-hand power grip is required, handle diameters should be from 1.25 to 2.0 in. A precision or fingertip grip for light tasks is accomplished most effectively when the handle diameter is 0.3 to 0.6 in.

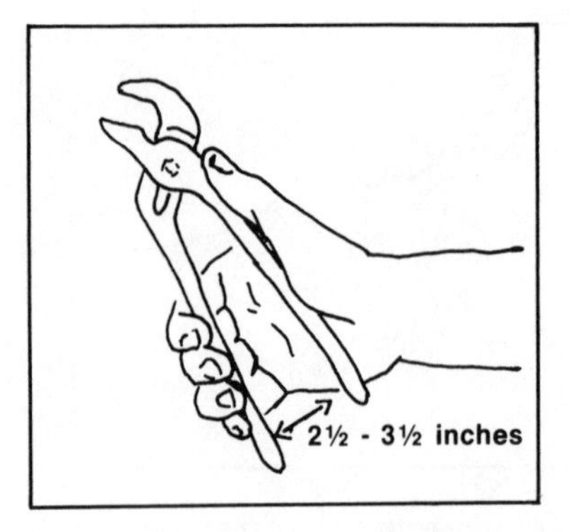

Fig. 5 Optimal grip span

Avoid Sharp Edges, Pinch Points, and Awkward Movements

Tool handles should not have sharp or protruding edges which can press into the hand and cause blisters or place undue pressure over nerves and arteries of the hand.

When two-handle tools are closed, there should be sufficient space between the handles to prevent the palm or fingers from being inadvertently pinched. Likewise, when these types of tools must be used on a repetitive basis, a means for opening the tool after use, such as a spring, should be provided to avoid awkward finger manipulations, as illustrated in figure 6. However, when a spring-type opening mechanism is used, the spring force should be low enough that it does not cause undue strain on the operator to keep the tool closed.

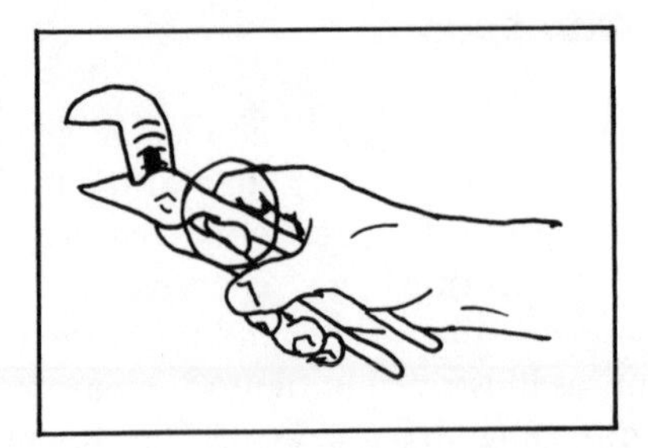

Fig. 6 Awkward finger manipulations required to open tool

Avoid Repetitive Finger Trigger Actions

A condition known as trigger finger can result when a single finger is used repetitively for operating a trigger, especially when tool handles are large, forcing the operation of the trigger to be performed by flexing only the tip of the finger while the middle joint remains straight. Trigger finger deprives the individual of the ability to actively extend the finger.

Use of the thumb for trigger operation is preferred over using a single finger, since the major muscles controlling thumb action are located in the hand. Location of a thumb trigger should be such that hyperextension of the thumb is not required, as illustrated in figure 7.

Preferable to thumb action are triggers requiring full four-finger action. This distributes the force requirements over a larger area of the hand.

Where practical, tools with pressure-sensitive starts or proximity switches are the most desirable triggering mechanisms. Proximity switches generally require a finger trigger action to initiate tool operation; as long as contact is maintained between the tool and work surface, however, no further pressure on the trigger is required. Welding, sanding, or polishing operations would be typical applications for a proximity switch where the duration of contact between tool and part is more than a few seconds.

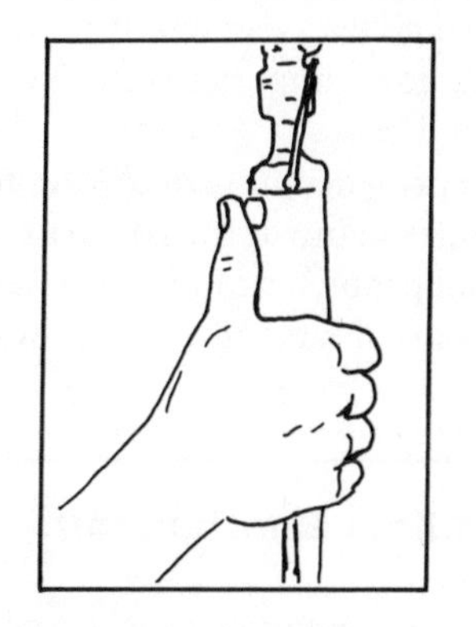

Fig. 7 Hyperextended thumb

Protect Hands from Heat or Cold

Tool handles should protect the hands from heat or cold generated by the tool. Heat exposure typically comes from electric motors or heat-producing tools such as soldering irons, welders, or tools which dispense heated glues or sealants. Rubber, plastic, or wooden handles are usually sufficient to protect the hands from heat produced by these tools.

Exposure to cold can come from air-powered tools, where the air is fed through the tool handle. When the handle is metal, this may be sufficient to cause discomfort and loss of dexterity and can result in the operator losing control of the tool.

Avoid Excessive Vibration

Prolonged use of vibrating tools can result in reduced blood circulation in the hands and fingers, a condition known as vibration white-finger syndrome. Compressible rubber handles on tools, as opposed to metal or wooden handles, can reduce transmission of vibration. Where this does not reduce vibration sufficiently, limited exposure through job rotation should be considered.

Use Gloves That Fit

Gloves are often worn in the manufacturing facility to protect the hands from adverse elements in the work environment. When gloves are used in conjunction with handtools, several factors must be considered. Gloves reduce both strength and dexterity. Tools with hand openings, such as scissors, must provide sufficient clearance for the gloved hand to operate comfortably. Loose fitting or excessively bulky gloves also present several hazards. Excess material may catch in rotating tool bits or snag on protrusions in the workplace, causing injury to the hand. Bulky gloves, with excess material between the fingers, can also give a false sensation of a secure grip by exerting pressure on sensitive nerge endings between the fingers, resulting in the tool slipping out of the hand.

Work gloves should be provided in several sizes to accommodate variations in hand size and minimize many of the adverse effects of gloves. Gloves should be kept clean to avoid problems of oils or other skin irritants soaking into the gloves or irritating particles getting caught inside the gloves and rubbing on the skin.

Handtool Questionnaire

The following questionnaire can be used to evaluate handtool design and use in repetitive operations by placing a check in the appropriate column. Checks in the "Yes" column will indicate areas where improvements in tool or workplace design can be of benefit.

Working Posture	**Yes**	**No**
1. Does the wrist deviate from the neutral position?	___	___
2. Is the elbow-forearm angle:		
— greater than 120°?	___	___
— less than 85°?	___	___
3. Is work performed above shoulder level?	___	___
4. Is the elbow elevated to the side or extended in front of the body?	___	___

5. If the tool is *not* counterbalanced, does it weigh more than 1 pound? ____ ____

6. Does the operator feel that excessive grip force is required to perform the task or maintain control of the tool? ____ ____

Tool Handle

1. Does the tool handle press into the palm of the hand? ____ ____

2. Are there finger grooves on the tool handle? ____ ____

3. Are there sharp edges or other pinch points on the tool handle? ____ ____

4. Is the tool handle excessively hot or cold? ____ ____

5. Is the hand prone to slipping when grasping the tool handle? (smooth handle tools) ____ ____

6. For two-handle tools:
   — are awkward motions required to open the tool? ____ ____
   — can the hand or fingers be pinched between handles when closed? ____ ____
   — is the grip span
   greater than 3.5 in.? ____ ____
   less than 2.5 in.? ____ ____

7. For circular handle tools:
   — If a full hand power grip is required, is the handle diameter:
   greater than 2.0 in. ____ ____
   less than 1.25 in. ____ ____
   — If the tool is used for precision work, is the handle diameter:
   greater than 0.6 in. ____ ____
   less than 0.3 in. ____ ____

Gloves

1. Are work gloves excessively bulky? ____ ____

2. Do work gloves present a hazard of catch points on the tool or elsewhere in the workplace? ____ ____

Power Tool Triggers

Does the tool have a trigger mechanism? If yes, check the type of activation method ____ ____
____ Full four-finger trigger
____ Thumb trigger
____ One-finger trigger

References

Ayoub, M.A. 1983. Tendinitis control program for the apparel industry. *IIE Ergonomics Newsletter* 18(1).

Dionne, E.D. 1984. Carpal tunnel syndrome — Part II: Some answers. *National Safety News* 129(4)

Eastman Kodak Co. 1983. *Ergonomic design for people at work*. Lifetime Learning Publications. Belmont, Calif.: Eastman Kodak Co.

Tichauer, E.R., and H. Gage. 1978. Ergonomic principles basic to hand tool design. *Ergonomics guide series*. American Industrial Hygiene Association.

***Sue Nemeth** is associate professor with the Industrial Engineering Department at GMI Engineering and Management Institute, Flint, Michigan.*

23

Screening and Job Placement

Mahmoud A. Ayoub, Ph.D.

The composition and characteristics of the American industrial workforce are changing rapidly. More women are now seeking industrial employment; the handicapped are no longer excluded from the potential job market; and the retirement age is no longer fixed at a predetermined figure. Current workplace regulations, notably those growing out of the Equal Employment Opportunity Act (EEO), mandate that employers justify their hiring practices by meeting the strict and comprehensive Equal Employment Opportunity Commission (EEOC) guidelines concerning the selection and placement of applications, including minority members (*Uniform Guidelines 1970*).

To this end, every employer is required to support in detail the rationale behind any screening program or selection criterion adopted, especially if the result is ''discrimination'' against any minority group (Sterling Transit). Ergonomics provides an attractive solution which encompasses all the requirements detailed by EEOC for pre-employment screening programs. Interest in job evaluation and development screening programs has been sustained over the years by industry, academia, and government. Accordingly, there exist many approaches, as well as designs, for the development and implementation of screening programs. (See references at the end of this chapter.)

In this chapter we will limit our treatment to programs typically used for screening applicants for physically demanding jobs. A sample of three specific programs is presented below.

Screening Programs

Psychological Tests

Use of psychological tests in pre-employment screening has been a common practice for years. The rationale behind such tests is that certain behavioral attributes can predict the success or failure of an individual's job performance. Measuring these attributes in applicants allows a more favorable workforce to be selected. Personal maturity, motivation, and aptitude for certain activities are commonly included in these tests. Since EEOC guidelines require that the predictiveness of these tests be validated if used in screening, the inclusion of test items must be based on extensive research relevant to the jobs under consideration and not merely on textbook recommendations. There is little doubt that behavioral tests are important tools for selection in many sedentary-type jobs, but their value in screening for physically demanding jobs is questionable. While it is important that workers be motivated to perform well in strenuous jobs, no amount of motivation can overcome a lack of physical capacity to work. No matter how hard an individual wants to lift a 200-lb block, it simply will not move if the strength capacity proves insufficient.

Rating Methods

Two screening methods come close to matching job demands and an applicant's work capacity. The first, known as the GULHEMP method, was developed by Koyl (Koyl and Hanson 1968). The other is the Hanman method (Hanman 1959), also known as the specific method, first proposed some thirty years ago.

The GULHEMP method rates both jobs and applicants on a seven-category scale. These are: (1) general physique, (2) upper extremities, (3) lower extremities, (4) hearing, (5) eyesight, (6) mentality, and (7) personality type. (Combining the first letters of the scale categories gives the name GULHEMP.) Each category is described in terms of a finite number of levels that vary from 1 to 7, with 1 representing highest demand or full capacity. For each category, the job being evaluated is assigned an appropriate level that best describes its demands. Similarly, an applicant's capacity is evaluated for each category. If the applicant cannot perform in a given category a value of 7 is assigned, indicating that he or she cannot perform the job as currently described in the particular category.

In contrast, if the applicant is fully capable of meeting job demands in that category, a value of 1 is assigned. An applicant is judged acceptable for hire if he or she is assigned levels equal to or below those determined for the detailed description of the categories and the meaning of the levels of each category. (See figure 1.)

GENERAL

G1 Fit for heavy manual work including digging, lifting, climbing, regularly as main occupation.

G2 Fit for manual work including incidental or occasional heavy work as in G1 — Can work on shifts.

G3 Fit for all employment except heavy labor, liable to deteriorate if meals are irregular, or if rest inadequate as with frequent shift changes.

G4 Fit for sedentary employment with regular hours and meals.

G5 Fit for restricted employment or part-time employment. "The handicapped worker" in home or out.

G6 Self care only.

G7 Bedfast.

G1 Fit for heavy manual work including digging, lifting, climbing, regularly as main occupation:

Can: Lift max. — own weight
usual — 150 lbs. @ 1 per 2 hours
— 50 lbs. @ 10 per hour
Stand or walk more than 8 hours
Carry max. loads short distances (i.e., 100 yards) 50 lbs. for 50 mins. per hour
Run, jump or climb — run or trot 10-20 mins. per hour. Climb 50 mins. per hour.
Climb and carry — could climb 1 flight — 18 ft. with max. load 50 lbs. up to 50 mins. out of hour
Bend back — 90° i.e., unrestricted
Environmental restrictions — nil

Fig. 1 A sample of Gulhemp Scale

Success of the GULHEMP method depends upon (1) a complete job analysis to define job demand and corresponding levels of the scale categories, and (2) judgment by an examining physician of the applicant's capability on each of the scale categories. The method does not offer the physician any specific objective tests for rating the applicants. Similarly, to define job demands, the process is entrusted to consensus ratings made by engineers, physicians, and personnel analysts, without requiring specific objective job evaluations. This lack of objectivity in determining job demands and applicant capacity opens the GULHEMP method to criticism. However, despite this serious drawback, the method is claimed to have been successful in a major demonstration project that lasted five years and involved hundreds of companies.

The essence of the Hanman method is rating both the job demands and the applicant's capacity to do work. In this respect, it is similar to the GULHEMP method; it differs substantially, however, in the specific factors used in the rating. The Hanman method deals with a detailed account of three primary attributes of job demands: weight, distance, and time. In addition, environmental factors are explicitly considered. An applicant is judged acceptable if he or she can meet the job demands in all categories (figure 2).

Advocates of the Hanman method attest to its success and usefulness as a pre-employment screening tool for many businesses and industries, including the Aluminum Company of Canada. Criticism of this method for a lack of objectivity in determining job demands and applicant capacity is as valid as in the case of the GULHEMP method.

Ergonomic Screening

A screening program should be predicated on the principle that it will separate the fit from the unfit, the normal from the unhealthy. The results should assure that job demands would not tax the individual's work capacity beyond safe limits. To accomplish this, jobs and the individuals that could perform them are defined using common scales and determinants; in other words, jobs and potential employees are described as a function of demands and capacities, respectively.

The capacity to do work or to exercise depends on the functional performance of the body's respiratory, cardiovascular, and muscular systems. To a worker, a job is simply a set of demands imposed on the body's physiological systems.

Job demands and human work capacity are typically described in terms of the following common descriptors or dimensions: reach demand/capability; strength demand/capability; energy expenditure demand/capability; and cardiac output demand/capability. The work demand positions the job requirements on a given scale, while capability locates the limiting physiological/physical value on the same scale.

When job demands and an individual's capabilities are known, decisions on employment can be reached on a rational and unbiased basis. This will mean that the individuals, male or female, who at the time of screening are assessed to be functionally qualified, will not be exposed to undue risk when assigned the targeted jobs. However, the success of such decisions rests upon two prerequisites: determination of job demands and assessment of the functional capacity and physiological efficiency of the applicants. Details of the ergonomic approach to screening and placement are given in the subsequent sections.

Form 1

Physical Demands Analysis Work Sheet

Job Title:

Job Location:

Physical Factors

	No.	Factor	Group
	1	1- 5	Lifting (Pounds) — Includes pushing and pulling effort while stationary
	2	6- 10	
	3	11- 25	
	4	26- 50	
	5	51-100	
	6	100+	
	7	1- 5	Carrying (Pounds) — Includes pushing and pulling effort while walking
	8	6- 10	
	9	11- 25	
	10	26- 50	
	11	51-100	
	12	100+	
	13	R	Fingering
	14	L	
	15	R	Handling
	16	L	
	17	R	Below Shoulders — Reaching
	18	L	
	19	R	Above Shoulders — Reaching
	20	L	
	21	R	Throwing
	22	L	
	23	Sitting	
	24	Total Time on Feet	
	25	Standing	
	26	Walking	
	27	Running	
	28	Jumping	
	29	Legs Only	Climbing
	30	Legs and Arms	
	31	R	While Sitting — Treading
	32	L	
	33	R	While Standing — Treading
	34	L	
	35	Stooping	
	36	Crouching	
	37	Kneeling	
	38	Crawling	
	39	Reclining	
	40	Twisting	
	41	Waiting Time	

	No.	Factor	Group
	42	Far — Snellen	Seeing
	43	Near — Jaeger	
	44	Color	
	45	Depth	
	46	Hearing	
	47	Talking	
	48	Other:	
	49	Other:	

Environmental Factors

	No.	Factor	Group
	50	Inside	
	51	Fair Weather	Outside
	52	Wet Weather	
	53	Hot °F	
	54	Cold °F	
	55	Sudden Temperature Changes	
	56	Humid	
	57	Dry	
	58	Moving Objects	
	59	Hazardous Machinery	
	60	Sharp Tools or Materials	
	61	Cluttered Floors	
	62	Slippery Floors	
	63	High Places	
	64	Electrical Hazards	
	65	Exposure to Burns	
	66	Explosives	
	67	Radiant Energy: (Kind)	
	68	Poor Lighting	
	69	Poor Ventilation	
	70	Toxic Conditions: (Kind)	
	71	Wet Quarters	
	72	Close Quarters	
	73	Vibration	
	74	Noise	
	75	Working With Others	
	76	Working Around Others	
	77	Working Alone	
	78	Shifts	
	79	Other:	
	80	Other:	

Job Analyst's Name — Verified With: Foreman's Name — Date

Fig. 2 Physical demands analysis work sheet

Predicting Job Demands

The performance of a job, from maintaining an erect posture to handling a heavy and bulky load, constitutes an external demand imposed on the human body to which a chain of coupled activities produces a predictable and quantifiable body response. The demand, regardless of type or characteristics, will require muscular activity involving one or more muscle groups.

Muscular work consumes energy that has to be supplied by oxidizing the substrata in the body. The oxidizing agent is the oxygen obtained from the atmosphere. To deliver the needed oxygen to the working muscles, the body mobilizes two primary systems — the respiratory system and the cardiovascular system.

The respiratory system delivers oxygen to the blood and clears out carbon dioxide produced in the oxidation process. On the other hand, the cardiovascular system responds to the imposed demand by pumping more oxygenated blood to meet the energy requirements of the working muscles. The functions of the three body systems (muscular, cardiovascular, and respiratory) in respose to job demand are highly correlated and can be predicted or assessed using several physiological measures.

Primary physiological measures of logical interest can be grouped according to their source of derivation under measures based on gas analysis and on the bioelectric responses of the body's muscular system. Gas analysis measures include oxygen consumption, ventilation rate, carbon dioxide produced, respiration rate and oxygen pulse. The bioelectric measures include heart rate, electrocardiograms and electromyograms (EMGs).

Over the years, physiologists have studied a host of jobs in the laboratory (under controlled conditions) and in industry. The fund knowledge gained from all these studies, performed by researchers from different countries studying a multitude of jobs, support the following assumptions regarding job demands and physiological responses:

1. At submaximal work, heart rate, oxygen consumption and ventilation rates are linearly related to each other regardless of the type or nature of the job performed.
2. The presence or absence of thermal stress has no effect on the oxygen consumption associated with job performance.
3. Heart rate is linearly related to the increase in thermal stress. When work is performed in hot environments, heart rate will increase linearly due to the combined effect of work stress and heat stress.
4. Maximum heart rate that can be reached by an individual is independent of the state of health or degree of fitness and depends only on age.
5. Maximum oxygen uptake that can be maintained by an individual can be predicted from knowing the maximum heart rate (see first assumption above).
6. Physiological responses of unfit or unhealthy individuals are markedly higher than those of normal individuals performing comparable jobs.
7. Physiological responses are linearly related to work intensity. This is true for all types of jobs performed under various conditions. This

linear relationship is usually presented in the literature in terms of an efficiency factor (or the slope of the linear line), which is a function of each individual's attributes (degree of fitness, state of health, etc.).

The above assumptions are well-defined in the literature and have been supported by numerous studies in work physiology and ergonomics.

The implication of the above assumptions should be very clear. First, once the work output is known, the levels of corresponding physiological responses can be predicted. Next, if the physiological efficiency of the person is known, a determination can be made as to whether the person will be able to perform the job without being exposed to unacceptable risk. In other words, to develop a screening program, the work output and strength requirement must be defined for each job and the physiological efficiency of each applicant must be determined.

Work Output and Strength

Performance of a job can be described simply in terms of the motions of the body segment involved in its execution. The motion of each segment, in turn, can be categorized in terms of three fundamental characteristics: displacement, velocity, and acceleration. These characteristics can be obtained experimentally through either photographic or electromechanical techniques. Using motion characteristics coupled with the principle of body dynamics, it is possible to compute the mechanical work output versus time for a given job.

In addition, information concerning the forces and torques acting on each articulation joint of the body during the motion can be obtained and presented as a series of profiles versus time. The forces and torque profiles represent the strength demand at any given time during execution of the job.

Experimental determination of work output is rather lengthy and time-consuming. In lieu of the exact experimental procedure, two other approaches can be considered.

1. *Using averages*. This is by far the most widely used and referenced approach in the literature. It determines the work output in terms of the work done in changing the body posture and the tool or object handled through the motion.
2. *Using models*. Through modeling, the motion characteristics and related dynamic descriptors can be predicted for the best and worst performances of a given job. Based on the characteristics of the job (workplace geometry, initial and final point of the motion, the weight and size of the object handled, etc.) and the basic anthropometric data on the individual performing the job, an optimization model can be developed.

Two classes of possible job motions are obtained by optimizing the model objective function subject to job and human constraints: motion associated with best performance — that is, job performed at minimum cost (mechanical energy) — and motion associated with worst performance, or a job performed at maximum cost.

With the extreme motions fully defined, two limits can be computed for both the total work output and peak strength. These limits are then used to predict the expected range of physical and physiological responses of job performance.

The attractiveness and perhaps the power of the modeling approach should be obvious, since a host of data concerning the dynamics of the job can be obtained based on a limited and rather general number of job and workplace descriptors.

Physiological Efficiency

The assumption is generally made (or perhaps implied) that persons seeking employment are free from any functional diseases which may impede or impair their physiological responses to job demands. This is simply not true, and in many cases the presence or absence of any impairment cannot be ascertained without actually exercise testing the person at submaximal work loads.

The functional capacity or state of health of an individual can be assessed using one of the three standard laboratory tasks: walking/running on a treadmill, exercising on a bicycle ergometer, and stepping up and down with a certain frequency on a step of standard dimensions. Using two or more different work loads (employing two frequencies of ten and twenty steps/minute for a step rest), the individual's physiological efficiency can be defined and expressed as a relationship between physiological measures and work output. In addition, from the test data, the individual's state of health can be determined.

Figure 3 shows how step-test data can be used to screen three applicants for a job with a known work load. Because the three applicants are the same age, their maximum heart rates are taken to be the same. However, due to the marked differences in their physiological responses on the step test, their employment potential varies, and they are classified as acceptable, marginal, and unacceptable.

On the other hand, for evaluating the physical capability of an individual, strength testing offers a simple, yet accurate, approach. An individual can be tested for arm, back and leg strength in a matter of minutes (see figure 4). From these values, a complete strength profile can then be developed, utilizing the fact that strength (force that can be exerted) is proportionate to the distance between the hands (point of exertion) and the back (point of support).

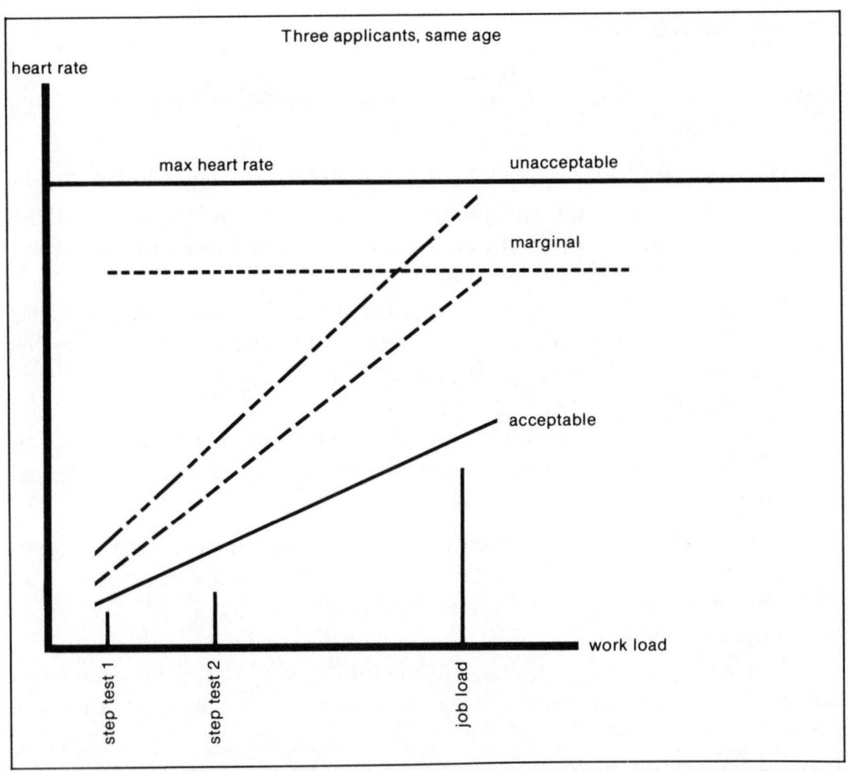

Fig. 3 Screening of three applicants based on a predicted job heart rate

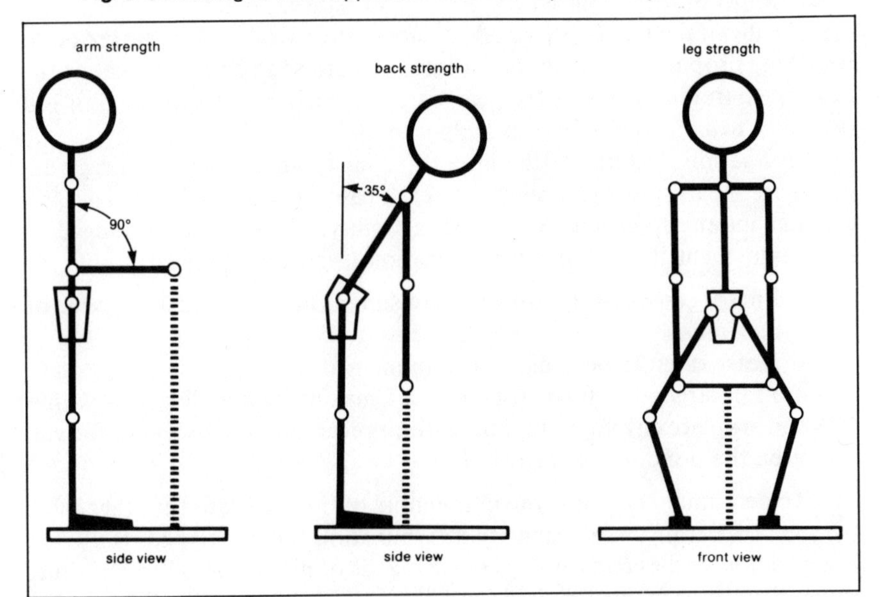

Fig. 4 Arm, back and leg strength tests

Implementation

The screening program detailed above can be implemented in accordance with the following steps:

Work capacity. For the application at hand, perform the following:

- Determine the heart rate that corresponds to two different work loads on the step test. From the data gathered, express heart rate as a function of work load (work output).
- Measure static strength for arm lift, back lift and leg lift. Starting with these three data points, develop a complete strength profile that gives the forces which can be exerted at any point in the workplace envelope.
- Determine the maximum heart rate based on the applicant's age. The maximum oxygen uptake from the person is given by the value that corresponds to this maximum heart rate.

Job demands. For the job to be filled, determine the total work output and strength requirement versus time. This information can be either obtained experimentally or predicted using job characteristics and appropriate (optimization) models.

Response prediction. Using the functional relationship between heart rate and work load developed in the first step, predict the heart rate that would correspond to the work output defined for the job. Next, from the predicted heart rate, determine the corresponding oxygen consumption (or energy expenditure) required for job performance.

Finally, if the job is performed in a hot environment, adjust the predicted heart rate proportionately to the increase in thermal stress above that of the neutral environment. Using the heart rate as a basis, predict the level of job difficulty to be perceived by the applicant.

Evaluation. Determine the level of capacity utilization for energy expenditure, heart rate and strength. In each case, this is a ratio between job demand and the applicant's predicted capability. The applicant is judged fit for employment if the following utilization levels are obtained:

- Energy expenditure (oxygen consumption): 40 to 50 percent of maximum
- Heart rate: 75 percent of maximum
- Peak strength: 50 to 70 percent of maximum for all points within workplace envelope. In most cases, prevention of muscle fatigue will be the deciding factor (Muller).

To determine the employment potential of the applicant for other jobs, the steps concerning work capacity determination can be skipped. If a given organization studies and catalogs the demands of major jobs ahead of time, some of the information required for determining job demands will be readily available without any further analysis or testing.

The approach to pre-employment screening detailed previously has been adopted for all the aluminum reduction plants of the Reynolds Metals Co. of Richmond, Virginia (Ayoub 1982). In regard to satisfying the requirements of the EEOC uniform guidelines, the design and subsequent implementation of the program are patterned around the concept of *content validity*. The screening steps detailed above have been summarized and presented in a manual to be used by the medical personnel.

Typically, an applicant can be tested and classified as acceptable, marginal, or unacceptable in about an hour (figure 5 shows the two parts of the test). In classifying an applicant, a set of charts can be used to determine levels of utilization for both strength and heart rate. The form used for collecting test data and results is shown in figure 6.

Screening results and feedback from the plants are positive and very supportive of the design and architecture of the program.

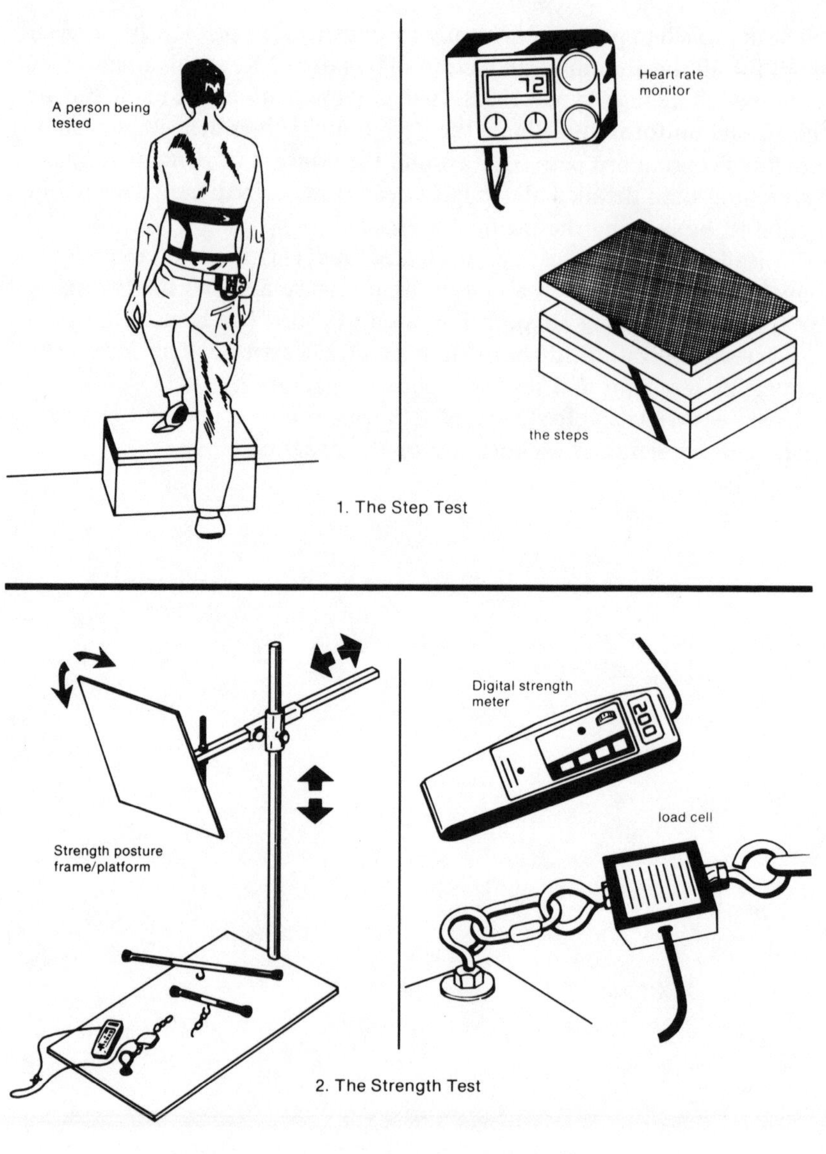

Fig. 5 The preemployment screening test

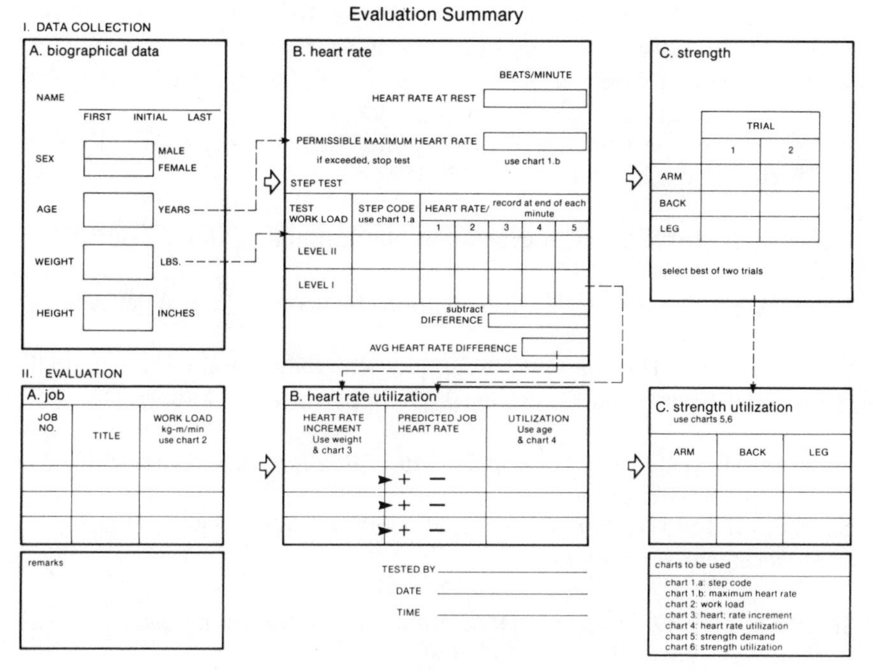

Fig. 6 The test form

Conclusions

The approach offered for the design and implementation of a pre-employment screening program is different from other available approaches in the following respects:

- It is integrative in nature because it considers all aspects of the physical and physiological characteristics of human work capacity.
- The screening is based on the individual's attributes (degree of fitness and state of health), determined through actual tests rather than predicted from data such as weight or height.

References

Ayoub, M.A. 1982. Control of manual lifting hazards, III: Pre-employment screening. *Journal of Occupational Medicine* 24(10):751-61.

Chaffin, D.B., et al. 1977. *Preemployment strength testing*. NIOSH Technical Report, DHEW (NIOSH) Publication No. 77-163.

Dotson, C.O., D.L. Santa Maria, and P. Davis. 1976. *Development of job-related physical performance examination for firefighters*. NFPCA, U.S. Department of Commerce.

EEOC v. Spokane Concrete Products, Inc. U.S. District Court, Eastern District of Washington, C-79-253, 1982.

Hanman, B. 1959. Clues in evaluating physical ability. *JOM* 1:595-602.

Jones, P.W. 1948. *Practical job evaluation*. New York: John Wiley & Sons.

Koyl, L., and P. Hanson. 1968. Age, physical ability, and work potential. National Council on the Aging, U.S. Department of Labor:21-2.

Slanway, H. Geddes. 1947. *Applied job evaluation*. New York: Ronald.

Sharkey, B.J. 1977. *Fitness and work capacity*. Washington, D.C.: U.S. Government Printing Office.

Shartle, C.L. 1949. *Occupational information: Its development and application*. New York: Prentice-Hall, Inc.

Snook, S.H. 1978. The design of manual handling tasks. *Ergonomics* 21(12):963-85.

Spriegel, W.R., and E. Lenham. 1953. *Job evaluation in automobile and automotive parts industries*. Austin, Tex.: Bureau of Business Research, University of Texas.

Sterling Transit Co., Inc., v. State of California. 121 Cal. App. 3rd, 791.

Uniform guidelines on employee selection procedures. Federal Register 42: 65542, December 30, 1970.

Mahmoud A. Ayoub *is professor in the Department of Industrial Engineering, North Carolina State University, Raleigh.*

REFERENCE SOURCES

24

Ergonomics Equipment

B. Mustafa Pulat, Ph.D.

Several sources of field study equipment are listed in this section, along with company addresses. Industrial engineers may find this information useful for evaluation of working conditions and quantifying task stress. For each equipment category, the manufacturer should be contacted for specific details such as cost. The list given below is in no way intended to be complete. Much safety-related equipment and manufacturer information are available from:

Best's Safety Directory
A. M. Best Company, Inc.
Ambest Road
Oldwick, NJ 08858

1. Accelerometers — Used for vibration testing and evaluating motion profiles of objects and body members:

   Bruel & Kjaer Instruments, Inc.
   185 Forest Street
   Marlborough, MA 01752
   (617) 481-7000

GenRad, Inc.
300 Baker Avenue
Concord, MA 01742
(617) 369-4400

2. Air velocity meters (anemometers) — Monitor the effectiveness of ventilation systems:

    Mine Safety Appliances Company
    600 Penn Center Blvd.
    Pittsburgh, PA 15235
    (412) 273-5000

    Davis Instrument Mfg. Com., Inc.
    519 E. 36th Street
    Baltimore, MD 21218
    (800) 368-2516

3. Audiometers — For pre-employment screening and periodic checking of hearing ability:

    Grason-Stadler, Inc.
    Box 5
    Littleton, MA 01460
    (617) 486-3514

    Maico Hearing Instruments, Inc.
    7375 Bush Lake Road
    Minneapolis, MN 55435
    (800) 328-6366

4. EMG (Electromyography) systems — Monitor muscle activity during work:

    Stoelting-Cyborg Company
    1350 South Kostner
    Chicago, IL 60623
    (617) 964-9020

    Lafayette Instrument Company
    P.O. Box 5729
    Lafayette, IN 47903
    (317) 423-1505

5. Industrial skills testing systems — Test for abilities such as finger and hand dexterity, eye-hand coordination, reaction time, and hand steadiness:

   Lafayette Instrument Company
   P.O. Box 5729
   Lafayette, IN 47903
   (317) 423-1505

   Marietta Apparatus Company
   118 Maple Street
   Marietta, OH 45756

6. Oxygen consumption meters — Evaluate oxygen uptake during work:

   Ambulatory Monitoring Inc.
   731 Saw Mill River Road
   Ardsley, NY 10502
   (914) 693-9240

7. Photography, video systems — Analyze motion patterns of limbs, trunk, other personnel, time-lapse photography:

   Lafayette Instrument Co.
   P.O. Box 5729
   Lafayette, IN 47903
   (317) 423-1505

8. Photometers — Measure illumination in a given environment, on work surface, etc.

   International Light, Inc.
   5 Dexter Industrial Green
   Newburyport, MA 01950
   (617) 465-5923

9. Portable physiograph systems — Allow for monitoring bioresponses such as heart rate, temperature, and muscle activity during work:

   Vitalog
   2484 Old Middlefield Way
   Mountain View, CA 94043
   (415) 857-0977

   Ambulatory Monitoring
   731 Saw Mill River Road
   Ardsley, NY 10502
   (914) 693-9240

10. Strip chart recorders — Obtain hard copy of bioresponse data collected:

    Lafayette Instrument Co.
    P.O. Box 5729
    Lafayette, IN 47903
    (317) 423-1505

    Ambulatory Monitoring
    731 Saw Mill River Road
    Ardsley, NY 10502
    (914) 693-9240

11. Sound-level meters, noise dosimeters — Sound-level meters measure intensity of sound at a given instant; noise dosimeters measure dose (total amount received for a given period):

    Bruel & Kjaer Instruments Inc.
    185 Forest Street
    Marlborough, MA 01752
    (617) 481-7000

    Metrosonics, Inc.
    P.O. Box 23075
    Rochester, NY 14692
    (716) 334-7300

12. Timers — For performance evaluation:

    Meylan Corporation
    264 West 40th Street
    New York, NY 10018

13. Toxic gas and vapor analyzers — For in-plant air monitoring:

    The Foxboro Company
    Foxboro, MA 02035

14. Vibration meters, vibration frequency meters — For vibration surveys:

    Metrosonics Inc.
    Box 23075
    Rochester, NY 14692
    (716) 334-7300

    IRD Mechanalysis, Inc.
    6150 Huntley Road
    Columbus, OH 43229

15. Vision testers — For visual screening or periodic vision checks:

American Optical Corp.
Safety Products
14 Mechanic Street
Southbridge, MA 01550

Titmus Optical Inc.
Box 191
Petersburg, VA 23803
(800) 446-1802

25

Ergonomics Software

B. Mustafa Pulat, Ph.D.

This section gives a selection of mainframe and microcomputer software available in the field of ergonomics. The source should be contacted as to specifics and accessibility information.

Time-Motion Models

1. SAINT (Systems Analysis of Integrated Network of Tasks) — A network modeling and simulation technique developed to assist a designer analyze a complex man-machine system:

   Source: Defense Technical Information Center (DTIC)
   Cameron Station
   Alexandria, VA 22314

2. HOS (Human Operator Simulator) — A generalized model which allows for the simulation of a total system performing a complex mis-

sion. Not only the behavior of the operator is simulated, but also the operating characteristics of system hardware and software:

Source: DTIC
Cameron Station
Alexandria, VA 22314

3. WAM (Workload Assessment Model) — Model developed to estimate operator workload in a man-machine system:

Reference: Edwards, R., R. Curnow, and R. Ostrand. 1977. Workload assessment model users manual. Report D180-20247-3. Seattle, Wash.: Boeing Aerospace

Workspace Design Models

1. CAPABLE (Controls and Panel Arrangement by Logical Evaluation) — Computer aided design system for laying out panels, anthropometric evaluation and workload balancing among limbs:

Reference: Bonney, M.C., and R.W. Williams. CAPABLE. A computer program to layout controls and panels. *Ergonomics:* V20, N3, 187-192, 1977.

2. CAPADES (Computer Aided Panel Design and Evaluation System) — A two-stage mainframe model developed for preparing layouts for large control panels for standing operators (in the control rooms of power plants, etc.):

Source: B. Mustafa Pulat
AT&T Technologies
7725 W. Reno Avenue
Oklahoma City, OK 73125

3. MAWADES (Multi-Man-Machine Work Area Design and Evaluation System) — A three-stage mainframe model developed for designing the workspace of a crew engaged in command, communications, and control activities at sit-stand duty:

Source: DTIC
Cameron Station
Alexandria, VA 22314

4. WODIM (Workplace Dimensions) — A microcomputer model which generates critical work station dimensions for seated and standing operators:

   Source: B. Mustafa Pulat
   AT&T Technologies
   7725 W. Reno Avenue
   Oklahoma City, OK 73125

Workspace Evaluation Models

1. SAMMIE — A 3-D anthropometric model of a person adjustable to various percentiles:

   Source: COMPEDA
   140 Route 17 North
   Paramus, NJ 07652

2. COMBIMAN — Model developed for design and evaluation of workspaces:

   Reference: Krause, H.E., and K.H.E. Kroemer. Combiman—A computer model of the operator at his workstation. In *Proceedings of the 17th Annual Meeting of the Human Factors Society*, California.

Task Evaluation Models

1. Metabolic Energy Expenditure Prediction Program — A microcomputer-based model which can estimate the energy requirement of a wide variety of manual materials handling jobs:

   Source: Center for Ergonomics
   IOE Building, 1205 Beal
   The University of Michigan
   Ann Arbor, MI 48109

2. Static Strength Prediction Program — A microcomputer-based, sagittal-plane, human-static-strength prediction and low-back stress evaluation model:

   Source: Center for Ergonomics
   IOE Building, 1205 Beal
   The University of Michigan
   Ann Arbor, MI 48109

3. NIOSH Lifting Model — Microcomputer-based model developed to evaluate lifting tasks based on the action limit (AL) and maximum permissible limit (MPL) as suggested by NIOSH:

   Source: Association of American Railroads
   Research and Test Department
   1920 L Street, N.W.
   Washington, DC 20036

4. ECOW (Energy Cost of Work) — Microcomputer-based model to estimate energy cost of work on common industrial tasks, and recommend rest durations where applicable:

   Source: B. Mustafa Pulat
   AT&T Technologies
   7725 W. Reno Avenue
   Oklahoma City, OK 73125

5. Manual Materials Handling — Microcomputer-based model to predict percentage of industrial population that would perform a user-defined lifting, lowering, pushing, pulling, or carrying task on voluntary basis.:

   Source: B. Mustafa Pulat
   Department of Industrial Engineering
   North Carolina A & T State University
   Greensboro, NC 27411

26

Ergonomics Bibliography

B. Mustafa Pulat, Ph.D.

The sources given below represent a selection for a practitioner who wishes to do extra reading in the field of industrial ergonomics. Several journal names are also provided.

General

Adams, Tack A. 1982. Issues in human reliability. *Human Factors* 24(1):1-10.

Alexander, D.C., C.G. Givens, and H.R. Kaudcwitz. 1981. Ergonomics and automation—A marriage that works in industry. *Human Factors Society Proceedings*. Rochester, N.Y. (October 12-16).

Beaumont, T. Graham. 1982. System requirements for interactive testing. *International Journal of Man-Machine Studies* 17(3):311-20.

Bennett, Corvin A. 1962. The business of human factors. *Human Factors* 4(2):101-3.

Birren, F. 1976. A colour code for safety. *Control* 3(2):53-8.

Brigham, F.R. 1975. Some quantitative considerations in questionnaire design and analysis. *Applied Ergonomics* 6(2):90-6.

Brown, C.R., and D.L. Schaum. 1980. User-adjusted VDU parameters ergonomic aspect of visual display terminals. E. Grandjean and E. Vigliani, eds., 195-220. London: Taylor & Francis Ltd.

Browning, A.C. 1975. City transport of the future—The high speed pedestrian conveyor. Part 2: Ergonomics considerations of complete conveyors systems. *Applied Ergonomics* 6(1):17-22.

Cairney, P., and Sless. 1982. Communication effectiveness of symbolic safety signs with different user groups. *Applied Ergonomics* 13(2):91-2.

Carbonell, J.R. 1969. On man-computer interaction-model and some related issues. *IEEE—Trans. on Systems Science & Cybernetics* V SSC-51 (January):16-26.

Christ, R.E. 1976. Review and analysis of color coding research for visual displays. *Human Factors* 17(6):542-70.

Christensen, Julien M. 1962. The evolution of the systems approach in human factors engineering (from the viewpoint of an engineering psychologist). *Human Factors* 4(1):7-16.

Clarke, M.M. 1982. Remote systems, some human factors issues in teleoperator and robot development: An interactive session. *Proceedings of the Human Factors Society 26th Annual Meeting*. Seattle, Wash. (October 25-29):763-5.

Cook, K.G. 1975. Human factors and related design aspects of pallets. U.S. Postal Service, Research and Development Department, Office of Postal Technical Research, Information and Human Sciences Division, Technical Note PTR-H433, 75-3 (June).

Cooper, M.B., A.C. Cox, and F. Garnham. 1979. Controls for remote-controlled zoom lenses. *Applied Ergonomics* 10(2):109-11.

Cordes, R.E. 1980. Software-user interface evaluation: Methodology and tools. *Proceedings of the Human Factors Society*. Los Angeles (October).

Daniel, J. 1970. Some psychological approaches for determining mental load. *Proceedings of the 4th International Ergonomics Association Congress.* Strasbourg (July 6-10).

Davis, P.R. 1983. Human factors, contributing to slips, trips, and falls. *Ergonomics* 26(1):51-9.

Drury, C.G. 1978. Integrating human factors models into statistical quality control. *Human Factors* 20(5):561-72.

Eskew, R.T., and C.V. Riche. 1982. Pacing and locus on control in quality control inspection. *Human Factors* 24(4):414-5.

Evans, S.M., and D.S. Kochar. 1982. Office automation and managerial productivity—Some issues. *Proceedings of the Human Factors Society 26th Annual Meeting.* Seattle, Wash. (October 25-29):64-8.

Gaines, B.R. 1978. Man-computer communication—What next? *International Journal of Man-Machine Studies* (October):225-32.

Grandjean, E. 1980. Ergonomics of VDUs: Review of present knowledge, ergonomics aspects of visual display terminals. E. Grandjean and E. Vigliani, eds., 1-12. London: Taylor & Francis Ltd.

——. 1980. *Fitting the task to the man: An ergonomic approach.* 3rd ed. London: Taylor & Francis Ltd.

Gupta, A. 1982. An overview of contemporary office automation technology. *Behavior and Information Technology* 1(3):217-36.

Gustafson, H.W. 1980. Efficiency of output in self-paced work, machine-paced rest. *Human Factors* 24(4):395-410.

Glencross, D.J., and G.A. Anderson. 1976. Operation response factors in the location and control of foot pedals. *Ergonomics* 19(4):399-408.

Holzmann, P. 1982. ABBAN—A new method for analysis of ergonomics effort. *Applied Ergonomics* 13(2):82-6.

Irvine, C.H. 1978. A human factors approach to slippery floors, slippery shoes, and ladder designs. *Proceedings of the 22nd Annual Meeting of the Human Factors Society.* Detroit, Mich. (October 16-19):583-7.

Ivergood, Toni. 1973. Use of ergonomics in the design of new industries, ERGOLAB, Stockholm, Sweden. *Applied Ergonomics* (September):150-3.

Kennedy, T.C.S. 1974. The design of interactive procedures for man-machine communication. *International Journal of Man-Machine Studies* 6(3):309-34.

Lee, D.R., and L.R. Buck. 1975. The effect of screen angle and luminance on microform reading. *Human Factors* 17(5):461-9.

Lyungberg, A.S., F. Gamberale, and A. Kilbon. 1982. Horizontal lifting: Physiological and psychological responses. *Ergonomics* 25(8):741-57.

Maltas, K.L., and J.R. Buck. 1975. Simulation of a large man/machine process control system in the steel industry, human factors in our expanding technology. *Proceedings of the Human Factors Society 19th Annual Meeting*. Dallas (October 14-16):193-205.

Mauro, C.L., and M.A. Maney. 1978. Problems in the presentation of anthropometric data for use by designers and engineers. *Proceedings of the 22nd Annual Meeting of the Human Factors Society*. Detroit, Mich. (October 16-19):684-5.

McCormick, E.J., and M.S. Sanders. 1982. *Human factors in engineering and design*. 5th ed. New York: McGraw-Hill.

Meister, D. 1982. Where and what are the data in human factors. *Proceedings of the Human Factors Society 26th Annual Meeting*. Seattle, Wash. (October 25-29):722-6.

——. 1982. The present and future of human factors. *Applied Ergonomics* 13(4):281-7.

Metz, B.G. 1976. Ergonomics & standards. *Ergonomics* 19(3):271-4.

Rosenberg, D.T. 1981. Human factors for portable products. *Proceedings of the 25th Annual Meeting*. Rochester, N.Y. (October 12-16):317-21.

Smith, S.L. 1979. Letter size and legibility. *Human Factors* 21(6):661-70.

Stewart, T.F.M. 1976. Displays and the software interface. *Applied Ergonomics* 7(3):137-46.

——. 1980. Practical experiences in solving VDU ergonomics problems. In *Ergonomics aspects of visual display terminals.* E. Grandjean and E. Vigliani, eds., 233-40. London: Taylor & Francis, Ltd.

U.S. Consumer Product Safety Commission. 1975. *Handbook and standard for manufacturing safer consumer products.* U.S. Consumer Product Safety Commission, Washington, D.C. (January):68.

Wisner, A. 1979. Application of ergonomics at various stages in the design of industrial establishments. *Ergonomics* 22(6):687-9.

Wright, P. 1979. The quality control of document design. *Information Design Journal* 1(1):33-42.

Equipment and Product Design

Agate, S.J., and C.G. Drury. 1980. Electronic calculators: Which notation is the better? *Ergonomics* 11(1):2-6.

Alden, D.G., et al. 1972. Keyboard design and operation: A review of the major issues. *Human Factors* 14:275-93.

Allen, J. 1978. An approach to reading machine design. *Human Factors* 20(3):287-94.

Biddle, H. 1981. Hand tools. *Engineering* 221(11):857-9.

Brunkow, G., and S. Konz. 1975. A biomechanical scissors. Human factors in our expanding technology. *Proceedings of the Human Factors Society 19th Annual Meeting.* Dallas (October 14-16):136-9.

Corlett, E.N., and H.J. Sinclair. 1972. Ergonomics and machine tools. *Production Engineering* 51(6):204-8.

Corlett, E.N. 1982. Design of handtools, machines, workplaces, office and buildings. In *Handbook of industrial engineering.* G. Salvendy, ed. New York: Wiley.

Cornog, D.Y. 1974. Letter sorting machines, human factors. U.S. Postal Service, Office of Postal Technology Research, Research and Engineering Department, Report No. 74-1-1 (February):82.

Coury, Bruce G., and Colin Drury. 1982. Optimum handle positions in a box-holding task. *Ergonomics* 25(7):645-62.

Curry, R.E., D.L. Kleinman, and W.C. Hoffman. 1977. A design procedure for control/display systems. *Human Factors* 19(5):421-36.

Department of Defense. 1974. Human engineering design criteria for military systems, equipment, and facilities. MIL-STD-1472B.

Drury, C.G. 1975. Application of Fitts law to foot-pedal design. *Human Factors* 17(4):368-73.

——. 1980. Handles for manual materials handling. *Applied Ergonomics* 11(1):35-42.

Drury, D.G., and B.G. Coury. 1982. A methodology for chair evaluation. *Applied Ergonomics* 13(3):195-202.

Ducharme, R.E. 1975. Problem tools for women. *Industrial Engineering* 7(9):46-50.

Fellmann, T.H., et al. 1982. An ergonomic evaluation of VDT's. *Behavior and Information Technology* 1(1):69-80.

Ferguson, D., and J. Duncan. 1974. Keyboard design and operation posture. *Ergonomics* (November):731-44.

Fisher, H.T. 1974. Large scale telescope and human factors. In *Proceedings of the Human Factors Society 18th Annual Meeting*. Huntsville (October 15-17):176-86.

Fraser, T.M. 1980. Ergonomics principles in the design of hand tools. International Labor Office, Geneva, Occupational Safety and Health Services, No. 44:93.

Grandjean, E., and E. Vigliani, eds. 1980. *Ergonomics aspects of visual display terminals*. London: Taylor & Francis, Ltd.

Greenberg, L., and D. Chaffin. 1977. *Workers and their tools*. Midland, Mich.: Pendell Publishing Co.

Harten, G.A., and P.M. Derks. 1975. A new ergonomically improved lathe. *Applied Ergonomics* 6(3):155-7.

Hoag, L.L. 1979. Data for designing hand tools for female craft workers. *Proceedings of the 23rd Annual Meeting of the Human Factors Society*. Boston (October 29-November 1):188-90.

Hughes, A.J.G. 1982. Ergonomics of equipment design and operations in forestry. *Ergonomics* 25(1):3-9.

Kaczmark, J. 1979. Ergonomics in the design of industrial equipment. *Ergonomics* 22(6):681-6.

Konz, S. 1974. Design of handtools. *Proceedings of the Human Factors Society 18th Annual Meeting*. Huntsville (October 15-17):310-1.

Kreifeldt, J.G., and P.H. Hill. 1974. Towards a theory of man-tool system designs applications of consumer products area. *Proceedings of Human Factors Society 18th Annual Meeting*. Huntsville (October 15-17):310-1.

Lawrie, W.B. 1974. Development of safety and health features in the design and construction of machinery and equipment. Paper presented at the 7th World Congress at the Prevention of Occupational Accidents and Diseases. Dublin (May 20-25):15.

Manro, C.L., and M.A. Maney, 1979. Anthropometry and the design of products for non-military use: Needs and limitations. *Proceedings of the 22nd Annual Meeting of the Human Factors Society*. Detroit (October 16-19):686-7.

McClelland, I., and J.S. Ward. 1976. Ergonomics in relation to sanitary ware design. *Ergonomics* 19(4):465-78.

Pezoldt, V.J., and J.J. Persensky. 1977. Power lawn mowers: Ease of pull. National Bureau of Standards, Report No. NBSIR 77-1298 (June). Washington, D.C.

Rabideau, G.F. 1974. Human, machine, and environment aspects of snowmobile design and utilization. *Human Factors* 16(5):481-94.

Roozbazar, A. 1977. Ergonomics of machine guarding. *National Safety News* 116(1):53-9.

Sheridan, T.B., and R.W. Mann. Design of control devices for people with severe motor impairment. *Human Factors* 20(3):320-38.

Shinar, D., and M.B. Acton. 1978. Control-display relationships on the four-burner range: Population stereotypes versus standards. *Human Factors* 20(1):13-7.

Tichauer, E.R., and H. Crage. 1977. Ergonomics principles basic to hand tool design. *American Industrial Hygiene Association Journal* 38(11):622-34.

Tomlinson, R.W., and E.N. Corlett. 1975. The ergonomics of openfronted C-frame presses. *Applied Ergonomics* 6(1):23-31.

U.S. Postal Service. 1971. Human factors checklist for mail processing equipment and operation. U.S. Postal Service, Rockville, Maryland, USA General Research Report No. 71-2 (March):36.

Yanase, T. 1978. A study of the psychological evaluation of the design of coffee cups. *Japanese Journal of Ergonomics* 14(6):327-34.

Job Design

Adams, S.K. 1973. Manual materials handling: A complex case for safety criteria and standards. *Proceedings of the 17th Annual Meeting of the Human Factors Society*. Santa Monica, Calif. (October 16-18):469-76.

Bielski, J., J. Wolowick, and A. Zeyland. 1976. The ergonomics evaluation of work stress in the furniture industry. *Applied Ergonomics* 7(2):89-91.

Bulat, V., et al. 1982. Rhythmical work in production lines and the humanization of work. *Proceedings of the 8th Congress of the International Ergonomics Association*. Tokyo (August 23-27): 104-5.

Caelli, Terry, and David Finlay. 1982. Does welding affect visual acuities or color sensitivity? *Human Factors* 24(1):115-9.

Chaffin, D.B., G.D. Herrin, and W.M. Keyserling. 1978. Preemployment strength testing—An updated version. *Journal of Occupational Medicine* 20(6):403-8.

Conry, B.G., and C.G. Drury. 1982. Optimum handle positions in a box-holding task. *Ergonomics* 25(7):645-62.

Davis, L.E., and J.C. Taylor. *Design of jobs*. 2nd ed. Santa Monica, Calif.: Goodyear Publishing Co.

Drury, C.G., C.H. Law, and C.S. Pawenski. A survey of industrial box handling. *Human Factors* 24(5):553-65.

Folkard, S., and T.H. Monk. Shiftwork and performance. *Human Factors* 21:483-92.

Gruver, W.A., M.A. Ayoub, and M.B. Muth. 1979. A model for optimal evaluation of manual lifting tasks. *Journal of Safety Research* 11(2):61-71.

Hall, A.J. 1976. Reducing sources of human error in transmission of alphanumeric codes. *Applied Ergonomics* 2:75-8.

Kamon, E. 1982. Physiological basis for the design of work and rest. In *Handbook of industrial engineering*. G. Salvendy, ed. New York: Wiley.

Kassab, S.J., and C.G. Drury. 1976. The effect of working height on a manual lifting task. *International Journal of Production Research* 14(3):381-6.

Kirjonen, J. 1982. Design of jobs in a man-computer system, an action research approach. *Proceedings of the 18th Congress of the International Ergonomics Association*. Tokyo (August 23-27):538-9.

Kroemer, K.H.E. 1978. Engineering controls for safe and effective manual material handling. *Proceedings of the 22nd Annual Meeting of the Human Factors Society*. Detroit (October 16-19):309-16.

Letbetter, D.G. 1982. Design criteria for safer manual lifting by men and women. *Proceedings of the Human Factors Society 26th Annual Meeting*. Seattle (October 24-25):503-7.

Mulder, F. 1982. Task allocation based human needs as a tool in the humanization of work systems. *Proceedings of the 8th Congress of the International Ergonomics Association*. Tokyo (August 23-27):112-3.

Pearson, R.G., and M.A. Ayoub. Ergonomics aids industrial accidents and injury control. *Industrial Engineering* 7(6):18-26.

Sen, R.N. 1981. Ergonomics study of tea-leaf plucking operations: Criteria for selection and categorization. *Applied Ergonomics* 12(2):82-5.

Smith, D.M. 1968. Job design from research to application. *Industrial Engineering* 19(10):477-82.

Vihma, T., M. Nurminen, and P. Mutanen. 1982. Sewing-machine operator's work and musculo-skeletal complaints. *Ergonomics* 25(4):295-8.

Webb, R.D., and J. Handyside. 1982. Brick-handling: A case study. *Applied Ergonomics* 13(3):191-4.

Wisner, A. 1980. Work at computer terminals: Analysis of the work and ergonomics recommendations. Paper presented at the Conference on Work Humanization through Job Redesign and Ergonomics. Helsinki (February 11-15):18.

Workplace Design

Ayoub, M.M. 1973. Workplace design and posture. *Human Factors* 15:265-8.

Ayoub, M.M., and C.G. Halcomb. 1976. Improved seat, console and workplace design: Annotated bibliography, integration of the literature accommodation model, and seated operator reach profiles. Pacific Missile Test Center, Point Mugu, Calif. Technical Publication No. TP-76-1 (December):342.

Buti, L.B., F. Denigris, and E. Moretti. Ergonomic design of a workplace for VDU operators. *Ergonomics aspects of visual display terminals*. E. Grandjean and E. Vigliani, eds., 283-8. London: Taylor & Francis, Ltd.

Coe, J. 1980. Proof and practice: The design of a VDU workstation. *Proceedings of the Ergonomics Society of Australia and New Zealand*. Sydney (November 27-28):187-97.

Cortlett, E.N. 1973. Human factors in the design of manufacturing systems. *Human Factors* 15(2):105-10.

Cortlett, E.N., and R.P. Bishop. 1978. The ergonomics of spot welders. *Applied Ergonomics* 9(1):23-32.

Cornog, D.Y. 1975. Evaluation of footrest for LSM operators. U.S. Postal Service, Planning and New Development Department, Office of Postal Technology Research, Information and Human Sciences Division. Technical Note PTR-H433-75-2 (January):14.

——. 1975. Evaluation of pneumatic adjustment features in chairs for LSM operators. U.S. Postal Service, Planning and New Development Department, Office of Postal Technology Research, Information and Human Sciences Division. Technical Note PTR-4433-75-1 (January).

Dannhaus, D.M., et al. 1977. Seating, console, and workplace design: Integration of literature and accommodation model. Gateways to the future. *Proceedings of the 21st Annual Meeting of the Human Factors Society*. San Francisco (October 17-20):88-91.

Deivanayagam, S. 1982. Human factors concerns in industrial robot applications. *Proceedings of the Human Factors Society 26th Annual Meeting*. Seattle (October 25-29):858-62.

Drury, C.G., and B.G. Coury. A methodology for chair evaluation. *Applied Ergonomics* 13(3):195-202.

Eastman Kodak Co. 1983. *Ergonomic design for people at work*. Lifetime Learning Publications. Eastman Kodak Co.

Gamst, F.C. 1975. Human factors analysis of the Diesel-electric locomotive cab. *Human Factors* 17(2):149-56.

Grandjean, E., and W. Hunting. 1977. Ergonomics of posture—Review of various problems of standing and sitting posture. *Applied Ergonomics* 8(3):135-40.

Haider, E., H. Luczark, and W. Rohmert. 1982. Ergonomics investigation of workplaces in police command control center equipped with TV displays. *Applied Ergonomics* 13(2):163-70.

Hayata, K. 1978. Human engineering applied to the design of a control room in a new factory. *Japanese Journal of Ergonomics* 14(3):111-6.

Hilliar, P. 1981. The DHSS ergonomics data bank and the design of spaces in hospitals. *Applied Ergonomics* 12(4):209-16.

Hunting, W., E. Grandjean, and K. Maeda. 1980. Constrained postures in accounting machine operators. *Applied Ergonomics* 11(3):145-9.

Kattan, A., and G. Naddler. 1969. Equations of hand motion path for work space design. *Human Factors* 11(2):123-9.

Konz, S. 1983. *Work design: Industrial ergonomics*. 2nd ed. Columbus, Ohio: Grid Publishing Co.

Kvalseth, T.O., ed. 1983. *Ergonomics of workstation design*. Kent, England: Butterworths.

Lewis, T.L. 1979. Operator station design system: A computer aided design approach to work station layout. *Proceedings of the 23rd Annual Meeting of the Human Factors Society*. Boston (October 29-November 1):55-8.

Mandal, A.C. 1976. Work-chair with tilting seat. 1976. *Ergonomics* 19(2):157-64.

Minsker, E.I. 1975. Ergonomics in the development of control consoles for machine tools in transfer lines. *Machines and Tooling* 46(11):10-5.

Murphy, J.W., and B. Shackel. 1970. Are we sitting comfortably? *Personnel Management* 2(8):30-2.

Parsons, H.M., and G.P. Kearsly. 1982. Robotics and human factors: Current status and future prospects. *Human Factors* 24(5):535-55.

Rabideau, G.F., and R.U. Luk. 1975. A Monte Carlo algorithm for workplace optimizations and layout planning—WOLAP. Human factors in our expanding technology. *Proceedings of the Human Factors Society 19th Annual Meeting*. Dallas (October 14-16):189-92.

Rebiffe, R., O. Zayana, and C. Tarriere. 1969. Determination of optimal areas for the location of controls in the workplace. *Ergonomics* 12(6):913-24.

Rozier, Carolyn K. 1977. Three-dimensional work space of the amputee. *Human Factors* 19(6):525-33.

Roth, J.T., M.M. Ayoub, and C.G. Halcomb. 1977. Seating, console, and workplace design: Seated operator reach profiles. *Proceedings of the 21st Annual Meeting of the Human Factors Society* San Francisco (October 17-20):83-7.

Sen, R.N., and A.K. Ganguli. Preliminary investigation into the loco-man-factor on the Indian railways. *Applied Ergonomics* 13(2):107-17.

Shackel, B., ed. 1974. *Applied ergonomics handbook*. Guildford, Surrey, U.K.: IPC Science and Technology Press.

Shackel, B., and L. Klein. 1976. Esso London airport refuelling control center redesign—An ergonomics case study. *Applied Ergonomics* 7(1):31-45.

Shahnavaz, H. 1982. Lighting conditions and workplace dimensions of VDU operators. *Ergonomics* 25(12):1165-75.

Siegel, A.I., J.J. Wolf, and J. Pilitsis. 1982. A new method for the scientific layout of workspaces. *Applied Ergonomics* 13(2):87-90.

Springer, T.J. 1982. VDT workstations: A comparative evaluation of alternatives. *Applied Ergonomics* 13(3):211-2.

Stoudt, H.W. 1978. Arm-leg reach and workspace layout. Anthropometric source book, vol. 1. E. Churchill, ed., 68. Abstract in Scientific and Technical Aerospace Reports. Report No. NASA-RP-1024, S-479.

Teel, K.S., and R.M. Springer. 1968. Assembly and inspection of microelectric systems. *Human Factors* 10(3):217-23.

U.S. Air Force systems command handbook 1-3. 1977. Human Factors Engineering. 3rd ed.

Weiner, J.S., and H.G. Maule, eds. 1977. *Human factors in work design and production*. London: Taylor & Francis, Ltd.

Wise, T.A., et al. 1979. Human-factors applications to the design of legal offices. *Proceedings of the 23rd Annual Meeting of the Human Factors Society*. Boston (October 29-November 1):106-10.

Worker Characteristics

Borg, Gunner, 1978. Subjective aspects of physical and mental load. *Ergonomics* 21930:215-20.

Caldwell, Leo S. 1962. Body stabilization and the strength of arm extension. *Human Factors* 4(3):125-30.

Corlett, E.N., and K. Mahadera. 1970. A relationship between freely chosen working pace and energy consumption curves. *Ergonomics* 13(4):517-24.

Corlett, E.N., and I. Manenica. 1980. The effects and measurement of working postures. *Ergonomics* 11(1):7-16.

Das, B. 1982. Relationship of work pace to worker physiological cost in a human-machine production task. *Proceedings of the Human Factors Society 26th Annual Meeting*. Seattle (October 25-29):556-60.

Davies, B.T., and B. Mebarki. 1981. Hand movement times and machine guarding. *Ergonomics* 24(5):387-91.

Davies, B.T., et al. 1980. Female hand dimensions and guarding of machines. *Ergonomics* 23(1):79-84.

Elliott, L.L. 1978. Development of communication aids for the deaf. *Human Factors* 20(3):295-306.

Evans, O.M., et al. 1983. Physiological responses to load holding and load carriage. *Ergonomics* 26(2):161-71.

Fine, Michelle. 1982. Cultures of drinking: A workplace perspective. *Social Work* 27(5):436-40.

Gaines, B.R. 1969. Linear and nonlinear models of the human controller. *International Journal of Man-Machine Studies*. 1(4):333-60.

Garg, A., A. Mital, and S.S. Asfour. A comparison of isometric strength and dynamic lifting capability. *Ergonomics* 23(1):13-27.

Grieve, D.W., and S.T. Pheasant. 1981. Naturally preferred directions for the exertion of maximal manual forces. *Ergonomics* 24(9):685-93.

Hammerton, M., and A.H. Tickner. An investigation into the effects of stress upon skilled performance. *Ergonomics* 12(6):851-5.

Ilmarinen, J. 1979. Training effects of stair climbing during office hours on female employees. *Ergonomics* 22(5):507-16.

Jorgensen, K., and Poulson. 1974. Physiological problems in repetitive lifting with special reference to tolerance limits to the maximum lifting frequency. *Ergonomics* 17(1):31-9.

Kaplan, A. 1975. The significance of anthropometrics. *Industrial Design* 22(6):51-3.

Kogi, K., and Y. Saito. 1971. Assessment criteria for mental fatigue—A factor analytic study of phase discrimination in mental fatigue. *Ergonomics* 14(1):119-27.

Konz, S.A., C.E. Jeans, and R.S. Rathore. 1969. Arm motions in the horizontal plane. *AIIE Transactions* 1(4):359-70.

Kroemer, K.H.E. 1970. Human strength: Terminology, measurement, and interpretation of data. *Human Factors* 12(3):297-313.

Legg, S.J., and C.M. Pateman. 1983. Human capabilities in repetitive lifting. *Proceedings of the Ergonomics Society Conference.* London:101-6.

Lewin, T. 1969. Anthropometric studies on Swedish industrial workers when standing and sitting. *Ergonomics* 12(6):833-902.

Lomon, B.F. 1979. The analysis of the operator's activities in the man-machine system. *Ergonomics* 22(6):613-9.

Mandal, A.C. 1982. The seated man: Theories and realities. *Proceedings of the Human Factors Society 26th Annual Meeting.* Seattle (October 25-29):520-4.

North, Klaus, 1981. Job analysis applied to the special needs of the disabled. *Ergonomics* 24:889-98.

Pheasant, S.T. 1982. A technique for estimating anthropometric data from the parameters of the distribution of stature. *Ergonomics* 25(11):981-92.

Pheasant, S.T., and T.G. Scriven. 1983. Sex differences in strength: Some implications for the design of handtools. *Proceedings of the Ergonomics Society's Conference.* London:9-13.

Redgrove, Tone. 1979. Fitting the job to the woman: A critical review. *Applied Ergonomics* 10(4):215-23.

Salvendy, G., et al. 1982. Impact of personality and intelligence on job satisfaction of assembly line and bench work: An industry study. *Applied Ergonomics* 13(4):293-9.

Shan, H.S. 1975. Human criteria in the design and arrangement of control elements. *Machinery and Production Engineering* (May 14):455-9.

Shephard, R.J. 1970. Comments on cardiac frequency in relation to aerobic capacity for work. *Ergonomics* 13(4):509-13.

Smith, J.L., L.A. Smith, and T.M. McLaughlin. 1982. A biomechanical analysis of industrial manual material handlers. *Ergonomics* 25(4):299-308.

Wald, A., and L.B. Harrison. 1975. Oxygen consumption and heart rate: Changes and relationships in static work. *Ergonomics* 18(3):299-309.

Wargo, M.J. 1961. Human operator response speed frequency and flexibility. *Human Factors* 9(3):221-38.

Warwick, J.D., et al. 1980. Maximum voluntary strengths of male adults in some lifting, pushing, and pulling activities. *Ergonomics* 23(1):49-54.

Welford, A.T. 1978. Mental workload as a function of demand, capacity, strategy and skill. *Ergonomics* 21(3):151-67.

Wyndham, C.H., et al. 1963. Influence of gross body weight on oxygen consumption and on physical working capacity of manual laborers. *Ergonomics* 6(3):275-86.

Yates, Y.W., et al. 1980. Static lifting strength and maximal isometric voluntary contractions of back, arm and shoulder muscles. *Ergonomics* 23(1):37-47.

Zink, D.L. 1982. Standards for time taken in self-paced training. *Proceedings of the Human Factors Society 26th Annual Meeting*. Seattle (October 25-29):845-9.

Environment Design

Ahmed, I., and C.A. Bennett. 1978. Discomfort glare, duration, intensity relationship. *Journal of the Illuminating Engineering Society* 8(1):36-9.

Allen, M.A., and G.J. Fisher. 1978. Ambient temperature effects on paired associate learning. *Ergonomics* 21(2):95-101.

Baxter, P.A. 1980. Environmental lighting in work area. *IES Lighting Review* 42(6):144-7.

Chapanis, A. 1978. Human engineering environments for the aged. *Gerontologist* 14(3):228-35.

Chauvel, P., et al. 1982. Glare from windows: Current views of the problems. *Lighting Research and Technology* 14(1):31-46.

Fortuin, G.J. 1963. Age and lighting needs. *Ergonomics* 6(3):239-45.

Greene, T.C., and P.A. Bell. 1980. Additional considerations concerning the effects of "warm" and "cool" wall colours on energy conservation. *Ergonomics* 23(10):949-54.

Griffin, M.J., et al. 1982. Vibration and comfort—IV. Application of experimental result. *Ergonomics* 25(8):721-39.

Hedge, Alan. 1982. The open office: A systematic investigation of employee relations to their work environment. *Environment & Behavior* 14(5):519-42.

Hokl, M.V. 1982. The effect of the environment on human performance. *Applied Ergonomics* 13(4):269-80.

Kanda, H. 1978. Mechanisms of visual acuity decrement associated with whole-body vibration. *Journal of Science of Labour* 54(4):179-88.

Laubli, T.H., W. Hunting, and E. Grandjean. 1980. Visual impairment in VDU operators related to environmental conditions. *Ergonomic aspects of visual display terminals*. E. Grandjean and E. Vigliani, eds., 85-94. London: Taylor & Francis, Ltd.

Lion, Judith S. 1984. The performance of manipulative and inspection tasks under tungsten and fluorescent lighting. *Ergonomics* 25(8):759-69.

Poulton, E.C. 1970. *Environment and human efficiency*. Springfield, Ill.: C.C. Thomas.

Stone, P.T. 1968. Ergonomics of environment. *Illuminating Engineering Society Transactions* 33(4):150-8.

Journals

Applied Ergonomics. Guildford, Surrey, U.K.: IPC Science and Technology Press

Ergonomics. London: Taylor & Francis, Ltd.

Human Factors. Santa Monica, Calif.: Human Factors Society

About the editors

David C. Alexander, P.E., is senior industrial engineer at Tennessee Eastman Company, Kingsport. Alexander has been involved in industrial ergonomics for more than ten years with Eastman and was the company's first human-factors engineer. He is a registered professional engineer and holds BSIE and MSIE degrees from the University of Arkansas. He has written numerous articles on industrial ergonomics and *The Practice and Management of Industrial Ergonomics* (Prentice-Hall, 1985). In addition, he was director of IIE's Ergonomics Division from 1980 to 1982, was IIE's Outstanding Young Engineer in 1984, and received the IIE Region III Award of Excellence in 1981. Alexander is on the Executive Committee of the President's Committee on Employment of the Handicapped and serves as chairman of that group's Worksite Committee. He has also served on the Ergonomics Task Group for the Chemical Manufacturer's Association.

Babur Mustafa Pulat, Ph.D., is with AT&T Network Systems, Oklahoma City. He holds a doctorate in industrial engineering from North Carolina State University and B.S. and M.S. degrees in industrial engineering from the Middle East Technical University in Ankara, Turkey. Pulat was awarded several scholarships, including the NATO scholarship for advanced studies, and has published numerous articles and technical reports on the relationship between ergonomics, and work design, workstation design, and industrial performance. He is a senior member of IIE and a member of the Human Factors Society.